A RAPID ACTION GUIDE

D0540325

When seconds count

● Every emergency demands urgent action. But sometimes the urgency is so pressing that seconds can mean the difference between minor and major damage or injury – in some cases, between life and death.

● This first 'Rapid action' section of *What to do in an emergency* is a guide to help you to cope with emergencies of the specially urgent kind that can occur in and around the home.

● The instructions give only the essential information needed for taking immediate action. Additional details about all of the emergencies dealt with here are given in the main sections of the book.

BLEEDING

If there is a large foreign body in the skin

1 Squeeze the edges of the wound together around the foreign body.

- *DO NOT TRY TO REMOVE IT, AS IT MAY BE PLUGGING THE WOUND.*

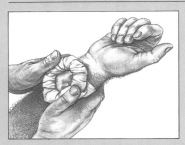

2 Put a piece of clean cloth over the wound. Then put a thick circular pad of clean material around the wound, preferably higher than the object, to prevent pressure on it (see page 58).

3 Bandage it with diagonally applied strips of material that do not go over the foreign body.

4 Telephone 999 and ask for an ambulance, or take the casualty to the Accident and Emergency Department of your local hospital.

If the bleeding will not stop

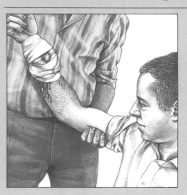

1 **A severely bleeding arm**
As a last resort, press your fingers between the muscles on the underside of the upper arm. This will compress the brachial artery, which roughly follows the seam of the sleeve. Press up and in, pushing the artery against the bone.

- *DO NOT MAINTAIN PRESSURE FOR LONGER THAN 10 MINUTES; YOU MAY CAUSE IRREPARABLE DAMAGE TO THE LIMB.*

- *DO NOT APPLY A TOURNIQUET.*

SEE NEXT PAGE

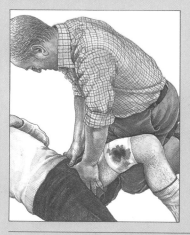

A severely bleeding leg

As a last resort, lay the casualty down with the injured leg bent. Press down in the centre of the fold of the groin with both thumbs, one on top of the other, against the rim of the pelvis. This will compress the femoral artery.

- *DO NOT MAINTAIN PRESSURE FOR LONGER THAN 10 MINUTES; YOU MAY CAUSE IRREPARABLE DAMAGE TO THE LIMB.*

- *DO NOT APPLY A TOURNIQUET.*

2 Tell someone to telephone 999 and ask for an ambulance.

If an injured person bleeds from nose, ear or mouth

1 This can indicate severe injury to the head or chest. Put the casualty in a half-sitting position, with the head inclined towards the injured side, to allow the blood to drain.

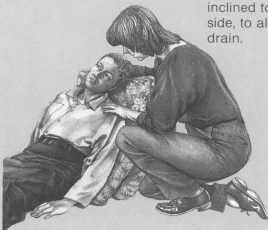

2 Cover the bleeding point, but do not apply pressure.

SEE NEXT PAGE

BLEEDING

3 Telephone 999 and ask for an ambulance.

4 If the person becomes unconscious, put her in the recovery position like this (see page 31).

BURNS AND SCALDS

Many burns need medical attention because of the risk of infection and shock. A young child or a sick or old person should always be taken to a doctor.

If the burn or scald is smaller than a 10p piece

Large burns and scalds ▶

1 If possible, remove rings, watch or constricting clothing before the area starts to swell.

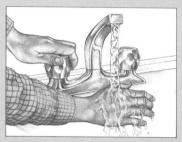

2 **Is it very painful?**
If so, the burn is probably superficial. Put it under slow-running cold water for ten minutes, or longer if pain continues.
Cover the burn with clean, non-fluffy material. A sterile dressing is best, but the inside of a folded handkerchief, bound on with cloth, will do.

Is it peeling or charred?
If the skin looks grey, and is peeling or charred and not very painful, the burn may be deep and serious. Cover it (see above) and take the patient to the doctor or to the Accident and Emergency Department of a hospital.

- *DO NOT USE PLASTERS.*
- *DO NOT APPLY FAT, OINTMENT OR LOTION.*
- *DO NOT BREAK A BLISTER OR TOUCH THE BURN.*

If the burn or scald is larger than a 10p piece

1 If possible, remove rings, watch or constricting clothing before the area starts to swell.

2 Cool the burn by running it under a cold tap for at least ten minutes, or longer if the pain continues. Cool a large area with a damp, clean cloth, but do not waste time before getting medical help.

SEE NEXT PAGE

3 Cover the burn with clean, non-fluffy material. A sterile dressing is best, but the inside of a clean folded handkerchief, bound on with a scarf or other cloth, will do.

4 See your doctor or go to the Accident and Emergency Department of your local hospital.

- *DO NOT USE PLASTERS.*
- *DO NOT APPLY FAT, OINTMENT OR LOTION.*
- *DO NOT BREAK BLISTERS OR TOUCH THE BURN.*

If the burn or scald covers a large area of the body

A person who receives burns over a large area of the body, such as an arm, thigh, lower leg or chest, is likely to suffer shock, and needs urgent hospital treatment.

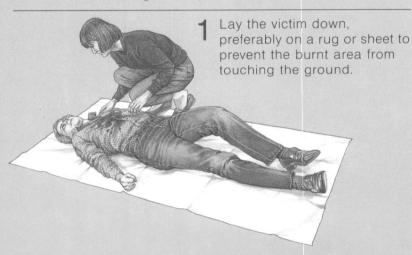

1 Lay the victim down, preferably on a rug or sheet to prevent the burnt area from touching the ground.

2 If possible, remove any rings, watch, shoes or constrictive clothing before the area begins to swell.

Remove clothing soaked in boiling liquid when it has begun to cool.

- *DO NOT REMOVE ANYTHING THAT IS STICKING TO THE BURN.*

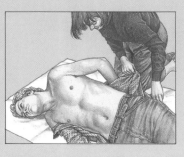

SEE NEXT PAGE

3 Ring 999 and ask for an ambulance, or arrange to take the victim to the Accident and Emergency Department of your local hospital.

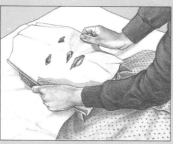

4 Cover the burn with clean, non-fluffy material, such as a freshly washed pillowcase. Fix it in place with a scarf or a piece of clean cloth.

- *DO NOT APPLY FAT, OINTMENT OR LOTION.*
- *DO NOT TOUCH THE BURN.*

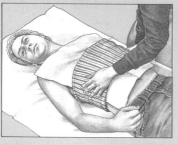

For burns to the face, make a mask from a clean pillowcase by cutting holes for nose, mouth and eyes.

- *DO NOT APPLY FAT, OINTMENT OR LOTION.*
- *DO NOT TOUCH THE BURN.*

5 If the victim is conscious, give frequent sips of cold water to replace lost fluid.

6 If a person with burns on the front becomes unconscious, put him in this recovery position. Turn the head to one side and tilt it back to open the airway. Raise the opposite side of the body by supporting it on a large cushion.

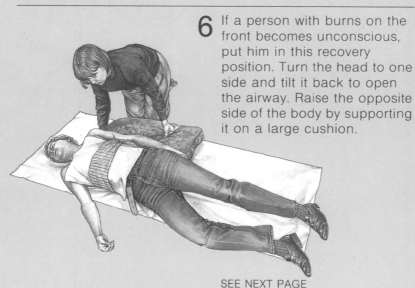

SEE NEXT PAGE

BURNS AND SCALDS

A person with burns on the back should be placed in the normal recovery position like this (see page 31).

BURST PIPE OR TANK

When water pours through a bedroom ceiling, it is probably coming from a burst pipe in the loft, or a corroded cold-water storage tank.

If water pours through the ceiling

1 Turn off the main stop tap. It is probably under the kitchen sink or in the cellar. In a bungalow it may be in the airing cupboard. This will stop water entering the cold-water storage tank.

2 Open all the taps in the house to drain the cold-water storage tank. When the water stops flowing from the taps, the flow from the leak will have stopped, or will stop shortly afterwards.

3 If water is running down a light fitting, switch off the light and remove the appropriate fuse from the main fuse box.

- *DO NOT REPLACE IT UNTIL EVERYTHING HAS DRIED OUT.*

4 If the ceiling plaster is bulging, put a washing-up bowl beneath the bulge and pierce the plaster with a screwdriver or chisel. Stand out of the way, and have spare buckets ready. This will limit ceiling damage to one area.

SEE NEXT PAGE

5 Switch off a gas or oil-fired boiler, or an immersion heater. Damp down a solid-fuel boiler, but there is no need to extinguish it as the hot-water cylinder will not have emptied.

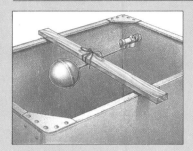

6 Find the source of the leak. If it was from a pipe supplied by the cold-water tank (see page 159), or if the tank itself was leaking, tie up the ball valve in the tank to stop it filling up again.

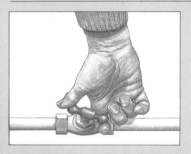

7 If you have tied up the ball valve, turn on the main stop tap. You now have cold water in the kitchen tap. And the lavatory cistern can be filled with a bucket.

8 Contact a plumber.

9 If possible, make an emergency repair to the burst pipe (see page 160).

CHOKING

Anything that goes down a person's windpipe, rather than the food passage, must be brought up again as soon as possible.

If the victim is conscious

1 Remove food or loose false teeth from the mouth. (Do not try to locate the object with your finger.) Encourage the victim to cough. It may be all that is needed to dislodge the blockage.

2 If this fails, help the victim to bend over with the head lower than the chest. He can be either sitting or standing. Slap him between the shoulder blades smartly with the heel of the hand up to four times. Each slap should be strong enough to dislodge the blockage.

Treating small children ▶

Treating babies ▶

Unconscious victim ▶

CHOKING

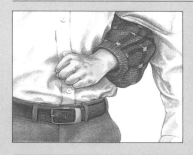

3 If the victim still cannot breathe, stand or kneel behind him. Clench your fist and put it, thumb inwards, between the navel and the bottom of the breastbone.

4 Hold your fist with the other hand and pull both hands towards you with a quick upward-and-inward thrust from the elbows. You are trying to pull the upper abdomen against the bottom of the lungs to drive out the remaining air and force out the blockage.
Repeat up to four times. Each thrust must be hard enough to move the blockage.

Treating small children

1 Encourage the child to cough. If this fails, lay the child over your knee with the head down. Support the chest with one hand while you slap him smartly with the heel of the hand up to four times. Each slap must be strong enough to dislodge the blockage.

2 If the child is still not breathing, sit him on your lap and perform abdominal thrusts (steps 3 and 4 on the previous page) – but use only one hand.

Treating babies

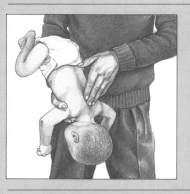

1 Lay the baby head downwards with the body lying along your forearm, using your hand to support the head and chest. Slap smartly between the shoulder blades with your fingers up to four times, using much less force than for an adult.

2 If the baby still does not breathe, hold him on his back with the head tilted well back to open up the airway. Apply abdominal thrusts with two fingers of one hand, pressing quickly forwards and downwards just above the navel. Repeat up to four times.

If the victim becomes unconscious

1 Start the kiss of life (turn to page 2). (turn to page 2)

2 If a third person is present, tell him to telephone 999 and ask for an ambulance. If you are on your own, do not stop the kiss of life until normal breathing resumes.

3 If the kiss of life does not inflate the lungs with the first two breaths, roll the victim onto the side nearest to you, with the chest against your thigh and head well back. Give up to four slaps on the back.

CHOKING

4 Look in the mouth to see if the blockage has become dislodged. If it has, hook it out with a finger.

5 If not, turn the victim onto his back and tilt the head well back. Straddle the victim's thighs, or kneel alongside. Put the heel of one hand between the navel and the bottom of the breastbone.

SEE NEXT PAGE

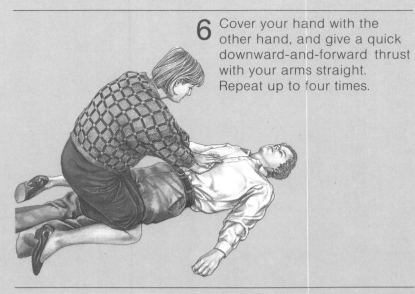

6 Cover your hand with the other hand, and give a quick downward-and-forward thrust with your arms straight. Repeat up to four times.

7 Check the mouth to see if the blockage has been dislodged. If it has, hook it out with a finger.

8 If not, resume the kiss of life.

9 If the lungs do not expand after the first two breaths, repeat steps 3 to 7 (see previous page).

DRUG OVERDOSE

An overdose of any drug (either an addictive drug or an ordinary medicine) is serious and requires urgent medical treatment. Symptoms of drug overdose include abnormal dilation or contraction of the pupils of the eyes, vomiting, difficulty in breathing, unconsciousness, sweating and hallucinations.

If a person takes a deliberate or accidental overdose

1 Ask the casualty what has happened. Obtain any information about the drug that you can as soon as possible. The casualty may become unconscious at any time.

- *DO NOT TRY TO INDUCE VOMITING. IT WASTES TIME AND MAY BE HARMFUL.*

2 If the person is unconscious, put her in the recovery position like this (see page 31).

Alcohol poisoning ▶

DRUG OVERDOSE

3 Telephone 999 and ask for an ambulance.

4 Collect a sample of vomit and any bottles or pill containers that are near the casualty. Send them to hospital with her as evidence to assist treatment.

If a person becomes unconscious from alcohol poisoning

1 Put him in the recovery position like this, so that he does not choke on his own vomit (see page 31).

2 Telephone 999 and ask for an ambulance.

DRUG OVERDOSE

ELECTRIC SHOCK

If someone receives an electric shock at home or at work, cut off the source of electricity before doing anything else.

How to deal with an electrical injury

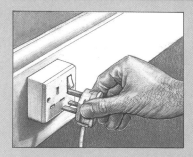

1 Stop the current by switching off at the socket or pulling out the plug. If you cannot reach the socket, switch off at the main fuse box.

- *DO NOT USE THE SWITCH ON THE APPLIANCE. A FAULTY SWITCH MAY BE THE CAUSE OF THE ACCIDENT.*

2 If there is no way to switch off, stand on dry insulating material, such as a thick layer of newspaper, a rubber mat or a wooden box, and push the victim's limbs away from the source with a broom or wooden chair.

- *DO NOT USE ANYTHING THAT IS DAMP OR MADE OF METAL.*

Alternatively, loop a rope, a pair of tights or any dry fabric around the victim's feet or under the arms, and pull her free.

- *DO NOT TOUCH THE VICTIM WITH YOUR HANDS.*
- *DO NOT USE ANYTHING WET, SUCH AS A DAMP TOWEL.*

3 If the victim is unconscious, and breathing, put her in the recovery position like this (see page 31)

SEE NEXT PAGE

4 If the victim has been unconscious, has suffered burns or is feeling poorly, telephone 999 and ask for an ambulance, or drive her to the Accident and Emergency Department of your local hospital.
Tell the hospital how long she was in contact with the electricity.

**ELECTRIC
SHOCK**

FIRE

When fire has taken hold in a house, get out fast. Smoke from plastic-foam upholstery can kill in less than two minutes.

If a chip pan or frying pan catches fire

1 Turn off the heat on the stove.

2 Cover the pan with a large lid or plate, or with a damp towel or a fire blanket.

- *DO NOT MOVE THE PAN.*
- *DO NOT THROW WATER ON IT.*
- *DO NOT LIFT THE LID OFF A CHIP PAN FOR HALF AN HOUR, EVEN IF THE FLAMES SEEM TO HAVE DIED DOWN.*

If an electrical appliance or fitting catches fire

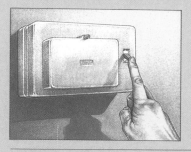

1 Switch off at the main fuse box.

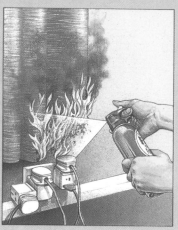

2 Extinguish the fire with water or a fire extinguisher, EXCEPT for a TV or computer fire (see next page).

- *DO NOT THROW WATER ON A BURNING APPLIANCE OR FITTING WHEN THE ELECTRICITY IS STILL TURNED ON.*
- *DO NOT TOUCH ANY SWITCH ON A BURNING APPLIANCE OR FITTING.*

TV set on fire ▶

Oil heater on fire ▶

Foam furniture on fire ▶

Clothing on fire ▶

Smell of burning at night ▶

Trapped on upper floor ▶

FIRE

If a TV or computer catches fire

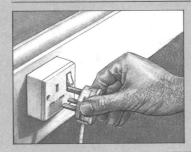

1 Pull out the plug or switch off at the main fuse box.

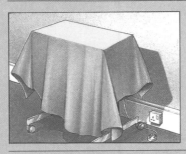

2 Smother the fire with a blanket or rug or a fire blanket.

- *DO NOT USE WATER OR A FIRE EXTINGUISHER, BECAUSE RESIDUAL ELECTRICITY MAY REMAIN IN THE SET.*

If an oil heater catches fire

Stand at least 6ft (2m) away, and throw on buckets of water. If doing so is likely to knock the heater over, smother the fire with a water-soaked blanket instead.

If a foam sofa or armchair catches fire

Burning plastic foam gives off choking black smoke that can overcome you in one minute. Do not try to put out the fire.

1 Get out of the room and close the door to prevent the smoke from spreading.

SEE NEXT PAGE

2 Telephone 999 and ask for the fire brigade.

If a person's clothes catch fire

1 Prevent the victim from rushing about in a panic; the movement will fan the flames.

2 Lay the victim down to prevent the flames from rising up to the head, and douse the fire with water or other non-flammable liquid (in a kitchen a bottle of milk might be nearest to hand).

Alternatively, wrap her tightly in a coat, curtain, blanket (not the cellular type) or other thick fabric, and simultaneously lay her on the ground.

- *DO NOT USE NYLON OR MAN-MADE MATERIAL TO SMOTHER THE FLAMES.*
- *DO NOT ROLL THE VICTIM ALONG THE GROUND. IT CAN BRING THE FLAMES INTO CONTACT WITH UNHARMED PARTS OF THE BODY.*

3 Treat the victim according to the extent of the burns (see pages 7, 8, 9 and 10).

If you smell burning at night

1 Alert everyone in the house.

2 If the fire is too big to deal with safely, get everyone outside. If you think the fire is well alight in a closed room, do not open the door to find out.

SEE NEXT PAGE

Trapped on upper floor ▶

FIRE

3 Shut all doors behind you to restrict the spread of flames and smoke.

4 Go to the nearest telephone, dial 999 and ask for the Fire Brigade.

- *DO NOT GO BACK INSIDE.*

If you are trapped on an upper floor

1 Go to a room at the front of the house, close the door and block up cracks with bedding or clothes.

2 Open the window and call for help.

- *DO NOT JUMP OUT OF THE WINDOW, EXCEPT AS A LAST RESORT.*

FIRE

GAS LEAK

Your first priority must be to cut off the flow of gas.

If there is a strong smell of gas

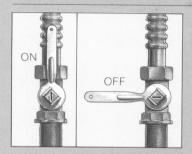

1 Turn off the main gas tap next to the meter.

2 Open doors and windows.

3 Put out cigarettes or naked flames; switch off electric fires.

4 Get an unconscious person into the open air and put him in the recovery position (see page 31).

5 Telephone 999 and ask for an ambulance.
Telephone your local area gas office immediately – day or night. Find it under 'Gas' in the phone book.

- *DO NOT TRY TO TRACE THE LEAK WITH A NAKED FLAME (MATCH OR LIGHTER).*
- *DO NOT ENTER A ROOM OR AREA WHERE THE SMELL OF GAS IS ESPECIALLY STRONG. THE BUILD-UP OF FUMES MAY OVERPOWER YOU.*

GAS OFFICE

Tel. ....

If there is a slight smell of gas

1 Trace the source immediately. Often the pilot light on a cooker or gas fire has gone out, or a burner on the cooker has blown out in a draught.
SEE NEXT PAGE

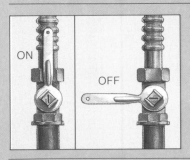

2 Turn off the pilot light or burner. If the pilot light does not have a tap, turn off the main gas tap next to the meter.

3 Put out cigarettes; extinguish naked flames; switch off any electric fire in the room.

4 Open doors and windows to let the gas disperse. Wait for the smell to go.

5 Relight the pilot light or burner.

6 If the smell persists or returns, telephone your local area gas office immediately – day or night. Find it under 'Gas' in the phone book.

- *DO NOT ATTEMPT REPAIRS YOURSELF.*

GAS OFFICE

Tel. ....

GAS LEAK

POISONING

A house contains many substances, such as bleach, insecticides and paint stripper, that are highly dangerous to children. Get medical help quickly if a child swallows one.

If a child swallows a household chemical

1 If the victim is conscious, try to discover what has been swallowed. Remember that he may become unconscious at any time.

- *DO NOT INDUCE VOMITING. IT WASTES TIME AND MAY BE HARMFUL.*

2 If the victim is conscious and has swallowed something that burns, such as bleach, cleaning fluid or paint stripper, give water or milk to drink slowly.

3 If the victim is unconscious, place him in the recovery position like this (see page 31).

Plant poisoning ▶

POISONING

4 Telephone 999 and ask for an ambulance.

SEE NEXT PAGE

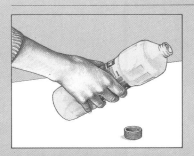

5 Give the ambulance men the poison container or a sample of vomit as evidence to assist treatment.

If a child eats a poisonous plant

The most common poisonous plants are the seeds and berries of laburnum and deadly or woody nightshade, green potatoes and death cap fungus. Symptoms of poisoning include vomiting, diarrhoea and stomach pains.

Telephone your doctor or take the child to the Accident and Emergency Department of your local hospital. Alternatively, telephone 999 and ask for an ambulance. If possible, give a sample of the plant to the hospital or ambulance men to help treatment.

POISONING

STROKE OR HEART ATTACK

STROKE SYMPTOMS There may be headache, paralysis down one side of the body, or difficulty swallowing and speaking. Possibly confusion and loss of consciousness.

HEART ATTACK SYMPTOMS Sudden crushing pain in the chest, often spreading to arms, neck and jaw. Possibly breathlessness.

Dealing with a possible stroke or heart attack

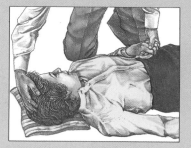

1 Suspected stroke
If the patient is conscious, lay her down with head and shoulders slightly raised and supported with a pillow. Place the head on one side to allow saliva to drain from the mouth.

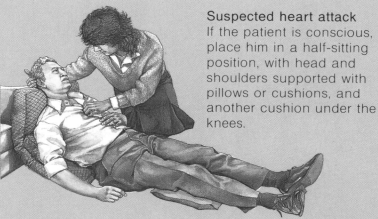

Suspected heart attack
If the patient is conscious, place him in a half-sitting position, with head and shoulders supported with pillows or cushions, and another cushion under the knees.

2 Call the patient's doctor, or telephone 999 and ask for an ambulance.

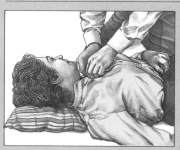

3 Loosen clothing around neck, chest and waist to help circulation and breathing.

- *DO NOT GIVE THE PATIENT ANYTHING TO EAT OR DRINK.*
- *DO NOT ALLOW A HEART-ATTACK PATIENT TO MOVE UNNECESSARILY; IT WILL PUT EXTRA STRAIN ON THE HEART.*

SEE NEXT PAGE

STROKE OR HEART ATTACK

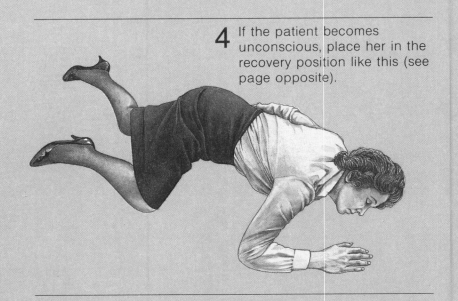

4 If the patient becomes unconscious, place her in the recovery position like this (see page opposite).

UNCONSCIOUS PERSON

Unless you suspect a fracture of the spine or neck, turn an unconscious, but breathing, casualty to the recovery position. This will prevent blood, saliva or the tongue from blocking the windpipe. The recovery position is a priority treatment.

Putting an unconscious casualty in the recovery position

1 Kneel beside the casualty, about 9in (230mm) away. Turn the head towards you and tilt it back to open the airway.

2 Lay the nearer arm along the casualty's side, tucking it under the body and keeping it straight. Place the far ankle over the near ankle. Put the other arm across the chest.

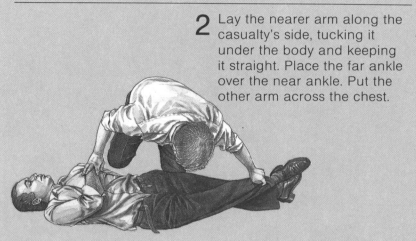

3 Cushion the head with one hand. Grip the clothing at the far hip with the other.

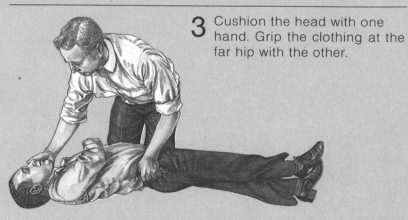

4 Turn the casualty onto his front by pulling quickly towards you, supporting him with your knees.

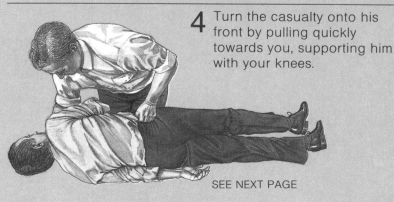

SEE NEXT PAGE

Turning a heavy person ▶

If an arm or leg is broken ▶

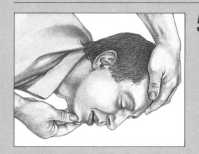

5 Tilt the chin forward to straighten the throat. This keeps the airway open, allowing the casualty to breathe freely.

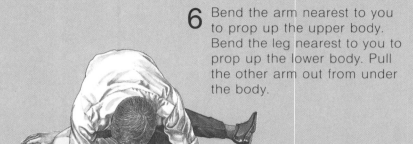

6 Bend the arm nearest to you to prop up the upper body. Bend the leg nearest to you to prop up the lower body. Pull the other arm out from under the body.

7 Telephone 999 and ask for an ambulance.

If the casualty is heavy

Grip the clothing at the hip with both hands and roll the body against your knees. If possible, get a second person to support the head while you turn the body.

Alternatively, the helper can kneel facing you and push the casualty while you pull.

If an arm or a leg is broken

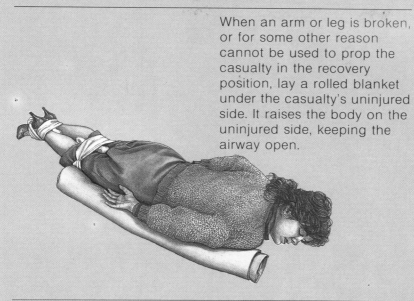

When an arm or leg is broken, or for some other reason cannot be used to prop the casualty in the recovery position, lay a rolled blanket under the casualty's uninjured side. It raises the body on the uninjured side, keeping the airway open.

WHAT TO DO IN AN EMERGENCY

was edited and designed by
The Reader's Digest Association Limited
London

First Edition
Copyright © 1986
The Reader's Digest Association Limited
25 Berkeley Square
London W1X 6AB

Reprinted with amendments 1987

Copyright © 1986
Reader's Digest Association
Far East Limited

Philippines Copyright 1986
Reader's Digest Association
Far East Ltd

Printed in Belgium

EMERGENCY

READER'S DIGEST

WHAT TO DO
IN AN EMERGENCY

PUBLISHED BY THE READER'S DIGEST ASSOCIATION LIMITED
LONDON · NEW YORK · MONTREAL · SYDNEY · CAPE TOWN

Contributors

WRITERS

Dr George Birdwood, MA, MB, ChB, MIL

Ted Clements
Chief Examiner
Institute of Advanced Motorists

Frank Eaglestone, Barrister, LLB, FCII, FCIArb
Insurance consultant
Co-editor, *Insurance Law Reports*

Fred Fearnley
Former survival and safety instructor
Special Air Service

Dr Max M. Glatt, DSc, MD, FRCP, FRCPsych, DPM
Medical Director, Addictive Disease Unit,
Charter Clinic, London;
Former Chairman, Medical Council on
Alcoholism

Anthony Greenbank
Author, *The Survival Handbook*;
Former Outward Bound instructor at Eskdale,
Cumbria, and Marble, Colorado, USA

Marcus Jacobson, MSc, CEng, FIMechE, FIMI
Former Chief Engineer
The Automobile Association

Dr Harvey Marcovitch, MA, MB, BChir, MRCP,
DObst.RCOG, DCH
Consultant Paediatrician
Horton General Hospital, Banbury

Dr Frank Preston, VRD, MBChB, DA, FFOM
Director Medical Services
British Airways

Tom Sanders, DLC
Water Safety Adviser
Royal Society for the Prevention of Accidents

Major Bertram Seymour
Former Chief Safety Officer
RCA Limited

Mike Stockman, MRCVS
Past President, British Veterinary Association;
Chairman, Breed Standards Committee
The Kennel Club

Superintendent Brian Turner,
Co-ordinator, Metropolitan Police Crime
Prevention Service
Scotland Yard

CONSULTANTS

Commander William Anderson, RN
Training manager
Royal Yachting Association

Dr Basil Booth, BSc, PhD
Former UK representative on UNESCO
Volcanic Hazards Committee

Malcolm Conway
Civil Aviation Authority

Dr James Cox, MD, BS, MRCGP, DObst.RCOG
General Practitioner
Caldbeck, Cumbria

Eric Franklin
Knotting Consultant to The Scout Association;
President, International Guild of Knot-Tyers

Geoff Good
Principal Coach
British Canoe Union

Dr Mark Harries, MB, MRCP
Consultant physician
Northwick Park Hospital and Clinical
Research Centre, Middlesex;
Medical Officer, British Olympic team, 1984;
Medical Adviser, Surf Lifesaving Association
and British Surfing Association;
Member of UK Resuscitation Council

Pippa Isbell
Association of British Travel Agents

Angela Large
Senior National Development Officer
Royal Life Saving Society

Dr W. Donald Mackenzie, MB, ChB, MFOM
Principal Medical Officer (Overseas)
British Airways

Contents

When emergency strikes

BE PREPARED

The time to read this book is *before* an emergency strikes, so that, forewarned, you know what to do as soon as danger threatens. Just as the middle of a darkening moor is no place to begin learning how to use a map and compass, the middle of a crisis is no time to begin discovering how to deal with it.

Safety experts also stress that, in any crisis, thinking is as crucial as doing. First assess the situation quickly, they say – then act. The experts identify three major rules to bear in mind: do not panic; improvise; and weigh the risks.

How this book is organised

WHAT TO DO IN AN EMERGENCY aims to cover all the crises that you are likely to run into. The first two sections – *When seconds count* and *First aid and medical emergencies* – are arranged alphabetically. In other sections, the information is arranged thematically: crises affecting swimmers, for example, are grouped separately from boating crises in the section called *Emergencies in the water*.

Within each section, there are also reassuring tips on ways of staying out of trouble, and real-life stories about people who have survived the most terrifying dangers by using their knowledge and their wits.

DO NOT PANIC

In any crisis, staying calm is the most important rule of all. Panic can turn a problem into a tragedy; and staying calm can do more than any other single factor to save a life – yours or someone else's.

A swimmer caught in weeds underwater can untangle himself with his hands if he keeps his head. If, in panic, he lunges blindly for the surface, he may pull the weeds tighter – and drown. Panic destroys judgment and paralyses the muscles.

Knowledge is one antidote to it. The best cure, though, is an unshakable determination not to give way to it. Keep telling yourself that panic will only make things worse.

IMPROVISE

No emergency is quite like any other. Treating a bad cut at home when you have a first aid kit to hand and an ambulance only a telephone call away is very different from trying to cope with the same problem when you are out camping far from help.

In any situation, if you do not have exactly what you need, be prepared to make do with whatever is to hand. Look around for possible substitutes. Keep looking until you find one.

A life buoy and rope, for example, are the best equipment for helping someone who has fallen into water. But if there is no life buoy nearby, a child's rubber ring, a couple of towels knotted together or even a pair of trousers can save a life, too.

WEIGH THE RISKS

Sometimes in a crisis there is no absolutely safe way out. There may be no choice but to take one risk in order to avoid a greater one. If your brakes fail on a steep hill, for instance, you may have to drive deliberately into a hedge – and risk wrecking your car – in order to avoid risking your life in an uncontrollable crash at the bottom.

In any emergency, only you, the person on the spot, can weigh the dangers of each possible course of action against the advantages, and pick the best.

To do that successfully requires clear knowledge and a cool head. This book will help you to achieve both.

First aid and medical emergencies

What you need in a first aid kit

A home first aid kit is mainly intended for minor injuries that you can treat yourself, but it should also be equipped to deal with more serious injuries until the victim gets professional medical help. It should be kept in a well-sealed plastic box, such as an old ice-cream container. Put the box on the top shelf of the hall cupboard or some other place out of the reach of children. Do not keep first aid materials in unsealed containers in the bathroom or kitchen; they may deteriorate in the damp air. When you go on family holidays, take the kit with you.

Write the address and telephone number of your doctor and the address of the Accident and Emergency Department of your local hospital on a piece of paper and fix it to the inside of the first aid box. Tape it to the underside of the lid, for instance.

Do not keep old medicines left over from a previous illness. Flush them down the lavatory or return them to the chemist.

First aid kits can be bought ready-made from chemists, but you can make up your own from the items shown here, and at the same time become familiar with what your kit contains.

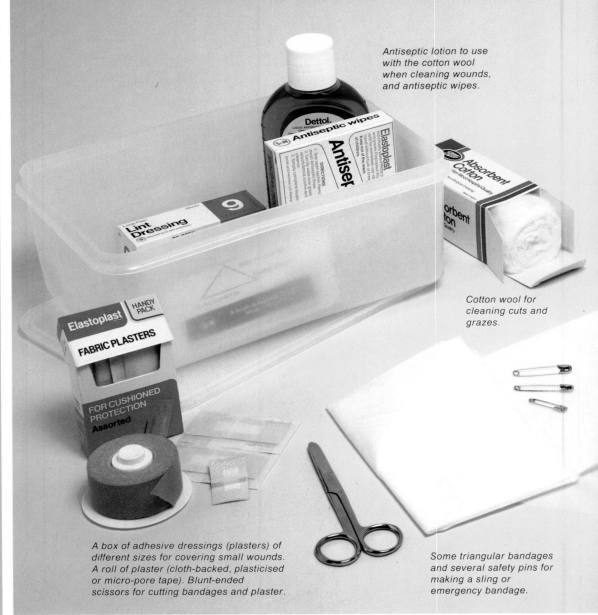

Antiseptic lotion to use with the cotton wool when cleaning wounds, and antiseptic wipes.

Cotton wool for cleaning cuts and grazes.

A box of adhesive dressings (plasters) of different sizes for covering small wounds. A roll of plaster (cloth-backed, plasticised or micro-pore tape). Blunt-ended scissors for cutting bandages and plaster.

Some triangular bandages and several safety pins for making a sling or emergency bandage.

A kit for hikers

On country walks – particularly in remote areas – take a small first aid kit which includes a foil blanket (also called a space blanket). The blanket can be wrapped around a casualty to preserve warmth in freezing temperatures.

The kit should also contain a triangular bandage, a crepe bandage for ankle injuries, some sterile dressings, adhesive dressings and a packet of antiseptic wipes for cleaning a wound when no water is available. Store the kit in a small plastic box.

How to improvise a dressing

If you have to treat a wound when no first aid kit is available, you can improvise dressings and bandages from a range of materials.
• For a dressing, take a clean handkerchief and fold it inside out so that the side that was protected from dirt can be placed on the wound. For a larger dressing, use a clean pillowcase or towel in the same way.
• Another way is to strip the wrapping off a packet of paper handkerchiefs and put the pad on the wound. Alternatively, discard the first few sheets of a toilet roll, then make a pad.

MAKING A TOILET-PAPER DRESSING *Wind toilet paper round your fingers to make a pad. Put its bottom, untouched side on the wound.*

• Do not put fluffy material such as cotton wool directly onto a wound because the fibres will become embedded in it.
• Whatever you make the dressing from, avoid touching the surface that will be in contact with the wound. Otherwise, dirt on your fingers could introduce infection.
• An improvised dressing can be bandaged on with any piece of reasonably clean material, such as a scarf, tie or old linen.

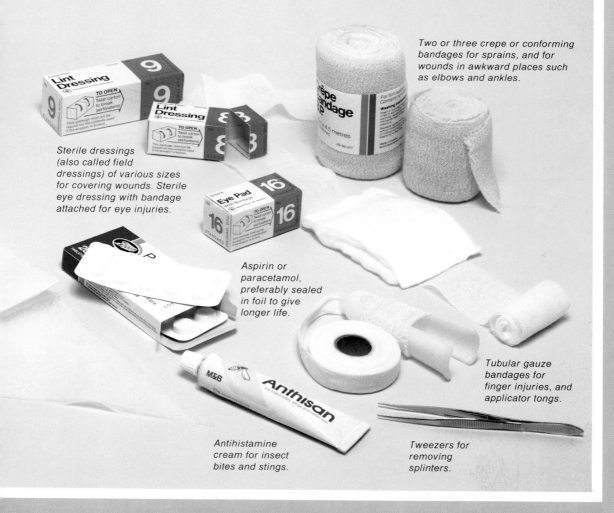

Two or three crepe or conforming bandages for sprains, and for wounds in awkward places such as elbows and ankles.

Sterile dressings (also called field dressings) of various sizes for covering wounds. Sterile eye dressing with bandage attached for eye injuries.

Aspirin or paracetamol, preferably sealed in foil to give longer life.

Tubular gauze bandages for finger injuries, and applicator tongs.

Antihistamine cream for insect bites and stings.

Tweezers for removing splinters.

Abdominal injuries

A car accident, a fall or a stab wound can cause serious injuries to vital organs inside the abdomen – the lower two-thirds of the trunk.

The abdomen contains organs such as the bladder, intestines and womb which are richly supplied with blood. An injury which damages the blood vessels can be as dangerous as one that affects the organs themselves.

Often the wound is clearly visible, and sometimes an organ may even be protruding.

If the wound runs lengthways on the body, lay the casualty flat on the back with the feet slightly raised on a cushion or folded jacket. If the wound runs across the body, lay the casualty on the back with the knees bent and the head and shoulders raised on a folded jacket or cushion. These two positions will help to hold the wound closed.

Treating the wound

Gently remove the clothing from around the wound, taking care not to cough, sneeze or even breathe on it, as it may become infected.

Put a dressing or a folded piece of clean linen over the wound to staunch the bleeding, and tie it in place with a bandage or scarf.

Cover the casualty with a coat or blanket, leaving the arms outside. Call for an ambulance, but do not leave the casualty alone.

Loosen any tight clothing – at the neck and

CASUALTY WITH A WOUND LENGTHWAYS TO THE BODY

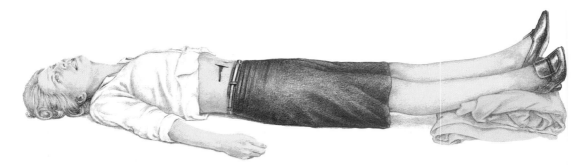

If the wound is running lengthways to the body, lay the casualty flat on her back with the feet slightly raised on a folded blanket, jacket or *other convenient support. Do not raise the head off the ground. This position tenses the muscles of the abdomen and helps to close the wound.*

CASUALTY WITH A WOUND ACROSS THE BODY

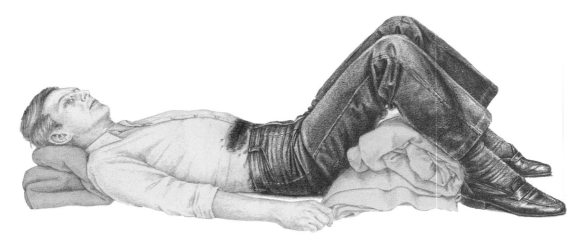

If the wound runs across the abdomen, lay the casualty on his back, with folded coats or blankets under the shoulders. Bend the knees *and support them, too, with anything to hand. This position relaxes the abdominal muscles and helps to keep the wound closed.*

waist, for example – to assist breathing and help blood circulation.

Do not offer anything to eat or drink, as the casualty may need a general anaesthetic at the hospital. If he complains of thirst, moisten his lips with water.

If the casualty becomes unconscious, carefully support the abdomen and gently turn him into the recovery position (see page 136).

If the casualty coughs or vomits, support the wound by pressing gently on the dressing to prevent internal organs from protruding.

If internal organs are already protruding from the wound, do not try to push them back or touch them.

Internal injuries of the abdomen

In some accidents there may be no external signs of injury, but the casualty may be bleeding internally.

All suspected cases of internal bleeding should be examined by a doctor as soon as possible. The warning signs are:
- Pain and tenderness in the abdomen.
- Tightening of the abdomen.
- Bruises and abrasions.
- Nausea and vomiting.
- Muscular spasms.
- Paleness, cold clammy skin and sometimes sweat on the forehead.
- Faintness.

HOW TO BANDAGE AN ABDOMINAL WOUND

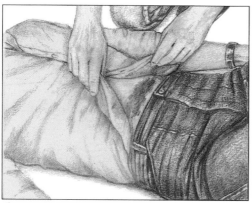

1 *Gently remove the casualty's clothing from around the wound to expose it for treatment. Do not cough, sneeze or breathe on the wound, as that may cause it to become infected. Do not touch the wound with your hands.*

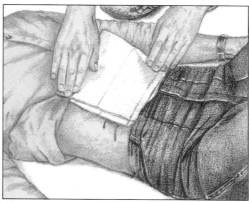

2 *Cover the wound and any protruding organs lightly with a large dressing, ideally a sterile dressing with bandage attached. Alternatively, use a piece of clean linen refolded so that the inside of the fold is now facing out.*

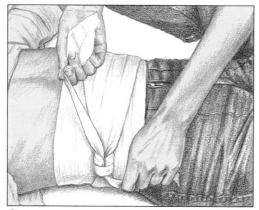

3 *Fix the dressing in place with a bandage, so that it covers, but does not press down on, the wound. Tie the knot away from the wound so that it does not press on the injury, either. If you cannot get a bandage under the casualty's back, secure the dressing with plaster.*

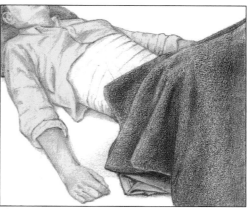

4 *Keep the casualty warm by covering him with a blanket or coat, leaving his arms outside so that you can check his pulse without disturbing him. Make sure that an ambulance has been called, but do not leave the casualty alone. Reassure him that help is on its way.*

Amputation

A finger, toe or major limb which has been severed in an accident can sometimes be sewn back on by microsurgery.

But do not waste time preserving the limb until you have taken care of the casualty, whose life is the first priority.

Do not try to restore the severed limb yourself – by binding it in place with surgical tape, for example. You will only cause the casualty great pain, and damage the tissues, which will make surgery more difficult.

What you should do
• Lay the casualty down and put a pad of gauze or clean linen, such as the inside of a clean, folded handkerchief, on the stump, and fix it in place with a bandage. A scarf will do.
• Immobilise an injured arm by bandaging it to the chest. If a leg is injured, bandage it to the other leg.
• Reassure the injured person and encourage him to keep still, then telephone 999 and ask for an ambulance.
• Once you have dealt with the casualty, try to find the severed limb. Wrap it in clean linen, such as a handkerchief or a pillowcase, and put it in a plastic bag.
• Keep it cool, if possible by packing ice around the plastic bag. Do not let the ice come in direct contact with the limb.
• Give the limb to the ambulance men, or doctor, to go to hospital with the casualty.

Animal bites

Bites from animals can introduce germs from the animal's mouth into the wound, possibly causing infection. There is a similar risk with human bites.

The area of any bite should be thoroughly washed, and if the skin has been broken the victim should see a doctor. Serious wounds should be treated at the Accident and Emergency Department of a hospital.

Report dog bites to the police, as failure to keep a dog under proper control is a legal offence.

CLEANING AND DRESSING A BITE

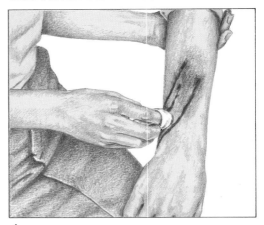

1 Wash the area thoroughly with soap and warm water, or a mild antiseptic. Dry gently, wiping down and away from the wound. Cover with a clean dressing.

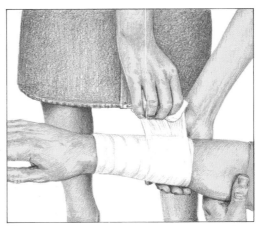

2 Hold the dressing in place with a clean bandage or plaster. Take the victim to a doctor, because injections against tetanus or a course of antibiotics may be required.

Ankle injuries

The ankle is the joint that most often suffers sprains – the stretching or tearing of a ligament linking the bones.

A sprain may be caused by twisting the foot as you walk or run. It causes pain in the joint, which becomes worse if it is moved, and the joint swells up.

The injury may take up to 14 days to heal, depending on the severity. For treatment, see *Sprains and strains*, page 132.

A serious sprain can be hard to distinguish from a fracture. So if there is any doubt, and the casualty cannot support himself on the ankle, assume that a bone is broken.

Treating a fractured ankle

A fracture of the ankle can follow a fall or a stumble that makes the ankle bend excessively, or it can be caused by falling on the foot from a height. The warning signs are:
• Immediate pain, which is often severe.
• The ankle soon becomes swollen or bruised.
• Pain when moving the ankle.
• It may be difficult or impossible to stand on the injured leg.

If you suspect a fractured ankle, apply a cold compress to limit the swelling, and see a doctor as soon as possible.

Make the cold compress by soaking a small towel or other material in cold water, wringing it out and wrapping it around the ankle. Or tie up some ice cubes in a plastic bag, wrap them in a cloth and crush them with a hammer. Then apply the compress to the ankle.

Appendicitis

Spasms of pain in the abdomen may be the first sign of appendicitis. The pain is caused by inflammation of the appendix, a short tube, closed at one end, that projects from the junction of the small and large intestines.

Appendicitis can occur if the open end of the appendix is blocked by fragments of hard waste matter, or if the appendix becomes kinked. As a result, infection sets in and the walls of the appendix become inflamed and swollen.

If the condition is left untreated, it may subside, only to recur – a condition known as chronic appendicitis.

If the condition is acute, however, the pain increases until the appendix finally bursts, spreading the infection through the area immediately around it, or throughout the intestine. This is a surgical emergency, requiring prompt treatment. For this reason, a doctor should be seen as early as possible in cases of suspected appendicitis, especially in children or old people.

The symptoms can take between 4 and 48 hours to develop. Because they are extremely variable, the condition can be difficult to diagnose. Call the doctor immediately if the pain gets worse, becomes continuous, or keeps the sufferer awake – and call him in any case if the pain lasts longer than four hours.

The danger signs

• Recurring spasms of pain. At first they may be felt near the navel, but sometimes in the lower right side of the abdomen.
• After a few hours, there is a constant severe aching in the lower right side of the abdomen.
• The lower right side of the abdomen is tender to the touch. The pain becomes more severe if the sufferer moves; it may interfere with sleep.
• The sufferer feels sick and may vomit. Often there is constipation, although the bowels may move normally, or even be loose.
• Food and drink are usually refused.
• It may hurt to walk, or to pass urine.
• The breath may smell foul.
• Body temperature generally rises to 39°C (102°F) in adults, and can be even higher in children. But sometimes it is only slightly raised.

What you can do to help

• Keep the sufferer lying still with a hot-water bottle wrapped in a towel on the abdomen.
• Rinse the mouth with sips of water, but do not give food or drink.
• Do not administer laxatives.

First aid and medical emergencies

Artificial respiration: the kiss of life

A person who has stopped breathing will die within minutes. After as little as three minutes without oxygen the brain can suffer irreversible damage. So it is urgent to get air into the lungs as quickly as possible. To tell if breathing has stopped, put your ear beside the casualty's mouth and nose and look along the chest. If he or she is breathing, you should be able to hear and feel it, and to see the chest moving.

When breathing stops, the lips, cheeks and ear lobes take on a bluish-grey tinge. Breathing may stop merely because the airway has become blocked for one of three reasons: the head may have fallen forward, making the airway narrower; the tongue may have slipped back in the throat, covering the airway; vomit or saliva may have collected at the back of the throat, blocking the airway.

• Your first step, therefore, must be to open the airway. Tilt the casualty's head backwards, push the chin up and clear out any obstruction in the mouth with your fingers.

• This may be enough to cause breathing to start spontaneously. In that case, turn the casualty over into the recovery position (see page 136) and call for an ambulance.

Breathing for a casualty

• If the casualty does not begin to breathe when the airway is opened, begin mouth-to-mouth respiration (the kiss of life) immediately.

• Pinch the nose shut, and seal your lips around the open mouth. Blow two full breaths into the casualty's mouth, making the chest rise. Then remove your mouth and watch the chest fall. Check the neck pulse with your finger while you watch.

• If there is no pulse, start external chest compression – but only if you have been trained in the technique (see page 52).

• Continue mouth-to-mouth respiration at your normal breathing speed – one breath about every three or four seconds.

• Once the casualty is breathing, turn him or her over into the recovery position (see page 136), *unless* you suspect a broken neck or back. Keep listening to the breathing: if it falters, restart artificial respiration.

Babies and small children

• When giving the kiss of life to a baby or a small child, seal your lips around both the mouth and nose, because the area is so small.

• Give the breaths a little more quickly than your normal breathing rate. For a small child, breathe more gently than you normally would. For a baby, deliver the air with gentle puffs.

If mouth-to-mouth is not possible

• Occasionally it is not possible to use a casualty's mouth for artificial respiration – perhaps because of mouth injuries. In such a case breathe into the nose, holding the mouth shut as you do so.

CLEARING THE PASSAGE FOR AIR

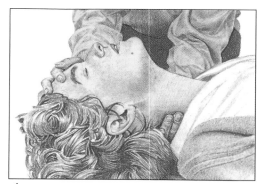

1 *Tilt the head back by lifting with one hand under the neck and pressing down with the other on the forehead. This opens the airway.*

MOUTH-TO-MOUTH RESPIRATION

1 *Ensure that the head and chin are tilted well upwards, so that the casualty's airway remains open. Pinch the nose shut with the finger and thumb of one hand.*

MOUTH-TO-NOSE RESPIRATION

Tilt the head and chin well upwards, holding the mouth shut with one hand. Seal your lips around the nose, and breathe into the casualty in the same way as for the kiss of life.

2 *Take your hand from the neck and push the chin up. This lifts the tongue away from the opening to the windpipe.*

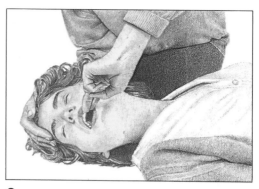

3 *If the casualty does not begin breathing, turn the head to the side and clear the mouth by sweeping inside it with two fingers.*

2 *Seal your lips around the open mouth and deliver two full breaths. Then remove your mouth and check the neck pulse (see* Has the heart stopped beating? *page 52).*

3 *Watch the chest fall. Replace your mouth and begin breathing into the casualty at your normal rate (every three or four seconds). Keep going until she starts breathing again.*

GIVING ARTIFICIAL RESPIRATION TO A BABY
Clear the airway and hold the baby with its head tilted back. Cover both nose and mouth with your mouth and puff in gently, making the chest rise. Remove your mouth and watch the chest fall. Then continue the puffs, slightly faster than you would normally breathe yourself.

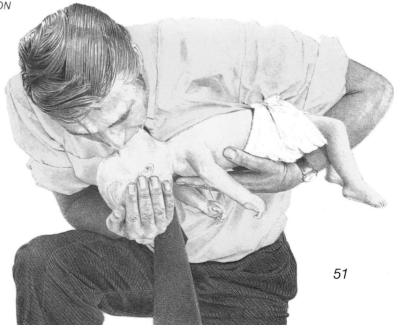

Artificial respiration: external chest compression

WARNING – THIS TECHNIQUE IS ONLY FOR PEOPLE TRAINED IN FIRST AID. IT IS DANGEROUS IF ATTEMPTED WITHOUT TRAINING.

If a casualty's heart stops beating, blood will no longer be pumped to the brain, and mouth-to-mouth respiration will be useless by itself. Brain damage will begin within minutes.

Squeezing the casualty's heart between the breastbone and the spine will make it work like a hand pump, forcing the blood around the circulatory system. If the brain continues to receive blood, the heart may spontaneously resume beating.

External chest compression is always used with mouth-to-mouth respiration (the kiss of life) to provide the blood with oxygen.

But chest compression can be a dangerous technique. The heart is sensitive, and if it is compressed while still beating faintly it may stop completely.

Compression should be used only by a person trained in first aid – and only after he or she has established conclusively that the casualty's heartbeat has stopped.

Consequently the information on these two pages is intended only as a memory aid for trained people. The technique should not be attempted without training, and should never be practised on a healthy person.

Compressing the casualty's chest

Compression is carried out on the lower half of the breastbone. The heel of the hand should be centred on a point two finger-widths up from the bottom of the breastbone.

• The pressure you apply should depress the chest of an adult by 1½in (40mm), and should be repeated at the rate of 80 per minute. If you are on your own, you should give 15 compressions, then inflate the lungs twice by mouth-to-mouth respiration.

HAS THE HEART STOPPED BEATING?

The only reliable way to discover if the heart has stopped beating is to feel the pulse of one of the carotid arteries in the casualty's neck to either side of the Adam's apple. The pulse on the wrist is not a reliable indication.

Feel the neck pulse after giving the first two breaths in mouth-to-mouth respiration. If there is no pulse, begin external chest compression.

Check the pulse again after one minute, and then after every three minutes. If the pulse returns, it means that the heart has started beating again.

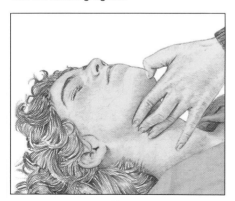

To feel the pulse of the carotid artery, place your fingers firmly in the hollow of the neck between the Adam's apple and the muscle at the side.

CHEST COMPRESSION ON AN ADULT

1 *Place the heel of one hand on the casualty's chest, two finger-widths up from the bottom of the breastbone. Keep your thumb and fingers raised, so that they do not press on the ribs.*

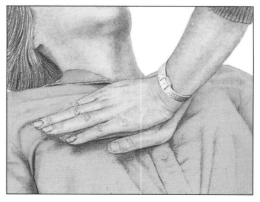

2 *Keep the heel of your hand in place and put your other hand over it. Press down 1½in (40mm), keeping your thumbs and fingers raised. Let the chest rise again.*

• If two trained people are giving artificial respiration together, the sequence is five compressions to one inflation.

• If necessary, continue the sequence until medical help arrives.

• When you detect a neck pulse, stop compression, but continue mouth-to-mouth respiration until breathing starts. Keep checking the pulse. If it stops, restart compression.

Treating children and babies

• Use one hand only to compress the chest of a child under ten.

• The depth of the compression should be slightly less than for an adult, and the speed a little greater – 80-100 times a minute, depending on the child's age.

• Give chest compression to a baby using two fingers only. The depth of compression must be no more than 1in (25mm), and the speed 100 times a minute.

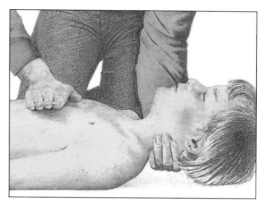

COMPRESSION ON A YOUNG CHILD
Press down the lower breastbone 1-1½in (25-40mm) at a slightly faster rate than an adult's pulse. Give 15 presses, then two lung inflations using mouth-to-mouth respiration.

COMPRESSION ON A BABY

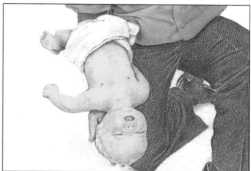

1 *Support the baby along one arm with your hand cradling its head, which should be slightly tilted down. You can also give mouth-to-mouth respiration in this position.*

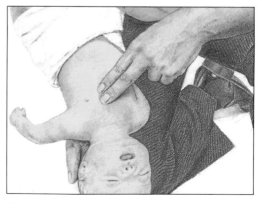

2 *Press down* the middle of the breastbone ½-1in (13-25mm), using two fingers only. Give 15 presses, then two lung inflations using mouth-to-mouth respiration.

3 *Give 15 presses at normal pulse rate, then inflate the lungs twice by mouth-to-mouth respiration. Repeat the sequence four times a minute. Check the carotid pulse after one minute, then every three minutes.*

Asphyxiation

A person suffering from asphyxiation (lack of oxygen in the blood) may die unless first aid is given promptly. Nerve cells in the brain can die after only three minutes without oxygen.

Common causes of asphyxiation
• Blockage of the airway by food, blood, vomit or broken teeth, or by the tongue falling to the back of the throat. Such blockages can occur with an unconscious person.
• Compression of the chest or damage to the lungs – possibly in a road accident.
• Gas poisoning – possibly from carbon monoxide given off by a car exhaust in a confined space.
• Electrical accidents.
• Suffocation – possibly from a plastic bag being placed over the head.
• Strangulation – possibly from attempted suicide by hanging.
• A severe attack of asthma or bronchitis.

Warning signs
• Breathing is difficult, and may become noisy and eventually stop altogether.
• The face turns blue, and the veins on the head and neck are swollen.
• The casualty gradually loses consciousness and may have fits.

What you should do
• If a person is suffocating because his mouth and nose have become blocked, remove the cause. If, for example, a plastic bag covers his head, tear it.
• Check for danger to yourself and to the casualty. If there is a continuing threat – from escaping gas, for example – stop it at the source or drag the casualty clear.
• If the casualty has been strangled, quickly cut or untie the cord or other material around the neck. If possible, keep the knot intact as possible evidence for the police.
• Check that the casualty is breathing. If not, clear the airway (see page 50).
• If breathing does not start, give mouth-to-mouth respiration (see page 50).
• If you suspect that the airway is blocked by food, treat for choking (see page 82).
• Once breathing is normal, turn the casualty into the recovery position (see page 136).
• Call for an ambulance but do not leave the casualty alone. Keep a careful watch on breathing, and give artificial respiration again if it falters.

Asthmatic attack

Most asthma attacks, while distressing, do not threaten life. However, a few particularly serious attacks are fatal each year.

During an asthmatic attack the muscles around the air tubes go into a spasm, impeding breathing. At the same time, the walls of the air tubes swell, and the tubes are further blocked by thick, tenacious mucus.

Warning signs of a severe attack
• Noisy, wheezy breathing.
• Pale or bluish-grey complexion.
• Beads of sweat on the forehead.
• An anxious expression.
• In a prolonged attack, mental confusion because of lack of oxygen.
• The victim struggles for breath, and is often

HOW TO HELP DURING AN ATTACK

1 *If possible, sit an asthma sufferer in an upright chair drawn close to a table or the back of another chair on which he can rest his forearms. His back should be fairly straight, and his elbows spread out.*

---

found sitting hunched up grasping the chair arms, a table-top or other support.

What you can do

- Most asthmatic attacks occur at night, often when the sufferer is in bed. In this case, open the window to provide fresh air and prop up the sufferer in bed with pillows.
- Even though the window is open, keep the room warm.
- Call the doctor for all but the mildest attack. Reassure the sufferer, telling him that expert help is on the way.
- If you have to take an asthma victim to hospital, transport him sitting up in the front passenger seat rather than lying down in the back.

Causes of asthma attacks

- Respiratory infection may cause inflammation of the air tubes.
- Allergy to various substances, including house-dust mites, animal fur or feathers, pollen and some foods.
- Night-time attacks in children are often associated with house-dust mites, down pillows or pets sleeping in the bedroom.
- Anxiety or excitement seems to bring on attacks in some people.

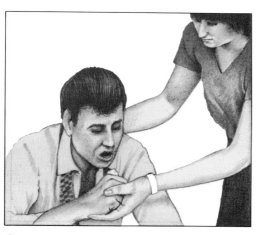

2 *If the sufferer has an inhaler, help him to use it. If he has an oxygen cylinder at home, give him oxygen only if you have been taught how to use it.*

Back or neck injuries

Mishandling a person whose back or neck is broken can cause permanent paralysis or even death.

A casualty with a suspected broken back or neck should be moved only if he is in immediate danger – in a burning building, for example. Otherwise leave him where he is. Any moving should be left to ambulancemen who have the right equipment.

Before you even touch an injured person, look for possible clues. For example, if he is lying at the foot of a ladder or a flight of stairs, it is possible he has suffered a back or neck injury.

Warning signs

- Loss of feeling and movement below the injured area, or a sensation of having been cut in half.
- Pain at the site of injury.
- A tingling sensation or pins and needles in the hands and feet (denotes neck injury).
- Inability to move fingers, wrists, toes or ankles when asked to do so, with no symptoms of a broken arm or leg.
- Inability to feel pain when the skin is gently nipped.
- Difficulty in breathing.

What you should do

- Tell the casualty to lie still.
- Cover him with a blanket and comfort him as much as possible. Do not raise the head or try to rest it on anything. Call for an ambulance.
- If the casualty is unconscious, and lying on his back, do not turn him over into the recovery position. Leave him face up, and clear his mouth of any obstructions to breathing with your fingers.
- Watch his breathing carefully. If it stops, begin mouth-to-mouth respiration (see page 50) immediately, even though tilting the head risks further damage to the spine. Be as careful and gentle as you can.

Bandages

In medical emergencies, bandages have three different uses. They keep a dressing in place over a wound, preventing dirt and germs from entering; they maintain pressure on a wound, controlling and absorbing bleeding; and they can be used to support or immobilise an injured part of the body (see *Slings*, page 121, and *Splints*, page 127).

Bandages are usually made of calico or gauze, but in an emergency they can be improvised from sheets, pillowcases, stockings, scarves or any other suitable material.

If no bandage is available, a dressing can be secured with strips of adhesive plaster.

Dressings, which are used to absorb blood and prevent infection, are usually a pad of cotton wool covered with gauze. Fluffy material such as cotton wool should not go directly on a wound because the fibres will stick.

In an emergency, a dressing can be made from a pad of any clean, dry, absorbent material. The inside of a folded handkerchief, a towel or pillowcase – even a pad of paper tissues or toilet paper – can all be used (see *How to improvise a dressing*, page 45).

Sterile dressings with a bandage attached, and sealed in a protective wrapping, can be bought from chemists. They are also known as field dressings, and will keep indefinitely in a family medicine cabinet.

Two other widely used types of bandage are the roller bandage, which varies in width from 1 to 6in (25 to 150mm), and the triangular bandage, with three sides about 3ft (1m) long.

APPLYING THE BANDAGE TO A WOUND

1 *Start by putting the end of the bandage on the limb and making a firm turn to hold it in place. Apply the outer surface to the skin so that you can unroll it easily. Bandage a limb in the position in which it is to remain.*

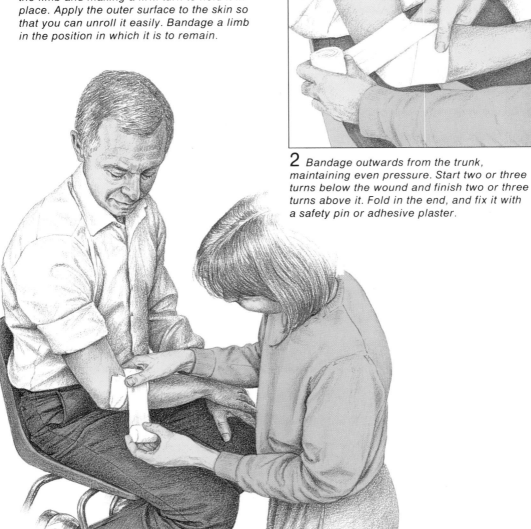

2 *Bandage outwards from the trunk, maintaining even pressure. Start two or three turns below the wound and finish two or three turns above it. Fold in the end, and fix it with a safety pin or adhesive plaster.*

How to use a roller bandage

Traditional roller bandages are made from non-stretch, open-weave gauze and are difficult to apply. Crepe, elasticated and 'conforming' bandages are easier to put on, and because they follow the contours of the body the pressure they exert on the wound is more evenly distributed.

Roller bandages can be bought in different widths for different purposes: a 1in (25mm) bandage for fingers and toes; 2in (50mm) for hands; 2½in (65mm) for arms; 3 or 3½in (75 or 90mm) for legs; and 4 or 6in (100 or 150mm) for the trunk.

Is the bandage too tight?

It is easy to bind a bandage so tightly that it interferes with the casualty's nerves or blood circulation. After applying a bandage, and again ten minutes later, check for the following warning signals.

- The casualty has a tingling feeling in the fingers or toes, or loses feeling altogether.
- The fingers or toes are very cold.
- The casualty is unable to move the fingers or toes.
- The beds of the fingernails or toenails are unusually pale or blue.
- The pulse of an injured arm is weak compared to the other arm, or completely absent.

If any of these danger signs occur, remove the bandage and apply it again more loosely.

Other types of bandage

Triangular bandages can be bought from chemists or they can be made by cutting a piece of

FINISHING OFF A BANDAGE WITH A KNOT

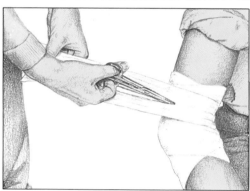

1 *If you do not have a safety pin or adhesive plaster, leave a piece of bandage free. The length will depend on the thickness of the area being bandaged. Cut the end of the bandage in half lengthways.*

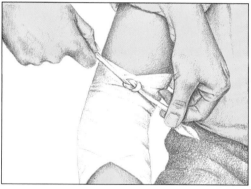

3 *Take the two ends around the limb again and tie them off, preferably with a reef knot (right end over left end, then left end over right). Once again, make sure that the knot does not press on the wound. Tuck in the ends.*

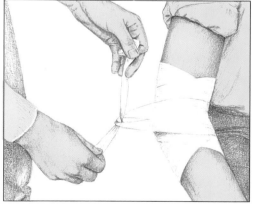

2 *Tie the two strips together with a single knot, pulling fairly tight at the bottom of the cut. This knot will stop the cut tearing further when you tie off the bandage. Make sure that the knot does not press on the wound.*

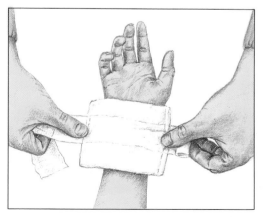

BANDAGE WITH DRESSING ATTACHED
A bandage and dressing combined, sealed in a wrapping, can be bought at chemists under the name of sterile dressing. The dressing is bound onto the wound, using the bandage.

linen or calico, about 3ft (1m) square, in half diagonally.

Unfolded, triangular bandages can be used as slings (see page 121).

They can also be folded into a broad bandage suitable for strapping up a broken limb, or into a narrow bandage for holding a dressing in place over a wound.

A triangular bandage can also be made into a ring-pad for a wound which contains a foreign object, or to protect an open fracture when a broken bone is jutting from the wound.

Seamless tubular bandages are easier to apply than conventional bandages, because they do not need to be tied.

Tubular bandages resemble stockings without feet, and they are available from chemists in various sizes to fit different parts of the body. They are all supplied with applicator tongs to slip them on over a dressing.

MAKING A RING-PAD

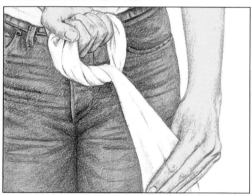

1 *Wind one end of a narrow bandage once or twice around your fingers, to make a loop. Bring the other end through the loop, under and back through again.*

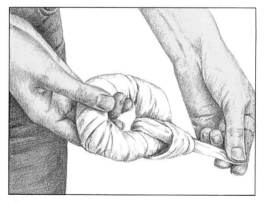

2 *Continue winding the free end around the loop until all the bandage is used up. You then have a pad to prevent pressure on a wound that has a foreign body, such as glass, in it.*

IMPROVISING WITH A TRIANGULAR BANDAGE

1 *To make a broad or narrow bandage in an emergency, spread the triangular bandage out on a flat, clean surface.*

2 *Fold the apex of the triangle to the centre of the base, and then fold it once more in the same direction. This makes a broad bandage.*

3 *To make a narrow bandage, fold a third time in the same direction. It can then be used like a roller bandage to bind wounds.*

PUTTING A TUBULAR BANDAGE ON A FINGER

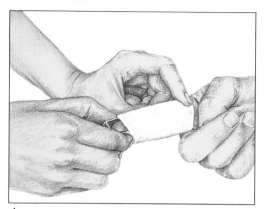

1 Cut a piece of tubular bandage 2½ times as long as the finger. Put the applicator over the finger and slide the bandage over the tongs.

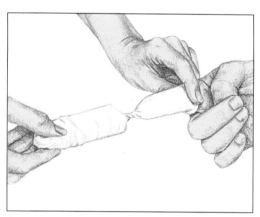

2 Slip the applicator off the finger, together with one end of the bandage. Turn the tongs so that the bandage is slightly twisted.

3 Push the tongs gently back down the finger, sliding the bandage off them as you go and leaving the finger covered with two layers.

Black eye

A blow to the eye socket and eyelid causes internal bleeding which colours the skin dark blue or black and produces a swelling.

Immediate treatment involves cold compresses. Do not put raw steak on a black eye; it is ineffective and wasteful.

There is always a possibility of damage to the eye itself or to the head, so have the injury examined by a doctor.

What you should do

• Put a cold compress over the eye to limit the swelling and relieve the pain. To make the compress, put crushed ice or ice cubes into a plastic bag, add some salt to encourage the ice to melt, seal the bag and wrap it in a cloth. Alternatively, soak a small towel in cold or iced water and wring it out.

• Cool the eye for at least 30 minutes, replacing the compress if it becomes warm.

• Take the casualty to a doctor as soon as possible to check that there is no serious damage to the eye or a fracture of the skull. A blow which is violent enough to blacken the eye may cause either.

First aid and medical emergencies

Bleeding

Although bleeding can be alarming and dramatic, most cases are not fatal, provided the injury is treated promptly.

Bleeding can usually be stopped by pressing down on the wound, which slows the flow of blood and allows clotting to take place. If there is a foreign object, such as a piece of glass, in the wound, apply the pressure alongside it. Pressure must be maintained for up to 10 minutes.

The clotting process can be assisted by raising the injured area, which also slows the flow of blood. If severe bleeding continues, it may be possible to stop it by pressing on the appropriate artery. But this is a last resort only (see page 62).

Detecting bleeding in the dark

Usually bleeding is obvious, but after an accident – particularly in the dark – a casualty's position may conceal a serious wound. In this situation feel all over and under the body for patches of sticky dampness, and assume they are blood until you are sure that they are not.

Other warning signs of severe bleeding are:
- Pale skin which is moist and cold to touch.
- Profuse sweating.
- Fast but weak pulse (the normal adult pulse rate is 60-80 per minute).
- Casualty complains of thirst.
- Casualty's vision becomes blurred and he feels faint and giddy.
- Breathing becomes shallow, with yawning and sighing.
- Casualty becomes restless and talkative.

A large foreign object in the wound

If a large object, such as a piece of glass, is embedded in a wound, do not try to remove it. You may make the injury worse. Moreover, the object may be plugging the wound, helping to restrict the bleeding.

Control the bleeding by pressing the sides of the wound together around the object. Then bind up the wound, using a ring-pad (see page 58) to keep pressure off the object.

Telephone for an ambulance, as the casualty will need hospital treatment.

HOW TO STOP SEVERE BLEEDING

1 *Lay the casualty down. Remove clothing from around the wound if you can without wasting time or causing distress. Press down hard on the wound with any absorbent material or your bare hands, unless something is embedded in it.*

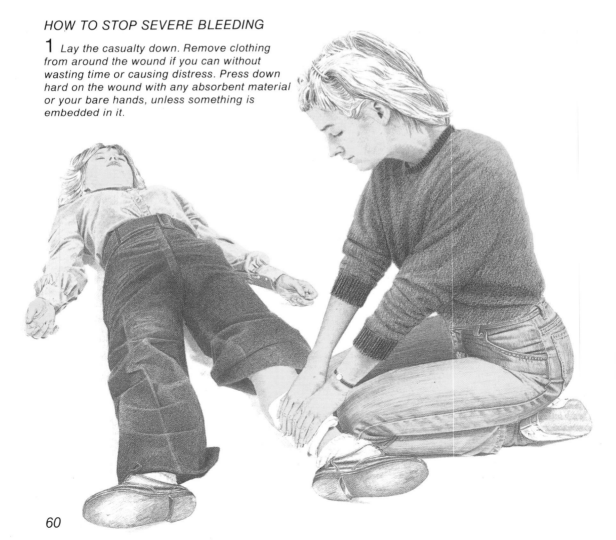

First aid and
medical emergencies

2 *If possible, raise the wounded area above the level of the heart to reduce the flow of blood. When the bleeding stops, put on an absorbent dressing, such as the inside of a clean, folded handkerchief.*

3 *If the blood seeps through the dressing, do not remove it. Put another dressing on top. Tie the dressing in place with a bandage or other material. Keep the casualty as still as possible and do not give food or drink.*

A LARGE WOUND
Squeeze the sides of a large wound together gently but firmly, and maintain the pressure for up to 10 minutes. Then treat as above and call an ambulance.

IF SOMETHING IS EMBEDDED

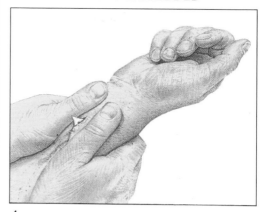

1 *To stop the bleeding, squeeze the edges of the wound together for up to 10 minutes. Do not try to remove the object.*

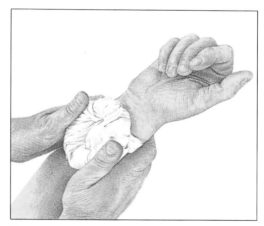

2 *Put a thick circular pad of clean material around the wound, preferably higher than the object, to prevent pressure on it.*

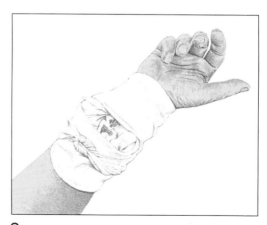

3 *Bandage the wound with diagonally applied strips of material that do not go over the object. Get the casualty to hospital.*

Stopping blood flow at a pressure point

If severe bleeding from an arm or leg cannot be stopped by direct pressure on the wound, or if direct pressure cannot be applied successfully, it may be possible to stop the bleeding by pressing on a pressure point.

Pressure points are places where an artery can be pressed against an underlying bone to prevent the blood flowing past. Use a pressure point to reduce severe bleeding only while a dressing is being prepared. Never maintain the pressure for more than 10 minutes, otherwise the tissues may be permanently damaged and the limb may have to be amputated.

There are two main pressure points. One is on the inner side of the arm where the brachial artery can be pressed against the bone. The other is high inside the thigh, where the femoral artery can be pressed against the pelvis.

When a varicose vein bursts

If a varicose vein in the leg bursts or is injured, severe blood loss can occur rapidly. The bleeding must be stopped as quickly as possible and the casualty taken to hospital.
• Lay the casualty down and press on the wound with a cloth pad, such as the inside of a folded handkerchief. If no pad is available, press with your bare fingers.
• Raise the leg onto your thigh and maintain the pressure for up to 10 minutes to stop the bleeding.
• Put a dressing on the wound and tie it firmly in place with a bandage or piece of material.
• If bleeding continues, lay further dressings and bandages over the first.
• Tell the patient to rest, and prop up the leg with pillows or on a chair seat.
• Call for an ambulance.

When blood flows from nose, mouth or ear

If an injured person bleeds from the nose, mouth or ear, he may be suffering from a severe internal injury to the head or chest.

A fractured skull may cause blood to trickle from the nose or ear. An injury to the lungs, caused by a fractured rib, may cause the casualty to cough up blood from the mouth.

Telephone for an ambulance as quickly as possible, and in the meantime place the casualty in a half-sitting position with the head tilted towards the side from which the blood is coming.

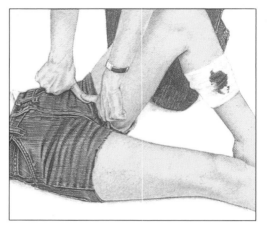

THE FEMORAL PRESSURE POINT
Lay the victim down and bend the injured leg at the knee. Press down firmly in the centre of the fold of the groin with both thumbs, one on top of the other, against the rim of the pelvis. Do not press for longer than 10 minutes.

THE BRACHIAL PRESSURE POINT
Hold the casualty's arm at right angles to the body. The brachial artery runs along the inner side of the upper arm. To control bleeding from the lower arm, put one hand under the upper arm and press your fingers against the bone.

First aid and medical emergencies

BLOOD FROM NOSE, MOUTH OR EAR

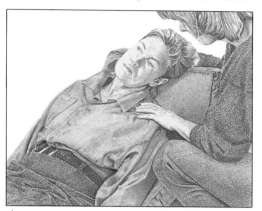

1 *Prop the casualty up in a half-sitting position, with the head tilted towards the side from which the blood is coming.*

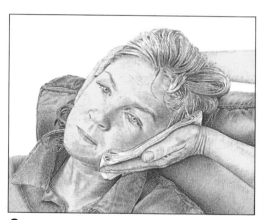

2 *Cover the bleeding point with a pad of clean material or cotton wool, but do not apply pressure. Telephone for an ambulance.*

3 *If the casualty becomes unconscious before the ambulance arrives, put her in the recovery position like this (see page 136).*

Blindness

Sudden blindness can occur in one or both eyes for a number of reasons, some much less serious than others.

Migraine

The most common cause is migraine, which can produce bright spots or zigzag lines in the vision, preventing the victim from seeing properly. The disturbances of the vision are seen with both eyes. The sight will return to normal in 30 minutes or less, and a severe headache is likely to follow.

After the first attack, see your doctor. Once the condition has been diagnosed it should not be necessary to see the doctor after subsequent attacks.

Snow blindness

People who spend long periods in the snow risk snow blindness if they do not protect their eyes with dark glasses. The ultraviolet rays from bright sunlight reflected from the snow inflame the cornea, causing loss of vision.

Cover the victim's eyes with improvised pads and get medical help as quickly as possible. With prompt treatment, normal vision should return in a day or two.

Circulation problems in the eye

High blood pressure and diabetes can bring about haemorrhages or clots in the blood vessels of the eye. These clots can cause sudden, painless loss of vision – either partial or total – in one eye.

The victim should rest in a chair with eyes closed until medical help is obtained. The doctor will almost certainly arrange emergency admission to an eye hospital.

Detached retina

A sudden painless loss or change of vision, sometimes preceded by flashing lights, can be the main symptom of a detached retina.

Alternatively, the victim may have the sensation of a curtain coming across the field of vision.

Get medical help immediately. With prompt treatment, the eyesight can be successfully restored.

Acute glaucoma

Severe pain in and around the eye, with blurring of the vision, can indicate glaucoma, a rare but serious eye ailment. It occurs most often in elderly people, particularly women.

The main attack is often preceded by blurring of the vision and discomfort in the eye, which is better after sleep.

Attacks often occur in the evening, and can be caused by excitement.

Call for a doctor immediately and keep the patient in a well-lit room until help arrives. Treatment with drugs and possibly surgery can lessen the damaging effects on the vision.

Blisters

Blisters caused by burns or friction to the skin usually heal within a week, whether they burst or not. A severe blister, affecting more than the outer layer of skin, will also heal completely but may leave a scar.

To burst or not to burst?

Do not burst a blister deliberately unless the taut skin is causing acute discomfort. Opening the skin increases the risk of infection.

If you decide to do so, observe scrupulous conditions of cleanliness.

• Wash the blistered area, and your hands, thoroughly.

• Pass a fine needle through a flame and let it cool for a moment. Do not wipe off any soot and do not touch the point.

• Hold the needle flat on the skin and press the point gently but firmly into the blister, just enough to burst it.

• Remove the needle and make a second puncture on the opposite side of the blister.

• Remove the needle and press gently on the blister with a clean piece of cotton wool.

• Wipe, and apply an adhesive dressing.

If a blister bursts by itself, expose it to the air as much as possible in hygienic conditions, but keep it covered with a bandage if there is a risk of dirt getting in.

See your doctor if a blister becomes infected, with a swollen, tender or inflamed area around it, or if blisters occur without any obvious cause. Multiple blisters are a symptom of several diseases, including shingles, chickenpox and impetigo.

How to avoid blisters

Blisters can be avoided by taking a few simple precautions.

• Take care when cooking or ironing. Cooks, for example, often receive burns on the arm when the oven door swings closed as they remove cooked food.

• Wear protective gloves for any heavy manual work to which you are not accustomed.

• Only buy shoes that fit well, and break them in with short periods of wear.

• For country walks, wear comfortable boots or shoes, with two pairs of socks to reduce friction on the feet. They can be a thin cotton pair next to the skin, with a thicker pair of woollen oversocks.

Boils

Most boils burst within a week of starting, but if the infection goes very deep it may take two weeks for the boil to 'come to a head'. The process can be speeded up by applying hot cloths or magnesium-sulphate poultices to the boil.

While waiting for the boil to burst, try to rest the affected area, and move it as little as possible. This allows the body's defences to work, and reduces the chance of the infection spreading below the skin.

Take paracetamol or aspirin to relieve the pain. Do not apply creams or antiseptics to the skin; they will not penetrate and so will not help to cure the boil.

When the boil bursts, cover it with a clean, dry dressing to prevent infection entering the wound.

Why do they occur?

Boils tend to occur in hairy parts of the body and areas where friction takes place, such as the nostrils, armpits, back of the neck and between the legs and buttocks.

They are caused by infection from bacteria, particularly in people with low resistance due to excessive tiredness, poor nutrition, diabetes mellitus or a blood disorder.

The bacteria create pockets of infection in the skin, often around a hair follicle. The follicle and surrounding cells in the skin are killed by the bacteria and form pus, which increases (or 'comes to a head') until it bursts through the skin and escapes.

A collection of boils, forming in several hair follicles, is called a carbuncle. The pocket of pus may be extensive, and can spread below the skin until two or more heads form and burst.

Boils tend to spread between members of a household, and sufferers should use their own towels and if possible sterilise underwear and handkerchiefs in boiling water or disinfectant while the boil is discharging.

It should be necessary to see a doctor only:

• If the boil is very painful.

• If the inflammation around the boil spreads without coming to a head.

• If the boil does not discharge pus, although a head has developed.

• If a person has many boils at the same time, or a sequence of infections.

The doctor may cut into the boil to release the pressure and ease the pain. Antibiotics may be prescribed to prevent the spread of infection. And tests may be made to discover any disease that is lowering resistance to infection.

To avoid boils in the future, eat a balanced diet and obtain plenty of rest to build up the body's resistance to infection. Control diabetes or any other disorders.

Bruises

Bruises are the visual sign of bleeding beneath the skin, usually as the result of a blow. Blood seeps into the tissues, causing swelling, soreness and discoloration.

The bruise is usually red or pink to start with, turning bluish and then greenish-yellow. These colour changes are caused by the gradual degeneration of the components of the blood as the bruise starts to heal.

Before treating a bruise check that there are no other injuries, particularly fractures.

Apply a cold compress to the bruised area to help to limit the swelling. The compress can be a small towel soaked in cold water and wrung out, or crushed ice cubes tied up in a plastic bag and wrapped in a cloth.

The cooling process slows down the blood flow. Apply the compress as soon as possible and keep it on for at least 30 minutes. Alternatively, instead of using a compress, hold the bruised area under a running cold tap.

A particularly severe blow can result in the outline of clothing becoming imprinted in the bruise. This is known as pattern bruising. If it should occur, see a doctor as the impact may have damaged internal organs.

See a doctor also:
• If the pain is severe, or if there is difficulty in moving the bruised part 24 hours later.
• If bruises occur without any apparent reason.
• If the lower leg is bruised in an elderly person or a person suffering from poor circulation.
• If the vision is disturbed as the result of a black eye (see page 59).

First aid and medical emergencies

TREATING A BRUISED ARM

1 Put the casualty in a comfortable position and get him to support the injured part before and during treatment. This helps to reduce the bleeding within the tissues.

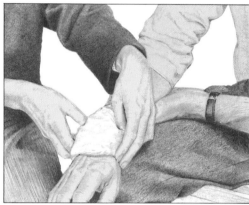

2 Apply a cold compress at once to help to minimise the swelling. If necessary, fix the compress in place with a stretch bandage, winding from below the injury to above it.

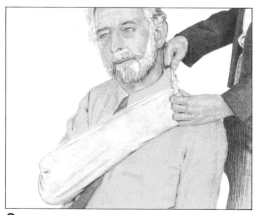

3 Support a bruised arm with a sling (see page 121). If a leg is bruised, lay the casualty down and prop up the leg on a pillow. For bruises on the trunk, lay him down with pillows below head and shoulders.

Burns and scalds

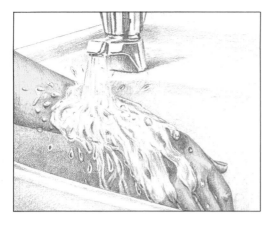

TREATING A MINOR BURN
A superficial burn smaller than a 10p piece can be treated by flooding it with cold water for at least ten minutes, or immersing it in any cold harmless liquid, such as milk or beer.

The seriousness of a burn or scald depends on how deep it is and how large an area it covers. All but minor burns and scalds are potentially serious and should be seen by a doctor. The treatment for burns and scalds is identical.

Do not put fat, ointment or lotion on a burn. It will have to be removed by hospital staff before they can give treatment, and may be a source of infection.

Do not apply any plasters, do not touch a burn and do not break any blisters. And do not remove anything that is sticking to a burn.

The first action in treating a casualty is to remove him from the source of heat. If the source is electrical, pull out the plug or switch off the power, taking care not to injure yourself.

If the burn is caused by a dry chemical, such as caustic soda or quicklime, brush away as much as you can with a duster or soft brush, taking care to protect your own hands. Remove contaminated clothing and check that the casualty is not lying on any of the chemical. For

REMOVING BURNT CLOTHING
When approaching a person with burning clothing, hold a blanket, rug or coat in front of you for protection. Wrap the material around him and lay him on the floor, burnt side uppermost. When the fire is extinguished, remove any hot clothing that can be taken off easily, but leave fragments that have stuck to the skin.

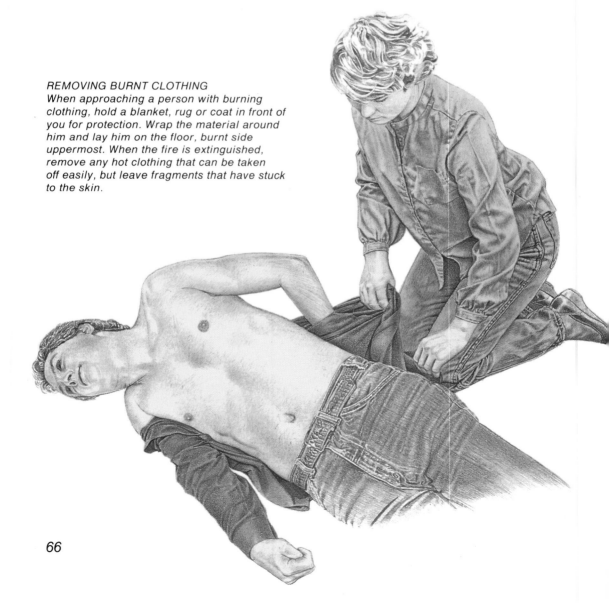

burns and scalds in the mouth, give the casualty ice cubes or ice cream to suck.

Treating a minor burn

If the burn is extremely painful it will probably be superficial, affecting only the outer layers of skin. It will be red, swollen and possibly blistered.

If a burn of this sort is smaller than a 10p piece, hold it under a slow-running cold-water tap or put it in cold water for at least ten minutes to cool the skin. If no water is available, use some other cold liquid, such as milk or beer.

Remove rings, watch or tight clothing before the area starts to swell, and finally cover it with a dressing of non-fluffy material.

Larger superficial burns

If a superficial burn is larger than a 10p piece, see a doctor or go to a hospital Accident and Emergency Department, because there is a danger of infection. Cool the burn in cold water and cover it with a clean dressing, but do not waste time before getting medical help.

Dealing with deep burns

If a burnt area of skin appears grey and is peeling or charred, the burn may be deep. It may not be particularly painful, as the nerves will have been damaged.

Whatever the size of a deep burn, do not immerse it in water. Cover it with a clean, non-fluffy dressing and get medical help at once, because there is a strong risk of infection.

Widespread burns

Burns covering a large area of the body, such as an arm, a thigh or the chest, are medical emergencies which must be treated in hospital as quickly as possible with minimum interference to the damaged skin.

Remove rings, watch or tight clothing before the area starts to swell. Remove scalding clothing as soon as you can handle it. Then dial 999 and ask for an ambulance urgently.

While waiting for the ambulance, cover the burn with clean, non-fluffy material, such as a freshly washed pillowcase. Fix it in place with a scarf or piece of clean cloth.

If the casualty is unconscious but breathing, put him in the recovery position (see page 136), before calling for an ambulance.

When a person's clothes catch fire

A person with burning clothes should be laid flat to prevent the flames rising to the head. Then douse the fire with water or any non-flammable liquid such as milk or beer (but *not* alcoholic spirits such as whisky or gin).

·If no liquid is available, wrap the casualty in thick, non-synthetic material, such as a rug, blanket or woollen coat, to smother the flames.

If your own clothes catch fire, wrap yourself in thick material and lie down.

DEEP OR WIDESPREAD BURNS

1 *Prevent infection by covering the burnt area with a clean dressing, such as a clean handkerchief or pillowcase. Hold it in place with a soft towel or other material.*

2 *Reassure the casualty and give sips of water to replace lost fluid. Adults should sip half a cup of water over ten minutes. Children should sip water continuously.*

3 *If the burn is widespread, lay the casualty down and treat for shock (see page 120). Call an ambulance as soon as possible. Do not try to cool deep or widespread burns with water.*

Chest injuries

Car accidents are the most common cause of chest injuries, particularly among drivers and passengers not wearing seat belts.

The other main causes are stab wounds and crushing by a heavy weight.

Serious chest injuries divide into two types, depending on whether the chest wall has been punctured.

'Sucking' wounds

If the chest wall has been penetrated by a sharp instrument, or by a fractured rib, the injury is known as a 'sucking' wound. As the casualty breathes, air is sucked into the chest through the wound, rather than down the airway, so that the lung does not inflate.

The lung on the uninjured side can also be affected, and the casualty can be in danger of dying from asphyxiation because of an inability to get enough air into the lungs.

Symptoms of a 'sucking' wound include:
- Pain in the chest.
- Difficulty in breathing.
- Blueness of the mouth and skin.
- Bubbles of blood-stained liquid emerging from the wound as the casualty breathes out.
- The sound of air being sucked through the wound as the casualty breathes in.

It is essential to seal the wound as quickly as possible so that the casualty can breathe.

Begin by placing the palm of your hand over the injury to provide immediate relief. Then, if

HOW TO TREAT A 'SUCKING' WOUND

1 *Rest the casualty in a comfortable position. Make him sit up and lean him towards the injured side. Leaning the casualty towards the injured side prevents blood draining across inside the chest and lessens the risk of the uninjured lung becoming affected. Lean him on cushions or against your knee. Slacken belt or waistband.*

possible, apply a dressing and create an airtight seal by covering the dressing.

For the covering, use a piece of polythene, or plastic film of the type used to wrap up food, or kitchen foil, and seal the edges with adhesive tape or plaster.

Tell someone to dial 999 and ask for an ambulance.

Complicated fracture of the rib cage

A fractured rib may damage internal organs, such as the lungs, without penetrating through to the outside of the chest.

This will cause bleeding inside the chest. The casualty will then cough up red, frothy blood.

Other symptoms include:

- Bruising and bleeding from the chest.
- Pain which may become worse if the casualty coughs.
- Shallow breathing.
- A tight feeling in the chest. If several ribs are fractured, you may also be able to hear a crackling noise, which is caused by the bone ends rubbing together.

Ask someone to call for an ambulance as soon as possible, and if possible put the arm on the injured side in a triangular sling to support the fractured ribs.

Crushed chest

If the rib cage is fractured in several places – as can happen when the chest has been crushed by

2 *Seal the puncture wound in the chest immediately with your hand – and a clean folded handkerchief if possible. Do not press hard if you suspect fractured ribs.*

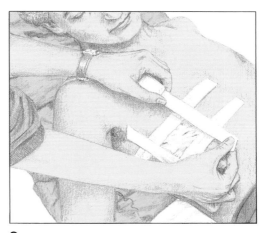

3 *To make a more permanent seal, cover the handkerchief with a sheet of polythene, plastic film or kitchen foil, securing it with plaster or any available adhesive tape to make it airtight.*

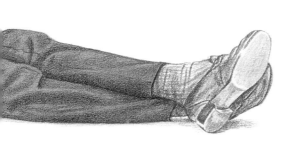

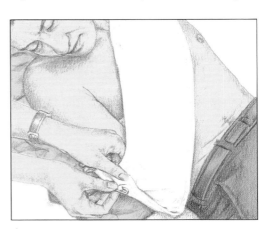

4 *While waiting for an ambulance, put the arm on the injured side across the chest to support the damaged area. Keep the arm in place with a triangular sling (see overleaf). Make the casualty as comfortable as possible.*

a heavy weight — a condition known as paradoxical breathing may occur.

The fractured ribs will be sucked in when the casualty breathes in, and pushed out as he breathes out. This is the reverse of the normal chest movement and can cause extreme difficulty in breathing.

A patient in this condition should be treated as for a complicated fracture of the rib cage.

TREATING A COMPLICATED FRACTURE OF THE RIB CAGE

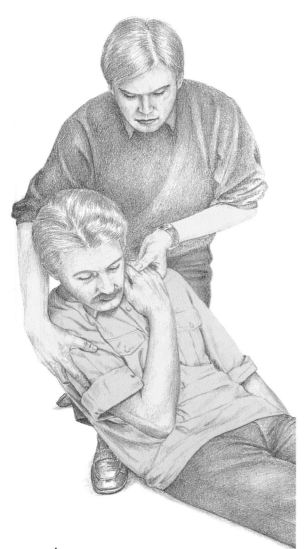

1 *Rest the casualty in a comfortable position. Make him sit up and lean him towards the injured side to help to drain blood and fluid away from the uninjured lung. Move the arm on the injured side diagonally across the chest, so that the hand rests on the opposite shoulder. The arm is now ready for a triangular sling.*

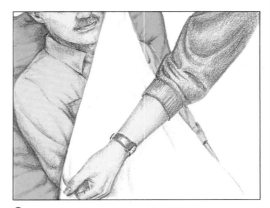

2 *Put one end of the base of the sling over the shoulder on the uninjured side, with the point extended beyond the elbow. The sling should hang over the arm.*

3 *Tuck the base under the hand, forearm and elbow. Bring the lower end up and around the back. Tie the ends together just above the collarbone on the uninjured side.*

4 *Fold the point of the sling at the elbow and fasten it with a pin or tape, or twist then tuck it in. Get the casualty to support the sling with the other hand if possible.*

Chest pain

Pain in the chest may be clearly related to breathing or quite unrelated to it.

In either case, the pain can be a danger signal of a serious condition – in the lungs or the heart – and should not be ignored.

Pain related to breathing

Painful breathing can be caused by chest injuries, which are usually obvious (see *Chest injuries*, page 68, and *Rib fractures*, page 120). It can also indicate a disorder of the lungs or their lining (the pleura), or of the bones, muscles or skin of the chest.

The pain forces the sufferer to take short and often rapid breaths. There is often a cough as well.

See a doctor as soon as possible if there is:
• Severe pain.
• Breathlessness.
• High temperature.
• Blood-stained spit.

Pain not related to breathing

Chest pain that is not associated with breathing may have a clear connection with exertion or with eating.

Pain brought on by exertion usually feels 'crushing', and may radiate to the neck, shoulders or arms. It passes off with rest. It is usually a symptom of a heart disorder, and is known as cardiac or anginal pain.

If the pain is associated with eating it may be caused by a problem in the digestive system such as indigestion or duodenal ulcer.

See a doctor immediately if:
• There is paleness of the skin and sweating.
• A heart condition is suspected – either because the patient has already suffered a heart attack or because the pain fits the description of cardiac or anginal pain given above (see also *Heart attack*, page 105).
• The pain is not improved after an hour's rest.

Treat indigestion by resting in a chair and taking a proprietary antacid or half a teaspoon of bicarbonate of soda in a glass of water.

Chickenpox

A highly irritating rash which starts on the body and spreads to the arms, legs, face and head heralds an attack of chickenpox.

The rash begins as raised pink spots which change to watery blisters. These then burst or shrivel up, and crust over to form scabs. The spots appear in crops over about four days, so that all stages of the rash may be on the body at the same time.

The patient has a raised temperature and may feel quite ill for three or four days.

What you should do

Most cases of chickenpox do not require medical attention, and can be treated at home.
• Keep the rash clean and dry by having a quick shower every day and patting the skin dry.
• Apply calamine lotion to the rash twice daily to ease the itching.
• Do not pick the spots, or they will leave little pockmarks.
• Drink plenty of liquid. It does not matter if the patient refuses food during the illness.
• Rest, and take painkillers in recommended doses to help to reduce fever and discomfort.
• There is no need to isolate an infected child from your other children, as it is better to have the infection in childhood than in adult life. But keep the patient away from children being treated for serious diseases such as leukaemia, because chickenpox could be fatal to them.
• Try to avoid spreading the infection to babies under six months and to women in late pregnancy. If a woman has the disease within a few days before giving birth, the baby may have chickenpox and be quite ill. But chickenpox in earlier pregnancy does not affect the unborn child.
• Avoid spreading the infection to elderly people. They may otherwise develop shingles, a painful and sometimes long-lasting disease.

When to see the doctor

Chickenpox can be complicated by infected blisters and by pneumonia and encephalitis, which are rare but serious. See your doctor if:
• The patient has a high fever, is vomiting or is coughing excessively.
• There is some alteration in the patient's state of consciousness, or if he develops a severe headache or becomes confused.
• The eyes themselves (not simply the eyelids) are affected.
• The spots become inflamed.

Chickenpox patients are infectious from about four days before the rash appears until all the blisters have formed scabs. The scabs disappear about a fortnight after they begin to form.

Chickenpox is mainly a disease of childhood, but it occasionally affects adults. It occurs in epidemics every two or three years and quickly spreads in schools. One attack ensures immunity to further attacks, but the virus may lie dormant in the body and cause shingles in later life.

First aid and medical emergencies

Childbirth

Most babies are born without difficulty. So your most important task in coping with an emergency delivery is to stay calm and reassure the mother and anyone else present.

Normally it is a criminal offence in Britain for anyone other than a doctor or midwife to supervise childbirth. But an unqualified person may have to take charge in an emergency, and the law recognises this.

Before doing so, however, every effort should be made to contact a doctor or midwife – dial 999 if necessary.

There are three distinct stages in labour:

Stage 1 lasts for several hours – up to 14 hours in a first pregnancy, less in later births.

During this stage the muscles of the body of the uterus begin to contract, opening up the neck of the uterus (the cervix) to let the baby's head pass through. The contractions cause pain in the back and lower abdomen, and at first they occur about every 30 minutes. Blood may seep from the vagina at the start. Gradually the contractions become more frequent.

A watery fluid runs from the vagina. This is 'the breaking of the waters' – the release of fluid which has surrounded the baby in the womb.

Stage 2, during which the baby is actually born, lasts between 15 minutes and an hour. The contractions become stronger and the mother feels an urge to bear down.

Stage 3 happens after the birth, and is vital to the health of the mother. The placenta, or afterbirth, to which the umbilical cord is attached, is expelled after further contractions.

What you should do to prepare

Between contractions, or before labour starts, try to make the following preparations (you may have to improvise):
• Line the bottom of a cot with a folded blanket, shawl or towel. Fold another blanket ready for when the baby is born. A baby's head is large in proportion to its body, so you do not need a pillow. If there is no cot, use a drawer or a cardboard box.
• Prepare a bed or a large clean surface such as a table for the mother to lie on. Spread a plastic sheet or newspaper over the surface and cover it with a clean sheet or towel.
• Find a clean pair of scissors and some string. Cut three pieces of string, each about 9in (230mm) long.
• If possible, sterilise string and scissors by boiling them in water for about ten minutes. Wrap them in a clean cloth. Do not touch the sterilised scissor blades.
• Fold a blanket in three from top to bottom to cover the mother's top during delivery. Wrap the blanket in a clean sheet if possible.
• Three or four more clean towels and several pieces of cloth or sheeting should be stacked ready, if available. Plus a sanitary towel for the mother to use after the birth, and a nappy for the baby.

Cleanliness is essential

• Wash your hands and scrub your nails under running water before assisting, and as often as necessary during the birth. Do not dry them on a towel. Shake them as dry as possible.
• Keep anyone with an open cut or infection away from the mother and baby.
• Make sure that bedding, towels, cloths and swabbing materials are as clean as possible. When they become soiled, discard them and get fresh ones if you can.

How you can help a mother during labour

• Give the mother occasional small drinks of milk or water, but nothing to eat. The body's digestive system shuts down during labour, so food will not be digested anyway.

DELIVERING THE BABY

1 *Tell the mother to lie on her back, or on her side if that is more comfortable, with her knees bent. Support her shoulders with pillows and cushions. When the baby's head first appears, put a clean towel or cloth under the mother's buttocks and a clean towel or sheet on the bed between her legs.*

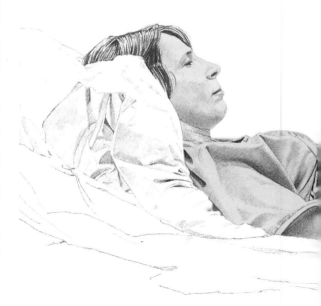

• As the contractions become more frequent, or if the waters break, tell her to lie on the bed (or other prepared surface) in the position most comfortable for her.

• If the pains are bad, it may help if she breathes deeply, in and out, with each contraction, and does not hold her breath.

• If she complains of tingling fingers or a trembling sensation when she does this, she is taking in too much oxygen. Cup your hands loosely over her mouth and nose during the contraction so that she re-breathes some of her own air. The tingling sensation should stop.

• During this first stage, encourage her to relax as far as possible between and during the contractions, and not to bear down.

As the second stage of labour begins, the mother will feel an unmistakable urge to bear down. By this time the contractions may be coming every two or three minutes, and the birth is imminent – though it may still take up to an hour to complete.

• Encourage her to lie on her back or side – whichever is more comfortable – and, with each contraction, tell her to hold her breath and bear down hard.

• Tell her to grip her thighs behind her knees, and pull her legs at the same time as she is bearing down.

Delivering the baby

Your first sight of the baby will usually be the top of its head, and it will usually become visible at the height of a contraction.

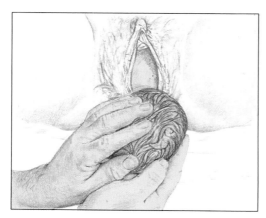

2 *When the baby's head is fully out, support it with clean, cupped hands. If a caul, or membrane, covers the baby's face, remove it gently but quickly.*

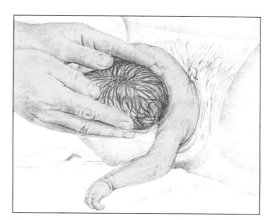

3 *As the shoulders emerge, support them gently but do not pull. One shoulder appears first. The second will follow easily if you gently raise the baby's head.*

Between contractions the head may slip back out of sight at first. This is normal.

Do not touch the baby's head as it emerges. Tell the mother to stop bearing down, and to pant in quick breaths to prevent the baby being thrust out too forcefully.

Once the shoulders are out, the rest of the baby will be born without difficulty.

Tying the umbilical cord

When the baby is breathing normally, use two pieces of string to tie off the umbilical cord and cut the cord between the two ties with clean scissors.

After the birth

Some 5 to 15 minutes after the birth, the uterus will contract again to expel the placenta.

• When these contractions start, place a bowl between the mother's legs. It will take between 5 and 20 minutes for the placenta to be pushed out.

• Do not pull the umbilical cord to speed delivery of the placenta – it will deliver itself.

• When the placenta is fully out, put it aside in the bowl, with the cord, to show a doctor or midwife later.

• Wash the mother, fix a sanitary pad or an improvised pad in place and give her fresh clothes if possible.

• Tidy up the room. If the mother wants something to eat or drink, she can now have it.

• Put the baby to the mother's breast if she wants to feed it.

• If the mother is asleep, lay the baby in a cot on its side (to drain any remaining mucus from the lungs) and with the head low (to ensure a good flow of blood to the brain).

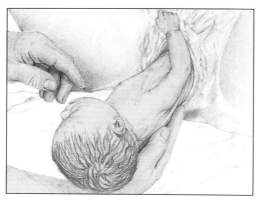

4 *The rest of the baby will be born without difficulty. Support the body with one hand. When it is fully born, wipe away any mucus or blood from the mouth with a clean cloth.*

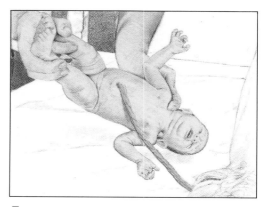

5 *If the baby does not breathe immediately, hold it with the head lower than the body to drain any mucus. Do not slap the baby. If necessary, blow hard on its chest.*

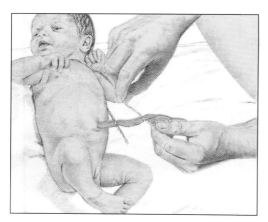

6 *Once the baby is breathing normally, which usually happens within a few seconds of birth, tie the cord with two pieces of clean string as tight as you can about 6in (150mm) and 8in (200mm) from the baby's navel.*

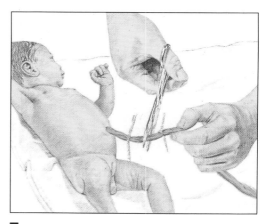

7 *Cut the cord with clean scissors between the two ties. Make a further secure tie about 4in (100mm) from the baby's navel. There is no need to cut the cord closer to the baby's navel. It will fall off on its own in a few days.*

Unusual deliveries

Most babies emerge head first and face down. Occasionally the baby emerges face up. Deliveries in this position tend to be slower, but present no special problems.

• In a small number of cases, the baby may appear with the umbilical cord around its neck. Hook a finger round the cord and loop it over the baby's head.

• In a very small number of cases, the baby may appear bottom first (breech birth). Support but do not pull the baby as it emerges. When the shoulders are out, hold the baby under them and ease the body up so that the mouth is clear to breathe.

If the baby does not breathe

A baby usually begins to breathe within a few seconds of birth.

• If it does not, hold it with the head down and blow hard on its chest. If it still does not breathe, open its mouth and clear out any mucus with your little finger. Clear the nose with a cloth, and lay the baby on one side with the head slightly lower than the body.

• Flick the bottom of the baby's feet sharply with your index finger to stimulate it into breathing. The child should breathe after a few taps. Do not smack the baby's bottom.

• If the baby fails to respond, give the kiss of life (see page 50), using very gentle puffs.

If the placenta fails to appear

Should the placenta not be expelled, or if it looks as though only part of the placenta has been expelled, get medical help as soon as possible. It may mean that the mother has serious internal bleeding.

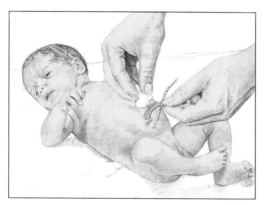

8 *Put a clean dressing over the end of the cord attached to the baby. Wrap the baby warmly. It will lose heat rapidly if left uncovered – particularly from the top of the head.*

9 *Give the baby to the mother and wrap her warmly in blankets. Now wait for the placenta to appear. Do not pull on the cord to speed delivery; it will deliver itself.*

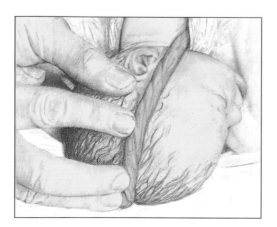

CORD AROUND THE NECK
If the baby appears with the cord around the neck, just hook a finger around the cord and loop it over the baby's head. Do not pull the baby or the cord.

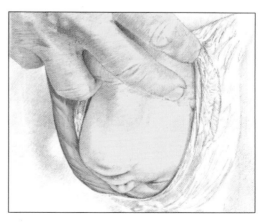

BREECH BIRTH
If the baby's bottom appears first, do not worry. Support it as it emerges, but do not pull. When the shoulders are out, ease the body up so that the mouth is clear to breathe.

Childhood illnesses

If you are worried that your child may be dangerously ill, ask yourself the following five questions. If the answer to any of them is 'yes', contact a doctor or go to the Accident and Emergency Department of a hospital without delay.

1 Is the child not fully conscious or unnaturally drowsy?
2 Has the child's colour become *and stayed* very pale?
3 Is there blueness around the face or lips?
4 Does the child have serious difficulty in breathing?
5 Is there a rash that looks like bleeding under the skin, and which does not go pale when you press firmly?

If the answer to all five questions is 'no', but the child still seems off-colour, use the charts on the following six pages to discover the best course of action. Begin by choosing the most appropriate major symptom, which is listed in capital letters at the head of each chart. Then start at the red box and follow the arrows, answering each question either 'yes' or 'no', to find the likely cause of the symptoms. Where paracetamol is recommended, follow the directions on the packet about the appropriate dose. Do not use aspirin without consulting a doctor.

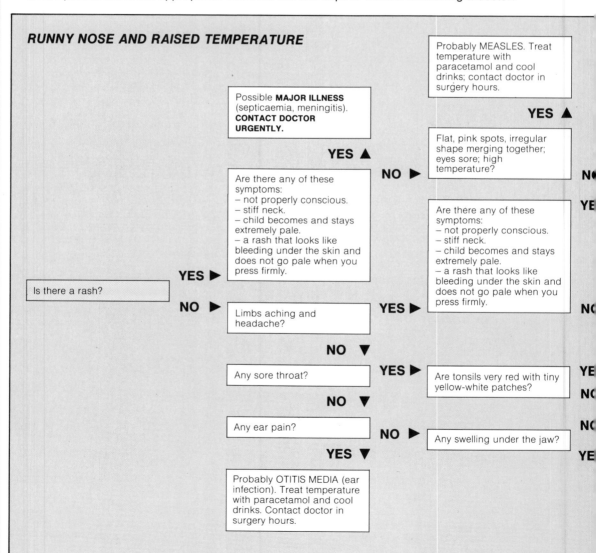

RUNNY NOSE AND RAISED TEMPERATURE

Probably MEASLES. Treat temperature with paracetamol and cool drinks; contact doctor in surgery hours.

Possible **MAJOR ILLNESS** (septicaemia, meningitis). **CONTACT DOCTOR URGENTLY.**

YES ▲

Flat, pink spots, irregular shape merging together; eyes sore; high temperature?

NO ▶

Are there any of these symptoms:
– not properly conscious.
– stiff neck.
– child becomes and stays extremely pale.
– a rash that looks like bleeding under the skin and does not go pale when you press firmly.

Are there any of these symptoms:
– not properly conscious.
– stiff neck.
– child becomes and stays extremely pale.
– a rash that looks like bleeding under the skin and does not go pale when you press firmly.

YES ▶

Is there a rash?

YES ▶

NO ▶ Limbs aching and headache?

YES ▶

NO ▼

Any sore throat? **YES ▶** Are tonsils very red with tiny yellow-white patches?

NO ▼

Any ear pain? **NO ▶** Any swelling under the jaw?

YES ▼

Probably OTITIS MEDIA (ear infection). Treat temperature with paracetamol and cool drinks. Contact doctor in surgery hours.

DIARRHOEA

Are there any of the following symptoms: listlessness, sunken eyes, very dry mouth, not properly conscious?

YES ▶ Possible **MAJOR ILLNESS** (gastroenteritis with dehydration, meningitis, septicaemia). **CONTACT DOCTOR URGENTLY.**

NO ▶ Is there sore throat, ear pain or aching limbs and headache?

NO ▶ Probably GASTROENTERITIS without dehydration. Give plenty to drink – fruit juice, squash, clear soup, water, but not milk. Contact doctor if no improvement in 6–8 hours, or immediately if signs of dehydration appear (see first question).

YES ▶ Could be TONSILLITIS, EAR INFECTION or FLU. Treat temperature with paracetamol and cool drinks. Contact doctor in surgery hours.

Probably RUBELLA (GERMAN MEASLES). Treat as for measles and keep patient away from women in early pregnancy.

YES ▲

▶ Tiny pink spots starting on face; tiny lumps behind ears; not very ill?

NO ▶ Raised blisters appearing in crops. High temperature?

NO ▶ Rash on face *only*?

YES ▼

Probably CHICKENPOX. Treat as for measles. Use calamine on skin.

YES ▼

Probably IMPETIGO. Make appointment with doctor for same or next day. Avoid contagion by reserving a flannel, towel etc for affected child.

▶ Probable **MAJOR ILLNESS** (meningitis, septicaemia). **CONTACT DOCTOR URGENTLY.**

▶ Possibly FLU. Give paracetamol and cool drinks Call doctor in surgery hours.

▶ Probably TONSILLITIS. Treat temperature with paracetamol and cool drinks, and call doctor.

▶ Probably COMMON.COLD. Treat temperature with para-cetamol and cool drinks.

▶ Probably MUMPS. Contact doctor in surgery hours; treat temperature with para-cetamol and cool drinks.

JERKY MOVEMENTS OF LIMBS

Is there a raised temperature?

YES ▶ Is the child properly conscious?

YES ▶ See *Runny nose and raised temperature*, page 76.

NO ▲

NO ▶ Was he or she unconscious for a time?

YE

NO ▶ Possible **MAJOR ILLNESS** (meningitis) but could be simple FEVER FIT. Place in recovery position (see page 136). **CONTACT DOCTOR URGENTLY.**

NO ▶ Is the child properly conscious?

YES ▶ Has he or she been unconscious?

YE

NO ▼

Is he or she a baby who might have stomach pain?

YE

NO

ABNORMAL BREATHING

Is there irregular gasping breath or blue lips, or both?

YES ▶ Possible **MAJOR ILLNESS** (pneumonia, epiglottitis). **CONTACT DOCTOR URGENTLY.**

NO ▲

NO ▶ Is the child properly conscious?

YES ▶ Is breathing noisy?

YE

NO

▶ Probably FEVER FIT. Remove clothes; sponge body down with lukewarm water; give paracetamol. If this is the child's first attack, **CONTACT DOCTOR URGENTLY**. But if the child has had attacks before, and the symptoms are unchanged, contact doctor in surgery hours.

▶ Possibly CONVULSIONS. If this is the child's first attack, **CONTACT DOCTOR URGENTLY**. But if the child has had attacks before, and the symptoms are unchanged, contact doctor in surgery hours.

▶ Is there diarrhoea or vomiting?

YES ▶
NO ▶

▶ Probably not serious; wait and see.

Probably GASTROENTERITIS. Is there listlessness, sunken eyes, very dry mouth?

YES ▶ Possible **MAJOR ILLNESS** (dehydration). **CONTACT DOCTOR URGENTLY**.

NO ▶ Give plenty to drink (not milk). Contact doctor if no improvement in 6–8 hours.

Probably COLIC. Give usual medicine; try rocking or cuddling. If very upset discuss with doctor or health visitor at next convenient surgery.

Probably ASTHMA. Use your regular asthma medicine and contact doctor without delay unless the wheezing is mild only.

YES ▲
NO ▶

Musical note to breathing with rapid breathing and/or cough? Has the child had this before?

Probably BRONCHITIS. Contact doctor during day unless you are very worried; then you should not delay.

NO ▲

▶ Hoarse sound with ringing or 'cow-like' cough?

YES ▶ Does the child look very ill?

YES ▶ Could be **MAJOR ILLNESS** (epiglottitis). **CONTACT DOCTOR URGENTLY**.

NO ▶ Probably CROUP. Nurse in steamy room and contact doctor if no better in 2 hours.

▶ Very rapid breathing with high temperature and/or chest pain?

YES ▶ Probably **MAJOR ILLNESS** (pneumonia). **CONTACT DOCTOR URGENTLY**.

NO ▶ Severe paroxysms of coughing, which may cause vomiting or going blue in the face, indicate WHOOPING COUGH. See doctor in surgery hours.

STOMACH PAIN

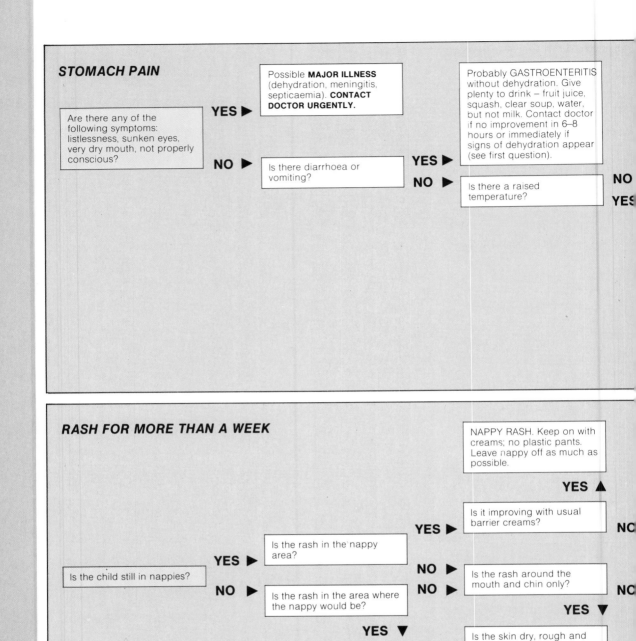

Are there any of the following symptoms: listlessness, sunken eyes, very dry mouth, not properly conscious?

YES ▶ Possible **MAJOR ILLNESS** (dehydration, meningitis, septicaemia). **CONTACT DOCTOR URGENTLY.**

NO ▶ Is there diarrhoea or vomiting?

YES ▶ Probably GASTROENTERITIS without dehydration. Give plenty to drink – fruit juice, squash, clear soup, water, but not milk. Contact doctor if no improvement in 6–8 hours or immediately if signs of dehydration appear (see first question).

NO ▶ Is there a raised temperature?

NO

YES

RASH FOR MORE THAN A WEEK

Is the child still in nappies?

YES ▶ Is the rash in the nappy area?

NO ▶ Is the rash in the area where the nappy would be?

YES ▶ Is it improving with usual barrier creams?

YES ▲ NAPPY RASH. Keep on with creams; no plastic pants. Leave nappy off as much as possible.

NO

NO ▶ Is the rash around the mouth and chin only?

NO

YES ▼ Is the skin dry, rough and largely unbroken?

YE

YES ▼ Could be THRUSH. Make an appointment with doctor.

NO ▼ If there are blisters, crusting over and golden-yellow, probably IMPETIGO. Make appointment with doctor for same or next day. Avoid contagion by reserving a flannel, towel etc for the affected child.

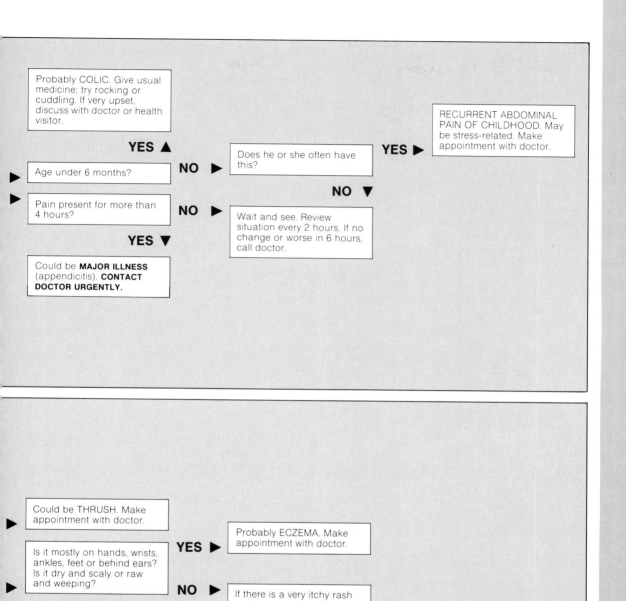

Probably COLIC. Give usual medicine; try rocking or cuddling. If very upset, discuss with doctor or health visitor.

YES ▲

Age under 6 months?

NO ▶

Pain present for more than 4 hours?

NO ▶

YES ▼

Could be **MAJOR ILLNESS** (appendicitis). **CONTACT DOCTOR URGENTLY.**

Does he or she often have this?

YES ▶

NO ▼

Wait and see. Review situation every 2 hours. If no change or worse in 6 hours, call doctor.

RECURRENT ABDOMINAL PAIN OF CHILDHOOD. May be stress-related. Make appointment with doctor.

Could be THRUSH. Make appointment with doctor.

Is it mostly on hands, wrists, ankles, feet or behind ears? Is it dry and scaly or raw and weeping?

YES ▶

NO ▶

Probably ECZEMA. Make appointment with doctor.

If there is a very itchy rash on the arms, legs or trunk, but not on the head, possibly SCABIES. Make appointment with doctor.

Probably ECZEMA. Make appointment with doctor.

Choking

A piece of food or some other object stuck in the airway will cause choking. In severe cases the victim cannot breathe at all, and if left untreated will die within minutes. It is vital, therefore, to act promptly.

Suspect choking if a person who is unconscious and not breathing is found anywhere near an eating area. However, choking can happen away from eating areas when the victim has been eating sweets, chewing gum or peanuts. Peanuts are a common cause of choking in young children, and should not be given to them.

Children can also choke on toys which they put in their mouths, and adults can choke on dislodged false teeth.

When choking occurs, the casualty may have a fit of coughing, his face turns blue and the veins on the head and neck are swollen.

He will instinctively make violent efforts to breathe, but the harder he tries to breathe in, the more firmly lodged the obstruction will become. Instant action is vital.

Treating a conscious casualty

• First, remove food or loose false teeth from the mouth and encourage the casualty to cough. It may be enough to dislodge the obstruction.
• If this fails, help the casualty to bend over with his or her head lower than the chest. He or she can be either sitting or standing.
• Slap him between the shoulder blades firmly with the heel of the hand up to four times. Each slap should be strong enough to induce an involuntary cough.
• When the casualty begins to breathe again, get him to sit quietly and take sips of water until he is fully recovered.

Small children and babies

• If the casualty is a child under about seven, encourage him to cough. If this fails to dislodge

BACK-SLAPS FOR AN ADULT
Bend the casualty over with his head lower than his chest so that gravity will help the obstruction to become dislodged. This can be done with the casualty either standing or sitting. Slap him between the shoulder blades forcefully up to four times, using the heel of the hand.

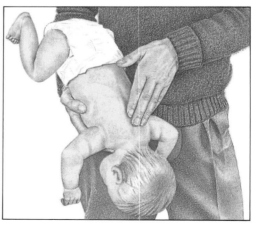

BACK-SLAPS FOR A BABY
Lay the baby along your forearm with his head downwards, and with the chest and head supported by your hand. Give up to four slaps between the shoulder blades with your fingers, using much less force than for an adult.

the obstruction, lay him over your knees with his head down.

• Support the chest with one hand while you slap him smartly between the shoulder blades with the heel of the other hand. Do this up to four times.

• Each of your slaps should be strong enough on its own to dislodge the obstruction.

• If a baby is choking, lay him along your forearm with his head downwards. Support the head and chest with your hand.

• Slap him smartly between the shoulder blades up to four times with the fingers of your other hand, using much less force than for an adult.

• Be extremely careful when removing anything from a baby's mouth. Put your finger into his mouth only if you can actually see the object. Take care not to push it farther down the throat, making the condition worse.

Abdominal thrusts

If the casualty still cannot breathe, administer abdominal thrusts. This is a dangerous technique, which can damage the liver and other internal organs. But it may dislodge the obstruction and restore the casualty's breathing, even

ABDOMINAL THRUST ON A CONSCIOUS ADULT

2 *When the throat is clear, reassure the casualty. Rest her in a comfortable position and give her frequent sips of water. Adults should sip half a cup of water over ten minutes.*

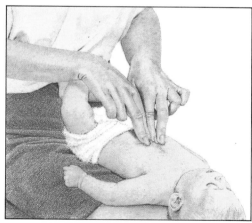

ABDOMINAL THRUST ON A BABY
Lay the baby on his back, with the head tilted well back to open the airway. Put two fingers of one or both hands between the navel and the bottom of the breastbone, and press quickly forwards and downwards. Repeat up to four times. Clear the mouth of any object. When he is breathing normally, give him water to sip.

1 *Stand behind the casualty. Put your arms around her waist, clenching the fist of one hand. Place the thumb knuckle against the stomach (above the navel and below the rib cage). Hold the fist with your other hand and give three or four quick, strong pulls diagonally upwards and towards you.*

if internal injuries have to be treated in hospital.
• Stand or kneel behind the casualty. Clench your fist and put it, thumb inwards, over the stomach between the navel and the bottom of the breastbone.
• Hold your fist with the other hand and pull both hands towards you with a quick upward-and-inward thrust from the elbows. You are trying to pull the upper abdomen against the bottom of the lungs to drive out the remaining air and force out the obstruction.
• Repeat up to four times.
• Even if the thrusts are successful, the casualty may be winded by the force and unable to breathe for a few moments.

• Check in her mouth to see if the obstruction has come up. If so, remove it.
• Abdominal thrusts can be performed on a child seated on your lap, but use only one hand to administer the thrusts.
• A baby should be laid or held on his back with the head tilted well back to open the airway. Apply abdominal thrusts with two fingers of one or both hands, pressing quickly forwards and downwards just above the navel. Repeat up to four times, if necessary.

An unconscious casualty

If the casualty becomes unconscious, the muscles of the throat may relax sufficiently to

ABDOMINAL THRUST ON AN UNCONSCIOUS ADULT

1 *Turn the casualty face up. Kneel astride her hips, or alongside, and put the heel of one hand between the navel and the bottom of the breastbone. Cover one hand with the other, and give a quick downward-and-forward thrust with your arms straight. Repeat up to four times.*

allow air to get past the obstruction. So begin mouth-to-mouth respiration to force air into the lungs (see page 50).

• If a third person is present, tell him to telephone 999 and ask for an ambulance. If you are on your own, do not stop mouth-to-mouth respiration until normal breathing resumes.

• If, however, the lungs do not inflate with the first four breaths, roll the casualty onto the side nearest you, with the chest against your thigh and the head well back. Give up to four hard slaps on the back.

• Look in the mouth to see if the obstruction has become dislodged. If it has, hook it out with a finger.

• If not, turn the casualty onto her back and tilt the head well back. Straddle the casualty's thighs, or kneel alongside. Put the heel of one hand between the navel and the bottom of the breastbone. Cover your hand with the other hand, and give a quick downward-and-forward thrust with your arms straight. Repeat the thrust up to four times.

• Check the mouth to see if the obstruction has been dislodged. If it has, hook it out with a finger.

• If not, resume mouth-to-mouth respiration. If the lungs again do not expand after the first four breaths, repeat the sequence of back-slaps, thrusts and mouth-to-mouth respiration.

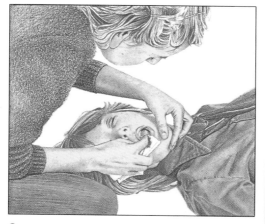

2 *With your finger, clear the casualty's mouth of any object that has been expelled by the abdominal thrusts. Once her breathing has returned to normal, put the casualty into the recovery position (see page 136).*

3 *Telephone 999 and ask for an ambulance. If the casualty becomes fully conscious before the ambulance arrives, get her to sit up, supporting her if necessary, and give her some water to sip.*

TWO METHODS OF SELF-HELP

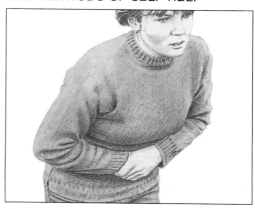

1 *Someone choking can perform abdominal thrusts on herself. Clench a fist and place it, thumb side against the stomach, slightly above the navel. With the other hand, jerk it firmly inwards and upwards several times.*

2 *Alternatively, lean over the back of a chair, supporting yourself by holding on to the sides with your hands. With the top sticking into you just above the navel, pull yourself downwards and forwards onto it three or four times.*

Concussion

A blow to the head or a heavy fall onto the feet can shake and disturb the brain, causing concussion. There is usually a brief period of unconsciousness, but it may be so short that it goes unnoticed.

If the casualty is unconscious for any length of time, his breathing may be shallow, his face pale and his skin cold and moist.

After the spell of unconsciousness – however brief – the casualty may suffer from nausea and vomiting and may remember nothing about the incident.

Anyone suffering these symptoms should see a doctor for examination in case a more serious condition called compression should develop.

While a person is unconscious, treat as described on page 136.

If a person feels very weak after a blow to the head, treat for shock (see page 120).

Recognising and treating compression

Any pressure on the brain – either from blood or fluid, or from a fracture of the skull – can cause the more serious condition of compression, which may develop up to 48 hours after the casualty appears to have recovered from concussion.

• The casualty's alertness and level of consciousness fall.
• There may be weakness or paralysis of one side of the body.
• Breathing may become noisy.
• The face may be flushed, and the casualty's temperature high.
• The pulse may be slow.
• The pupils of the eyes (the dark parts) may be unequal in size.

Usually most of these symptoms occur, but the absence of any of them does not mean that compression is not present.

Telephone 999 and ask for an ambulance. If the casualty is unconscious, treat as described on page 136.

Cramp

The sudden, involuntary spasm of muscles known as cramp causes acute pain, but it is usually dangerous only if a swimmer is affected (see *If you get into difficulties while swimming*, page 234). Cramp may be caused by chilling during or after exercise such as swimming, by poor muscular coordination during exercise, or by loss of salt through severe sweating, vomiting or diarrhoea. It can also occur during sleep for no apparent reason.

The spasm is generally relieved by stretching the affected muscles. This can be done by the sufferer, but it is often easier if another person can help gently to force the limb straight.

Cramp in the hand
• Straighten your fingers, using gentle force if necessary.
• Spread your fingers and press down on the outstretched tips.
• Massage the affected muscles as you stretch them.

Cramp in the calf
• Straighten your leg and stand up.
• Press down on your heel and toes alternately. Lean forward slightly to stretch the calf muscles.
• Massage the muscles as you stretch them.

Cramp in the foot
• Stand on the ball of the foot so that your toes are forced up. Alternatively, sit down and pull

HELPING A CRAMP VICTIM
To relieve cramp in the calf, the foot or the thigh, lay the victim down, straighten the knee and toes, and press the foot firmly up towards the shin. Massage the affected muscles.

your toes up towards the shin with your hand.
• Massage the muscles as you stretch them.

Cramp in the thigh

• Sit on the floor and straighten the leg. Then bear down at the knee to stretch the thigh muscles. If there is someone to help, get him to raise your leg by the heel and press down on the knee with the other hand.
• Massage the muscles.

If cramp persists

Cramp caused by loss of salt from the body – through sweating, vomiting or diarrhoea – can persist for some time. It is often felt as a gripping pain in the stomach.

To treat it, drink plenty of slightly salted water. Use half a teaspoon of salt to a pint of water (about a teaspoon to 1 litre).

Crush injuries

Someone who has been trapped for more than a few minutes under a heavy weight, such as fallen masonry or a car, may suffer severe internal damage, even if there is little external sign of injury. Without treatment the damage can lead to shock, kidney failure and death.

The warning signs

• Redness, swelling, bruising or blistering of the trapped part.
• Numbness or tingling.
• Continued swelling and hardening of the injured tissue.
• Shock – symptoms can include pallid clammy skin, dizziness, fainting, blurred vision, nausea, vomiting, thirst, anxiety and restlessness.

What you should do

• Treat severe injuries as far as possible while the casualty is still trapped.
• Once he has been released, keep the casualty on his back with his legs raised if possible.
• Do not let him move.
• If the casualty is unconscious, place him in the recovery position (see page 136).
• Get medical attention as quickly as possible. Make sure that the doctor or ambulance attendant is told that there may be crush injuries. Tell him how long the crushing lasted.

Minor crushing – what to do

• If fingers, hand or foot are crushed for a short time only, hold the injured part under cold running water.
• Show the injured part to a doctor in case it is fractured.

Crying baby

Normal babies generally cry only when they are hungry, angry, lonely, uncomfortable or in pain, and the crying will stop when you put right whatever is upsetting them.

It takes time for a new parent to learn what the different sorts of crying mean. The only way to find out is by discovering what stops it. There are some babies, however, who cry for no obvious reason.

What you should do
- Consult the chart and see if you can find a remedy.
- If you are feeling jumpy and nervous yourself, remember that this can affect the baby.
- Find some way to keep calm.
- Be sure to get enough rest. Perhaps you can persuade your partner to help out more than usual. Alternatively, get help from relatives,

ELEVEN REASONS WHY A BABY CRIES

Reason	Evidence
Hunger	Some hours since feed, or last feed not large enough.
Thirst	Hot weather. Baby feverish or sweating.
Passing urine	A sudden shriek.
Discomfort	Nappy rash, eczema, wet nappy, cold fingers and toes.
Colic	Restless, draws up legs, sudden cry, then relaxes. Passes a lot of wind.
Loneliness and boredom	Cries when he is alone, stops when you come in.
Habit	Usually cries at night. Stops when you come in.
Teething	May cause crying but less often than most people think.
Tiredness	Has missed a nap. A particular sort of moaning cry.
Personality	No other cause found.
Illness	Off feeds. Feverish. Signs of cold. Pulls at ear. Vomiting, diarrhoea. Pain is suggested if crying is severe, fails to stop when baby is picked up and comforted, or is accompanied by pale skin or drawing up of legs.

friends or neighbours. Your rest should come before housework or entertaining.
• If you feel desperate and unable to cope, seek the help of your health visitor or your local infant welfare clinic.
• If your worries are about housing, money or the state of your marriage, get advice from a social worker who can be contacted at your local council's social services department.

Remedy

Offer a feed.

Offer water.

Change nappy.

Treat or remove discomfort.

Carry baby over shoulder. Rock in cradle. Take for a drive. Check hole in teat if bottle-fed. Consult doctor or health visitor.

Keep him with you. Prop him up so that he can see you or other members of the family.

Let him cry for a few minutes before going in; he may go to sleep again. Lift him out and hold him for a few minutes; perhaps sing a lullaby. You may decide to take him to bed with you, but this can start a habit that may be difficult to break.

Look for some other cause first. Consult a doctor if severe.

Try to get the baby to settle to sleep.

Consult doctor if worried.

See pages 76–81.

First aid and medical emergencies

Cuts

Minor cuts do not need medical help unless infection has set in or the wound was caused by a dirty or rusty object.

The amount of blood lost and the extent of the injury usually show whether the wound is serious, but puncture or stab wounds are deceptive because the surface damage may be small. Get medical help for a puncture wound after giving first aid (see *Stab wounds*, page 133).

When treating a minor cut, first stop the bleeding by pressing on the wound with a piece of clean cloth. Then clean the skin around it with gauze or cotton swabs and lukewarm water with soap or a mild antiseptic. Wipe outwards and away from the cut and make sure the water you are using does not run into it. Use each swab once and then change to a fresh one.

If the bleeding is severe, see page 60.

HOW TO TREAT A CUT

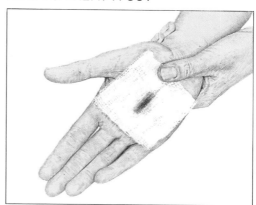

1 *Press a clean piece of cloth on the cut, or around the edges if a foreign body is in it. When bleeding stops, take the pad away and remove any foreign bodies that come out easily.*

2 *Gently wipe the wound outwards with a swab soaked in warm, soapy water. Renew the swabs frequently. Dry around the wound with a new swab. Apply a plaster or bandage.*

Diabetic coma

A diabetic who appears to be drunk may be suffering from low blood sugar, a condition known as hypoglycaemia. It is brought on by taking too much insulin or eating too little food. It can also occur after exercise has burnt up the sugar in the blood.

Low blood sugar affects the brain and leads to coma. Death could possibly follow in as little as 20 minutes.

The condition can be distinguished from drunkenness by the person's breath, which will have no smell of alcohol.

Low blood sugar can lead to rapid deterioration in the diabetic, with the following symptoms:
- Pale appearance, with sweating, rapid pulse, shallow breathing and possibly trembling.
- Confused state, sometimes resembling drunkenness.
- Faintness, leading to unconsciousness in 15 to 20 minutes.

What you can do

If a diabetic collapse comes on quickly, you can assume that the patient needs sugar. If he is conscious, give him three or four teaspoons of sugar, some cake or biscuits, honey, jam, chocolate, or a sweet soft drink.
- If the patient is unconscious, put him in the recovery position (see page 136), then telephone 999 and ask for an ambulance.

The opposite condition of too much sugar in the blood (hyperglycaemia) can also eventually lead to coma, but it comes on much more slowly, and the diabetic will usually become aware of it and treat himself by taking insulin. If he does not take insulin, the symptoms will be:
- Flushed appearance with dry skin.
- Deep, sighing breathing, with the breath smelling of acetone (pear drops).
- Eventually unconsciousness.

If the person becomes unconscious, put him in the recovery position (see page 136) and get immediate medical attention. If he is conscious, tell him to take some insulin at once.

What the patient can do

A person who is subject to hypoglycaemic attacks should carry a card or wear a bracelet giving his condition and emergency instructions. This can avoid the danger of being mistaken for being drunk when, in fact, all he really needs is some sugar.

A diabetic on insulin should avoid driving or using dangerous machinery unless he has had some food in the previous two hours. Consequently, regular mealtimes are important.

Dislocated joints

A bone that is wrenched out of place at a joint is said to be dislocated. The injury is usually accompanied by torn ligaments (a sprain) and sometimes by a fracture.

The symptoms may include severe pain, swelling and bruising, deformity of the joint and difficulty in moving the joint. Never try to push a dislocated bone back into place, but treat it as though it were broken.

In a case of dislocation, always assume there might be a fracture as well – the symptoms are similar (see page 98).

TREATING A DISLOCATION
Put the casualty into the most comfortable position possible, and support the dislocated joint with pillows or a rolled blanket. Telephone 999 and ask for an ambulance. If the dislocation is in the arm, you may be able to support it with an arm sling (see page 121).

Drowning

Death by drowning happens because, as the victim struggles for breath, water enters the airway. The water causes a spasm of the epiglottis, a cartilage flap at the back of the tongue, and this spasm blocks the air supply. Quick action can still save a victim's life.

Each year in Britain there are nearly 1000 deaths from drowning. Two-thirds occur in fresh water, because it is impossible to provide the same rescue facilities on rivers, lakes and canals as are available on holiday beaches. Most of the victims are able to swim, and most drown within 10yds (9m) of land.

Assume that anyone you see in the water fully clothed is a potential victim, and be ready to help. A swimmer who develops cramp or becomes exhausted is less easy to recognise. If he is having breathing problems, he may be unable to draw attention by shouting, and if he raises an arm to wave he may sink.

Warning signs
• As he gets more tired, the victim's body tends to sink until it is vertical and only his head shows above the water.
• The victim's strokes become erratic and his movement through the water appears jerky or simply stops.
• The victim's face – particularly the lips and ears – become congested and may turn a bluish-purple colour.

Rescuing a drowning person
For methods of getting a drowning person out of the water in a variety of different situations, see pages 231 and 240.

REVIVING A DROWNING PERSON

1 *If the drowning person has stopped breathing, start mouth-to-mouth respiration as quickly as possible (see page 50). Begin while still in the water if necessary – as soon as you can stand up or sooner if you are a strong swimmer. Remove any debris from the mouth with your index finger, tilt the head back and begin breathing into the mouth. Either press your cheek against the victim's nose to stop air escaping, or pinch the nose between finger and thumb. Move towards land between breaths. Once out of the water, continue artificial respiration, or begin if it is not already under way.*

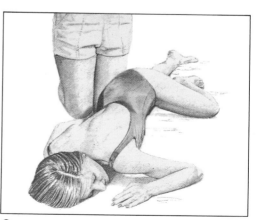

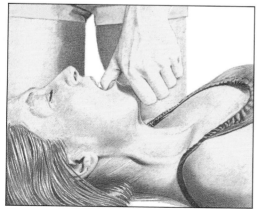

2 *Victims of drowning sometimes swallow water, which is brought up with food during artificial respiration. Turn the head to one side and regularly clear the mouth of any debris.*

3 *Once breathing has re-started, turn the victim into the recovery position (see page 136). Cover her and treat any injuries. Get medical help as soon as possible.*

Drug overdose

Anyone who takes an overdose of a drug needs immediate medical attention. This applies to an overdose of a prescribed medicine as much as an addictive drug such as heroin.

A drug overdose is likely to cause a stronger than normal reaction in a person who suffers from asthma, kidney disease or hypersensitivity to certain medicines.

While waiting for medical help to arrive, gather any information you can about the drug by talking to the casualty, collecting pill bottles or taking samples of vomit.

Generally, do not try to induce vomiting. Inducing vomiting is worth doing only if you know that the overdose has been caused by barbiturates or tranquillisers. For details of how to treat overdoses of either of these drugs, see *Barbiturates*, page 358.

Do not try to keep the casualty awake by giving him black coffee or walking him about. Physical activity will only speed up the absorption of the drug into the body.

How to recognise an overdose
Symptoms depend on the size of the overdose and the type of drug, but they can include any of the following:
• Vomiting.
• Difficulty in breathing.
• Unconsciousness.
• Sweating.
• Hallucinations.
• Dilation or contraction of the pupils of the eyes (the dark parts).

What you should do
• Ask the casualty what has happened. Obtain any information about the drug as soon as possible, because the casualty may become unconscious at any time.
• If the casualty is unconscious, put him in the recovery position (see page 136).
• Telephone 999 and ask for an ambulance.
• Collect a sample of vomit and any bottle, pill container, hypodermic syringe or glue container that is near the casualty. Send them to hospital with him as evidence to assist treatment.

Alcohol poisoning
If a person collapses unconscious after drinking a large amount of alcohol, put him in the recovery position so that he does not choke on his vomit (see page 136).

Then telephone 999 and ask for an ambulance (see also *Spotting and coping with a drink problem*, page 350).

Ear injuries

Damage to the middle or inner ear can be caused by injuries to the head, loud noise, explosions, or probing in the ear – to remove a foreign body, for example.

The most serious injury to the ear itself is a perforated eardrum, but bleeding from the ear or discharge of watery, straw-coloured fluid can be a sign of a fractured skull (see page 102).

Symptoms of ear injury
• Severe earache.
• Dizziness and loss of balance.
• Deafness in one ear following an injury.
• Headache.
• Possible unconsciousness.
• Discharge of blood or watery fluid.

What you can do
• If the casualty is conscious, stop him from hitting the side of his head to try to restore hearing; this will only make the damage worse.
• Sit the casualty up with his head tilted over on the injured side so that blood or fluid can drain out.
• Cover the injured ear with a piece of clean cotton or gauze as protection. Bandage it lightly in place. Get medical attention.
• Do not attempt to plug the ear. This can cause a build-up of pressure in the middle ear.
• If the casualty is unconscious but breathing, place him in the recovery position with the injured ear downwards and a clean pad underneath it (see page 136). Get medical attention.
• If the casualty's breathing stops, begin artificial respiration (see page 50).

Foreign body in the ear
Children often push objects into their ears. This usually causes no more than temporary deafness, but if the object is pushed hard and deep into the ear the eardrum may be perforated.

The symptoms are variable:
• There may be no symptoms at all, just the knowledge that something is in the ear.
• Discharge from the ear.
• Pain or buzzing in the ear.
• Deafness on the affected side.
Do not attempt to remove a foreign body. If there are no symptoms, get medical attention in 24 hours. Go sooner if there are symptoms.

Insect in the ear
If an insect crawls or flies into a child's ear its buzzing can sound frighteningly loud.
• Calm and comfort the child.
• Stop him from putting a finger in the ear. If the insect has a sting, this may provoke an attack.
• Hold his head still with the ear angled towards the ground. The insect may crawl out.
• If, after a minute or two, it has not come out, gently flood the ear with tepid water.
• If all attempts fail, or if it stings while inside, get medical help.

Electric shock

Electricity can kill or produce a wide range of injuries, including severe burns and asphyxiation. The extent of the injuries it will cause depends on three main factors: the strength of the charge; how long the victim was exposed to it; and how well he was insulated – by wearing rubber-soled shoes, say, or standing on a dry wooden floor.

• Never touch the victim of an electrical accident until you are certain you are not risking a shock yourself. If the casualty is still touching the source of the electricity – such as an electric drill that has gone 'live' – cut off the power first. Switch off the appliance at the socket and pull out the plug. If the plug itself is causing the trouble, wrench it free by the flex or turn off the power at the main fuse box.

• If you cannot turn off the electricity, and the casualty is still in contact with it, move him away using a piece of wood or fabric, which do not conduct electricity. Use a broom handle to lever

the casualty away, or loop a dry towel around an arm or leg and pull him free.

• Because water is an excellent conductor of electricity, use only dry wood or cloth, and preferably stand on insulating material such as a rubber mat or a folded newspaper.

High-voltage electricity

Electricity from high-voltage sources, such as power lines, overhead railway cables and some industrial equipment, can give a fatal shock up to 20yds (18m) away. Stay clear until you can get an expert to cut off the power. Railway stations and many pylons and substations display an emergency telephone number.

When lightning strikes

Another form of high-voltage electricity is lightning, which can do anything from merely stunning the victim to killing him (see *If you are caught in a lightning storm*, page 298).

First aid and medical emergencies

HOW TO RESCUE A VICTIM OF ELECTRIC SHOCK

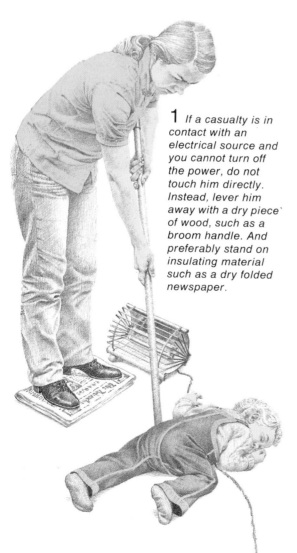

1 *If a casualty is in contact with an electrical source and you cannot turn off the power, do not touch him directly. Instead, lever him away with a dry piece of wood, such as a broom handle. And preferably stand on insulating material such as a dry folded newspaper.*

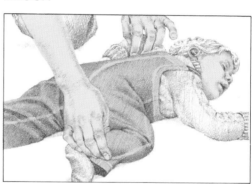

2 *If the casualty is unconscious, put him in the recovery position (see page 136). Dial 999 and ask for an ambulance. Cut off the power to the electrical source, but do not touch it.*

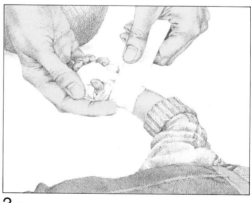

3 *Treat burns by cooling them with cold water. Then cover them with a dressing, such as the inside of a folded handkerchief, and secure it with a piece of clean cloth (see page 66).*

Epileptic fit

A major epileptic fit, also called *grand mal,* involves unconsciousness, convulsions and noisy breathing. Sufferers from epilepsy often carry an identifying card or bracelet which may reveal how long attacks normally last.

A series of fits, without the casualty regaining consciousness in between, is called *status epilepticus,* and is a serious condition which requires hospital treatment.

A minor epileptic fit, also called *petit mal,* usually involves only momentary inattention or confusion without loss of consciousness. Make sure that the sufferer is not in danger (from traffic, for example) and stay with him until he is once more quite alert.

The warning signs

• A sufferer from major epilepsy sometimes experiences a few seconds' warning of an attack. The warning may involve seeing flashing lights, or a sensation of noise, taste or smell.
• Loss of consciousness occurs.
• The limbs and neck stiffen for a few seconds; then the whole body is overcome by rhythmic and often violent twitching.
• The casualty may bite his tongue, froth at the mouth or urinate involuntarily.
• Finally the muscles will relax and the casualty may remain unconscious for some minutes.
• When consciousness returns, the casualty may be drowsy and confused for as much as an hour.

What you can do

• Do not try to restrain a victim of a major epileptic attack. Try only to stop him from hurting himself.
• If he is about to fall, catch him and lay him gently on the ground, or cushion his fall.
• Clear a space around him. Remove furniture and other objects that he may bump into.
• If possible, loosen clothing around the neck and place something soft under the head.
• Do not put anything in the mouth or try to force it open.
• When convulsions end, place the casualty in the recovery position (see page 136), and wait for him to regain consciousness. Do not leave him alone until he is fully recovered.
• Do not give him anything to drink until you are sure that he is quite alert.
• Call an ambulance only if the casualty has a series of fits without regaining consciousness in between, if he injures himself or if he takes longer than 15 minutes to regain consciousness.

Eye injuries

The most common injury to the eye is a small object, such as an eyelash or a piece of grit, lodged in it. Other injuries can be caused by corrosive chemicals or sharp objects, such as flying fragments of glass or metal.

Injury can also occur if contact lenses get displaced or stuck to the eyeball. If you have any difficulty with a contact lens, get medical help rather than risk hurting the eye.

Foreign body in the eye

If a person has something in his eye, tell him not to rub it. Turn the casualty's face up to the light. With your thumb and forefinger, push the eyelids away from the eyeball. Ask the casualty to look left, right, up and down while you look for the object.

REMOVING GRIT FROM THE EYE

1 *Tilt the head back, and gently raise the eyelid with your finger (or draw down the bottom eyelid). Lift off the piece of grit or eyelash with the corner of a clean handkerchief.*

TREATING CHEMICAL BURNS

1 *Tilt the casualty's head, with the injured eye downwards. Flood the open eye with gently running water from a tap or jug for at least ten minutes. Or splash water onto it from a basin.*

First aid and medical emergencies

Do not attempt to remove anything if it is on the pupil or iris (the black or coloured parts of the eye), or if it is sticking firmly to the eye. Leave the object and cover the eye with a clean, non-fluffy pad, such as the inside of a clean, folded handkerchief. Bandage it loosely in place and get medical help.

If you can see the object, try to wash it out. Tilt the casualty's head to the injured side, and gently run cold or lukewarm water over the eye from a tap or jug. Alternatively, get the casualty to blink his eyes underwater.

If no water is available, or flushing is not effective, try to lift the object off the eye with a moistened piece of clean gauze or the corner of a clean handkerchief.

If you are still unsuccessful, see a doctor.

Chemical burns to the eye

If chemicals – either liquid or solid – get into the eye, flood the eye with water immediately as they can cause serious damage.

You may need to force the eyelids open if they are shut tight in a spasm of pain.

Object impaled in the eye

Do not attempt to remove any object which is embedded in the eye, because you might cause irreparable damage. First, protect the eye, taking great care not to touch it or apply any pressure, by covering it with a paper or plastic cup. Then put a bandage over both eyes so that the casualty is not tempted to move them.

Telephone 999 and ask for an ambulance. Reassure the person while you wait for it.

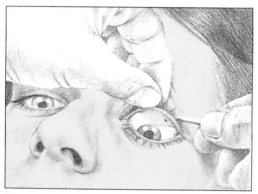

2 *If the grit is on the underside of the eyelid, press down the lid with a matchstick and pull up the lid against the matchstick with your finger and thumb.*

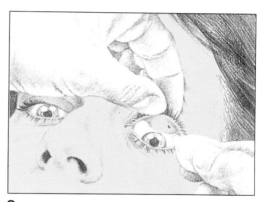

3 *Remove the grit with the corner of a clean handkerchief. Replace the lid by pulling down gently on the lashes. The same treatment can be used for the bottom lid.*

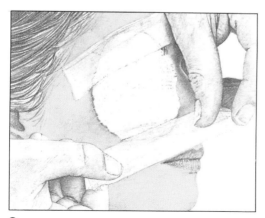

2 *When you have thoroughly flushed the chemical from the eye, dry the face and put a clean dressing lightly over the eye. Get the casualty to hospital as soon as possible.*

DEALING WITH AN IMPALED OBJECT
Do not try to remove any embedded or impaled object from the eye. Instead, cut a hole in a piece of clean cloth and put it over the eye. Place a paper or plastic cup or a ring-pad (see page 58) over the cloth and hold it in place with a bandage. Cover the uninjured eye with the bandage as well. Call an ambulance.

Fainting

If the blood supply to the brain is suddenly and temporarily reduced, a person may faint. Fainting is usually the result of the victim being in a hot, stuffy atmosphere.

But an emotional stimulus, such as an unpleasant sight, a fright or bad news, can also cause fainting. So can a drop in blood sugar due to missed meals or dieting, or standing still for long periods of time.

Sometimes there may be a more serious cause such as illness or injury, in which case a doctor should be consulted.

Someone who is standing still for a long time can reduce the risk of fainting by rocking gently from the heels to the balls of the feet.

The warning signs
- A person who is about to faint becomes pale or greenish-white. He may yawn frequently, showing that he is lacking oxygen.
- The skin is cold and clammy.
- Beads of sweat appear on the face, neck and hands.

What you can do
If someone says he is about to faint, tell him to sit down. Loosen tight clothing at the neck and waist, and put his head down to his knees.

A person who actually faints should have the feet raised above the level of the head to increase the blood circulation to the brain.

Recovery from a faint is usually rapid and complete, but check for any injury that may have been received during a fall. If the fall resulted in a blow to the head that was hard enough to

cause a cut or wound, the casualty should see a doctor, because there is risk of a fractured skull or concussion (see page 86).

Do not give the casualty anything to eat or drink until full consciousness returns, and then only sips of cold water. Do not give the casualty any alcohol, such as brandy. It lowers the rate of the body's vital activities, and may make the condition worse.

If you are in any doubt about the casualty's condition, get medical advice.

TREATING SOMEONE WHO FAINTS
Lay an unconscious casualty on her back with her legs raised above the level of her head. Hold the legs up, or prop them on a chair or anything suitable. Loosen clothing at the neck, chest and waist, and ensure that the casualty gets plenty of fresh air. If she is indoors, open the windows; outside, protect her from the sun. She should recover after a few minutes, but tell her to stay seated for a few minutes more.

Flu

Epidemics of influenza (commonly called flu) occur during most winters. The illness is a virus infection, which spreads rapidly through an area for two or three weeks and then quickly subsides.

Flu leads to high temperature and aching muscles, and can be an emergency if it strikes a person with heart disease, chronic lung disease or diabetes, or someone over 65. The doctor should be called to a patient in any of these categories.

The warning signs
- Headache.
- Aching muscles and back.
- High temperature with the sensation of feeling cold.
- Sweating.
- General weakness.
- Coughing, and pain behind the breastbone which is made worse by coughing.
- Nasal catarrh and sneezing.

What you can do
- Put the patient to bed.
- Give extra fluids to replace losses caused by fever.
- Give painkillers in the doses recommended on the packet.
- To help ease coughing and chest pain, give hot lemon-and-honey drinks or a proprietary cough mixture.
- Do not allow the patient to return to work or school until the main symptoms are over – usually in about three days. It will increase the risk of bringing on pneumonia, and will spread the disease.

How long will it last?
The worst of the illness will be over in two or three days, but aching muscles, headache and fever may persist for a week.

General weakness may continue for a few weeks more, possibly accompanied by a period of depression.

Preventing an attack of flu
Each year a vaccine is produced against the viruses that are expected to cause flu in the following winter. Anyone over 65, and sufferers from heart disease, lung disease or diabetes, should be immunised in September or October. But if an epidemic is caused by a new strain of virus, immunisation may not be effective.

Food poisoning

Severe vomiting and diarrhoea, usually with pain in the abdomen, are the main symptoms of food poisoning (also called gastroenteritis).

Two main types of bacteria cause the ailment. Staphylococcal bacteria multiply in reheated or half-cooked food and produce severe vomiting from two to eight hours after the food is eaten.

Salmonella bacteria usually come from food handlers, flies or unhygienic cooking utensils. The bacteria multiply in the victim's bowel, and the symptoms begin with severe diarrhoea after 12 to 36 hours.

What you should do
- Give the patient sips of water. Do not give food or milk drinks. The stomach is trying to get rid of an irritant; do not irritate it any more. Let it rest.
- A medicine containing antidiarrhoeal and pain-killing drugs may be given to an adult.
- After the stomach has begun to settle for a few hours, give the patient dry biscuits, jelly, blancmange or clear soup. Avoid tea or coffee, or acid drinks such as lemon or orange; they may cause irritation, and vomiting could recur.
- Most attacks of food poisoning settle after two or three days, and the patient can be put back on a fuller, non-irritating diet.
- Call the doctor if there is abdominal pain, blood in the faeces, other unexpected symptoms, or if the symptoms are severe and last longer than three days.

How to avoid food poisoning
- Avoid any creamy foods, processed meat or fish which have been left too long at room temperature. The time depends on the air temperature, but in summer all such foods should be kept in a refrigerator.
- Avoid food which you suspect has been unhygienically prepared. This is especially important in hot climates.
- When heating up cold meat, make sure that it is thoroughly re-cooked.
- Discard any containers of food whose contents show signs of spoiling.

First aid and medical emergencies

Fractures

A fracture is a cracked or broken bone. It can be caused by direct force, as when a car hits a person on the thigh, or by indirect force, as when a person falls on an outstretched hand and breaks the collarbone at the top of the arm.

There are three main types of fracture. A closed fracture leaves the skin unbroken, although it may be heavily bruised. An open, or compound, fracture either has a bone protruding through the skin or a deep gash leading down to the bone. In either case germs may enter the wound, causing serious infection. A greenstick fracture, most common in children, involves a bone splitting as it bends.

The warning signs

• Often, the casualty will have heard or felt the bone break. There may be the feeling of broken bone ends grating together, which can sometimes be heard.
• The casualty may not be able to use the injured part of the body, and will feel pain when he does.
• The area around the break may be tender to the touch, swollen or bruised.
• A limb may be in an unnatural position or deformed when compared to the uninjured side.

What you should do

All doubtful cases of injured bones should be considered as fractures. The principles of treatment are the same in all cases.

TREATING AN OPEN FRACTURE OF THE LEG

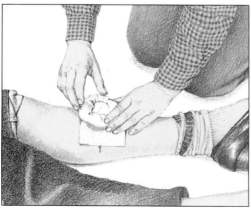

1 If the ambulance is going to take more than half an hour, or if you have to carry the casualty, you must protect the wound and immobilise the leg. First gently remove clothing from the area of the fracture.

2 Cover the wound with a piece of clean non-fluffy cloth (not cotton wool). Then put a ring-pad (see page 58) or two crescent-shaped pads of material around the protruding bone.

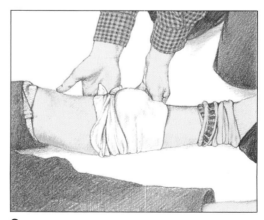

3 Put a bandage around the leg, over the ring-pad. Try to get a helper to support the leg carefully as you do so. The pad will reduce pressure on the wound.

- Do not move the casualty unless it is absolutely necessary.
- Telephone 999 and ask for an ambulance.
- Deal with any severe bleeding (see page 60), unconsciousness (see page 136) or difficulty in breathing (see page 50) before doing anything to the fracture.
- Put the casualty in the most comfortable position possible, and provide support for the injured limb with a rolled-up blanket or coat, or with cushions.
- Do not move the fractured part unnecessarily.
- To limit the dangers of shock, see page 120.
- If it is essential to move the casualty – and time allows – immobilise the injured limb by bandaging it to an uninjured part of the body.

Supporting a fractured leg

Tie a fractured leg to the other leg (see page 127), using scarves, neckties or any other piece of material, preferably something that is at least a few inches wide. This will support the leg until an ambulance arrives. If you need to improvise a stretcher, see page 115.

If a knee is broken, it will be extremely painful and may be bent in an unnatural way. Do not try to force it straight. Lay the casualty down with the leg in the most comfortable position.

Then put a cushion or folded jacket under the knee, and other soft supports such as rolled-up coats or rugs around the leg for further support. Call an ambulance.

Treating a broken arm

Support a broken arm in an arm sling (see page 121). Secure the arm to the chest by tying a broad bandage around the body, passing over the arm. Then take the casualty to hospital.

Never use force to bend a broken arm. If it will not bend, strap it to the body (see page 127) and wait for an ambulance.

Frostbite

In freezing weather, exposed parts of the body, such as the nose, ears, cheeks and chin, may develop frostbite as the skin cools and the blood vessels become constricted, cutting off the blood supply. The hands and feet can also become frostbitten, even when they are enclosed in gloves and boots. In severe cases, gangrene may develop unless the affected part is warmed up and the circulation restored.

The warning signs

- The affected part of the body feels cold and stiff, with a prickling pain.
- The skin becomes hard, and turns blue or white.
- The area becomes numb, and the feeling of cold and pain disappears.

What you should do

- If possible, get the casualty into shelter.
- Remove clothing from the frostbitten area; take off rings and watch from an affected hand.
- Warm the area with skin-to-skin contact. The casualty can put a frostbitten foot into your armpit, for instance. Cover ears, nose or cheeks with warm hands.
- Do not warm the area with dry or radiant heat. Slow thawing is essential.
- Do not rub or massage the frostbitten area.
- When warmth returns, wrap a frostbitten foot or hand in a towel or other cloth, and then cover that with a blanket or sleeping bag.
- To relieve swelling and pain, raise the affected area above the level of the casualty's chest.
- As the area thaws, it may become blue and develop blood-filled blisters. Do not break the blisters or apply any medication.
- Telephone 999 and ask for an ambulance, or get the casualty to the Accident and Emergency Department of a hospital.

First aid and medical emergencies

4 *Immobilise the leg by tying the two legs together with bandages, putting padding between the ankles and knees. Tie below, then above the fracture – but not on it.*

THAWING A FROSTBITTEN FOOT
When feeling begins to return, wrap the foot in a triangular bandage, towel or sweater, then cover it again with a sleeping bag or jacket.

Gas poisoning

The use of natural, non-toxic gas in the home has greatly reduced the number of deaths from accidental gassing. But there are many other danger sources, including propane and butane gases which are widely used in industry, ammonia which is used in refrigeration plants, the fumes given off by burning polyurethane foam found in furniture, and carbon monoxide from car exhaust fumes.

The warning signs
• The casualty may suffer from unsound judgment and may be difficult and uncooperative.
• The casualty may be confused, stupefied or unconscious.

What you should do
Whatever the cause of gassing, the treatment is always the same: try to cut off the source of gas and get the casualty into the open air.

If possible, before attempting a rescue tell someone else to call expert help, such as the fire brigade. Do not attempt a rescue if you are likely to become a casualty yourself.

RESCUING AN UNCONSCIOUS VICTIM

1 *Try to cut off the source of the gas, but be careful not to place yourself in danger. Take a few deep breaths of clean air, then drag the casualty into the open air. Pass your arms under the casualty's armpits and link them across the chest, grasping one of your wrists.*

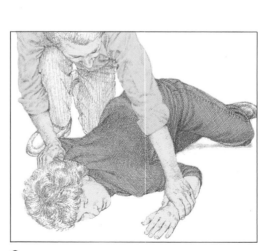

2 *Put your ear close to the casualty's nose and mouth to check her breathing. Check the rise and fall of her chest. If she is not breathing, give artificial respiration (see page 50).*

3 *Once she is breathing normally again, turn her into the recovery position (see page 136). Call an ambulance. Continue to check her breathing until help arrives.*

German measles

The main danger of German measles, known medically as rubella, is that it may affect an unborn child if contracted by a woman in early pregnancy. About 25 per cent of babies whose mothers get German measles in the first 16 weeks of pregnancy are born deaf or blind – sometimes with heart disease as well – or are stillborn. The risk is as high as 60 per cent in very early pregnancy.

The disease, which is otherwise not serious, is spread by contact with someone who has already been infected.

The warning signs

• The patient may feel unwell for a few days without any obvious symptoms.
• A rash of tiny pink, slightly raised spots then appears behind the ears or on the face, spreading downwards to the rest of the body.
• The glands become swollen, particularly behind the ears. The joints may swell and become painful, sometimes severely so, especially in young women.

Duration of the disease

The patient is infectious to others from five days before and until four days after the rash appears. The rash lasts from one to five days, but the joint pains may last for up to 14 days.

What you should do

A patient with German measles should be kept away from pregnant women, and should stay indoors for four days from the onset of the rash. If necessary, painkillers can be given to ease the discomfort.

You should consult your doctor if the joint pains become severe or if the patient develops a high temperature, a severe and persistent headache or becomes drowsy.

A woman who is in contact with German measles in early pregnancy, and does not know if she is immune, should also see her doctor. Blood tests will confirm whether she has been infected. If so, the doctor may ask the patient if she wishes to terminate her pregnancy, rather than risk having a child with deformities.

Developing immunity

German measles is very serious in pregnant women, so children should obtain immunity by catching the disease – you cannot get it twice.

Immunisation is now routinely offered to girls at about 13 if they have not had the disease.

Women of child-bearing age who have not already had German measles, and who may wish to become pregnant, should be immunised. Pregnancy should be avoided for at least two months after the injection, as immunisation might affect the unborn child during this period.

Older women who do not know if they have had the disease can have a blood test. And immunisation after childbirth is usually offered to women who have no immunity.

Grazes

Minor grazes of the sort usually suffered by children rarely need medical attention. But if dirt or grit is embedded in the wound, there is a risk of infection, and the casualty should see a doctor.

What you should do

• Wash your hands before treating the wound.
• Clean the area around the graze with a clean gauze or cotton swab which has been dipped in lukewarm soapy water.
• Wipe outwards, away from the wound.
• Carefully remove any loose dirt or gravel, either by washing or with tweezers.
• Dry the area with a clean swab.
• Cover a small graze with an adhesive dressing (plaster) and a large graze with a sterile dressing. If you do not have a sterile dressing, dress the wound with a clean, folded handkerchief turned inside out so that the untouched side is on the wound. Fix it in place with a bandage or sticking plaster.
• Do not cough on the injury or on the dressing. You could introduce infection.
• Do not dress the wound with cotton wool, because the fibres will stick to it.
• See a doctor straight away if the wound is very dirty or if it was caused by a rusty object. The casualty may need a tetanus injection or a course of antibiotics.
• If pus starts to ooze from the wound later, or the wound becomes sore and inflamed, see a doctor about it.

First aid and medical emergencies

Gunshot wounds

Most gunshot wounds are caused by shotguns, which are widely used in field sports. But all types of firearms – even airguns – are potentially dangerous.

In all types of gunshot accidents the pellet or bullet may leave two wounds – one at the point of entry into the body and another, larger one, at the point of exit.

When treating a gunshot wound, check both the point of entry and the other side of the casualty's body for an exit wound. The casualty may be aware only of the entry wound.

If there is no exit wound, the pellet has either deflected off the body, leaving a wound similar in appearance to an entry wound, or it is lodged inside.

A bullet will cause a great deal of tissue damage, and it may hit and splinter a bone. All gunshot wounds require expert medical attention urgently.

FIRST AID FOR A BULLET WOUND
Cover the wound with a clean pad or your bare hands to stop the bleeding. If there are entry and exit wounds, cover both. Once the bleeding has slowed, dress and bandage the wound (see page 56) and get medical help.

Head and face injuries

Any head injury which is severe enough to cause bleeding or a bruise could also fracture the skull or cause concussion (see page 86). So anyone who has suffered a head injury should be taken to a doctor or to the Accident and Emergency Department of a hospital for examination – even if, superficially, the injury does not appear to be serious.

Head injuries are common in road accidents, but they are also caused by falls – off a ladder or down a flight of stairs, for example. Old people are particularly prone to falls.

Sports are also a source of head injuries, particularly rugby. In cricket and hockey, the

HOW TO BANDAGE A SCALP INJURY

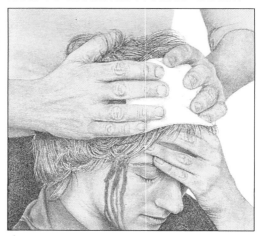

1 *Gently feel the skull around the wound. If part of it seems to move, suspect a fracture and do not press on it. Otherwise, press a clean pad on the wound to stop the bleeding.*

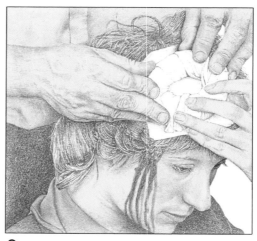

2 *Put a fresh cloth pad over the first. If you suspect a fracture, or if something is embedded, put the dressing on lightly, with a ring-pad to lessen pressure (see page 58).*

players may be hit on the head by the ball. Golfers, too, can be at risk.

Brain damage can occur without any obvious sign, except perhaps for brief unconsciousness. In elderly people, particularly, any slight knock to the head may cause internal bleeding which, if it is not recognised and treated, can result in permanent damage.

The warning signs
If you suspect that someone may have suffered a blow to the head, look for any or all of the following symptoms:
• The eye pupils (the black parts) may be unequal in size, and the casualty may have double vision and noisy breathing.
• Cuts, bruises and swellings on the scalp, face or jaw.
• Headache.
• Confusion or drowsiness, which may be followed by unconsciousness.
• Loss of memory of events before or at the time of the accident.
• Weak pulse and shallow breathing.

Bleeding scalp and face injuries
An injury to the scalp may bleed profusely because the scalp has a rich supply of blood.

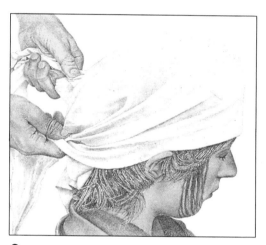

3 *Secure the dressing with a triangular bandage. Put the long edge across the forehead and the point at the neck. Bring the two ends around to the neck and cross them.*

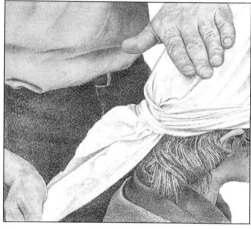

5 *Gently place one hand on the bandage to stop it slipping. With the other, draw the point downwards, parallel with the back of the neck, so that the bandage is snugly over the scalp.*

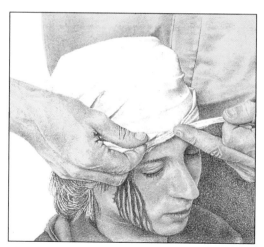

4 *Bring the two ends around to the forehead and tie them together, securing the bandage. Keep the casualty's head as steady as possible while you put the bandage on.*

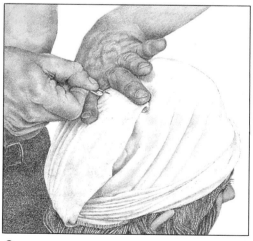

6 *Bring the point of the bandage up to the crown and fix it lightly in place with a safety pin or adhesive tape. Alternatively, tuck the point into the edge of the bandage at the front.*

Because the skin is stretched tight over the head, the wound may also gape open and look much more serious than it really is.

However, there is always the danger of a fracture to the skull, and the casualty should be examined by a doctor or at the Accident and Emergency Department of a hospital. In the meantime, control the bleeding by holding your hand or a cloth pad, such as the inside of a clean, folded handkerchief, on the wound.

A wound on the face will also bleed profusely, and may look much worse than it really is. But if it is deep, take the casualty to hospital because the wound may need to be stitched. If the wound followed a blow to the head, also get medical treatment at once.

A broken jaw

A person who has suffered a broken jaw will often have a wound inside the mouth. The casualty may have difficulty in speaking and there may be an excessive flow of saliva, often tinged with blood, and broken teeth. Usually only one side of the jaw will be broken.

Put a bandage under the casualty's chin and tie it in place on top of the head to support the jaw while you get the casualty to hospital. Do not tie the bandage too tightly.

TREATING A BLEEDING FACE

1 *A cut face may produce such severe bleeding that the wound may look worse than it really is. Press the inside of a clean, folded handkerchief, or a pad of paper tissues, against the wound. Do not use cotton wool.*

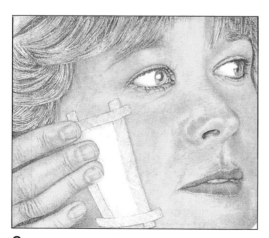

2 *When the bleeding slows (which may take 15 minutes), put a fresh handkerchief or pad on the wound – on top of the old one – and fix it in place with sticking plaster. If blood seeps through, put another pad on top.*

SUPPORTING A BROKEN JAW

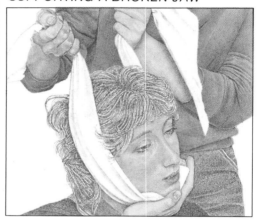

1 *If the jaw is broken or dislocated, make sure first that the mouth is clear of blood and broken teeth to avoid the risk of choking. Then put a pad of cloth under the point of the chin, and get the casualty to hold it in place.*

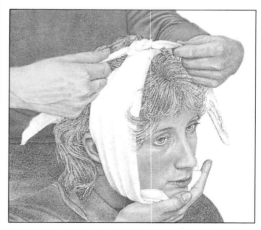

2 *Put a bandage or scarf over the pad, bring the ends to the top of the head, and tie them together in a reef knot. The bandage should be tight enough to support the jaw, but not so tight that the teeth are clenched.*

Heart attack

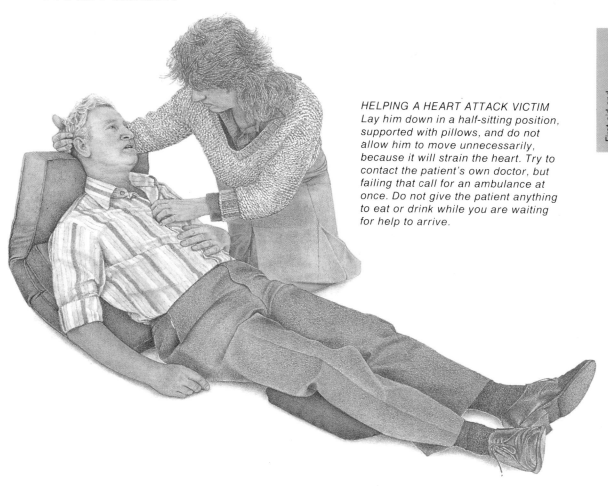

HELPING A HEART ATTACK VICTIM
Lay him down in a half-sitting position,
supported with pillows, and do not
allow him to move unnecessarily,
because it will strain the heart. Try to
contact the patient's own doctor, but
failing that call for an ambulance at
once. Do not give the patient anything
to eat or drink while you are waiting
for help to arrive.

Severe, crushing pain in the chest, often spreading to one or both arms, the neck and the jaw, is the main symptom of a heart attack. It comes on suddenly and, unlike anginal pain, is not related to exertion. It does not pass off if the patient keeps still.

The patient may also become breathless and sweat profusely. He may suffer sudden giddiness, causing him to sit down or lean against something for support.

During the weeks before an attack, the patient may have experienced unusual tiredness, shortness of breath and unaccustomed indigestion.

What you should do

• If the patient is conscious, put him in a half-sitting position, with head and shoulders supported with pillows, and knees bent.

• If possible, contact the patient's own doctor, as there may be a history of heart disease. If his doctor is not obtainable, telephone 999 and ask for an ambulance, and make it clear to the ambulance service that you suspect a heart attack.

• Loosen the patient's clothing around the neck, chest and waist to help circulation and ease his breathing.

• Do not give the patient anything to eat or drink.

• Do not allow him to move unnecessarily; it will put extra strain on the heart.

• If the patient becomes unconscious, put him in the recovery position (see page 136).

Preventing heart attacks

Most heart attacks are caused by a blood clot in one of the arteries supplying blood to the heart muscle. The process is known medically as coronary thrombosis.

The likelihood of coronary thrombosis is increased by smoking, obesity, diabetes, raised blood pressure, lack of exercise, faulty diet and a family history of heart attacks.

The following five rules will help you to avoid a heart attack:

• Stay within your ideal weight for height.

• If you smoke, give it up.

• Take regular exercise.

• Eat only modest amounts of meat from chickens, cows, sheep and pigs, as the fat from the meat may be deposited in the arteries, interfering with the flow of blood.

• If you suffer from diabetes or high blood pressure, follow your doctor's advice carefully.

Heat exhaustion and heat stroke

People who exert themselves during a summer holiday in a hot climate, or long-distance runners on a warm day, may suffer from heat exhaustion, or from an even worse condition known as heat stroke.

Both conditions can lead to unconsciousness and they both require medical treatment.

The body can become overwhelmed by heat when its mechanism for keeping cool breaks down. Usually it cools itself in three ways:

• It produces sweat which evaporates and cools the skin – just as water that seeps through an unglazed jug will cool the remaining water when it evaporates off the outside.

• The capillaries of the skin enlarge and carry more blood to the surface, where it loses its heat. This produces the flushed look a hot person often has.

• Breathing increases, carrying surplus heat from the lungs.

The effects of heat exhaustion

Profuse sweating on a hot day leads to an excessive loss of moisture and salt, which is contained in sweat.

This brings on muscle cramps in the legs and body, and weakness – although the sweating prevents the body's temperature from rising. If the fluid and salt are not replaced, the condition will get worse and the casualty will collapse.

Other symptoms of heat exhaustion are dizziness, headache and nausea. The temperature stays normal and the skin feels cold and moist. The face looks pale.

The breathing is fast and shallow, and the pulse is fast and weak.

The condition can be made worse if the sufferer has had a stomach upset with diarrhoea or vomiting, causing even greater loss of fluid.

• To treat heat exhaustion, lay the casualty in a cool place, preferably indoors, and give cold, salted water to drink.

• If the casualty becomes unconscious, put him or her in the recovery position (see page 136) and get medical help.

TREATING HEAT EXHAUSTION

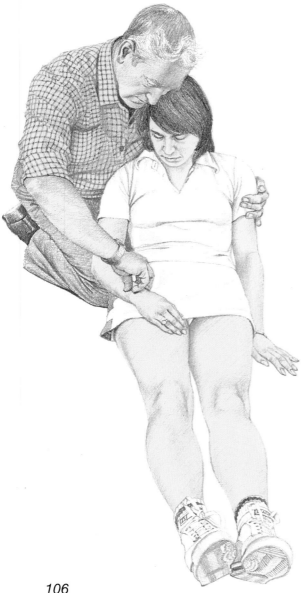

1 *Put the casualty in a cool place, preferably indoors. Remove any heavy clothing. If she is suffering from heat exhaustion, her pulse will be fast and weak. Check her temperature; if it is higher than normal she may be suffering from heat stroke. If she becomes unconscious, put her in the recovery position (see page 136).*

2 *If the casualty is conscious, give her a cup of weakly salted water every ten minutes. Use a quarter of a teaspoon of salt to each cup. Add fruit juice to improve the taste.*

Heat stroke: how to treat it

When humidity, as well as temperature, is very high, sweat is less able to cool the body as it cannot evaporate into the already moisture-laden air. It takes from three to six weeks to adjust to these conditions, and a person may suffer heat stroke before he has acclimatised.

Heat stroke may occur suddenly, with the body temperature rising to 40°C (104°F). The casualty's skin feels hot and may be dry. He may complain of headache, dizziness and nausea. As the condition worsens, he may become confused and lapse into unconsciousness.

TREATING HEAT STROKE

Treatment for heat stroke must be given quickly or the casualty may die. Babies and old people are particularly at risk.

• Move the casualty to a cool place. Remove the clothing and cover the body with a wet sheet. Keep it wet with cold water, and fan the casualty until the body temperature drops to 38°C (100°F).

• Call a doctor or ambulance as soon as possible. If the casualty becomes unconscious, put him in the recovery position (see page 136), and continue the cooling treatment.

How to deal with prickly heat

An intensely irritating skin rash, which may develop in hot, humid weather, is known as prickly heat. It is caused by swelling of the skin cells because of excessive sweating, and mostly affects babies and fat people. Pimples or small blisters appear, particularly in the skin creases and where clothing has been tight.

There is no quick remedy, but some relief will be gained by wearing loose clothing and lying under a fan during the heat of the day. Have frequent baths in cool water, using little soap, and apply calamine lotion to the affected area.

It may be necessary to see a doctor if the irritation becomes too severe to bear, or if the sufferer becomes weak and lethargic.

The skin will rapidly return to normal when you return to a cool climate.

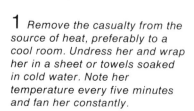

1 *Remove the casualty from the source of heat, preferably to a cool room. Undress her and wrap her in a sheet or towels soaked in cold water. Note her temperature every five minutes and fan her constantly.*

2 *When the casualty's temperature is down to 38°C (100°F), replace the wet sheet with a dry one. Continue fanning. If her temperature rises again, restart the cooling treatment.*

First aid and
medical emergencies

Hiccups

Most attacks of hiccups are over in 10 to 20 minutes, but occasionally attacks can last for days, causing distress and interfering with sleep. Persistent hiccups suggest some abdominal disorder requiring medical treatment.

Most hiccups are caused by irritation of the diaphragm – a muscular partition which separates the chest cavity from the abdomen. This occurs when the sufferer has overfilled the stomach with a large amount of food or drink, especially hot drinks. The diaphragm then goes into repeated and involuntary spasms.

What can be done to stop hiccups

Carbon dioxide gas – one of the products of breathing – inhibits hiccups. Simply holding the breath several times will cause carbon dioxide to build up in the body, and the hiccups may stop without further treatment.

Breathing in and out of a paper bag works in the same way. But *do not* use a plastic bag. It can mould itself to the mouth and nose, and obstruct breathing altogether.

Most other household remedies work by making the sufferer hold his breath. Drinking water slowly, sucking ice or pulling on the tongue are all ways of building up carbon dioxide.

If the hiccups last more than a day, the sufferer should see a doctor, who may prescribe sedatives or arrange a supply of 5 per cent carbon dioxide to be inhaled. The doctor may also examine the patient for kidney, liver, lung or abdominal disorders which could be causing the hiccups, although such disorders are rare.

ONE WAY OF STOPPING HICCUPS
Breathing in and out of a paper bag builds up carbon dioxide in the body, which can bring the spasms of the diaphragm to a stop. But on no account use a plastic bag.

Hypothermia

If a baby in a cold room begins to look bright red, becomes lethargic and refuses food, it may have hypothermia, a serious condition in which the body's temperature drops below normal.

Unless the drop in temperature is reversed the baby may die in a few hours.

Old people are also at risk. At first they may complain of the cold. If these warnings go unnoticed or are ignored, the condition will grow worse until the victim becomes mentally confused and tired, with stiff muscles. Uncontrollable shivering may also occur or speech may be slurred.

Eventually the victim becomes unconscious, suffers brain damage and then dies.

(For hypothermia in outdoor conditions, see *Exposure: the silent killer*, page 301.)

How hypothermia sets in

Hypothermia begins when the body's temperature drops below about 35°C (95°F) from the normal level of 37°C (98.6°F).

With babies, the cause of hypothermia is usually a cold bedroom at night. Premature babies and babies which are suffering from illness are the most susceptible.

One problem in recognising the condition is that the red colour of the skin that develops may be mistaken for a healthy glow.

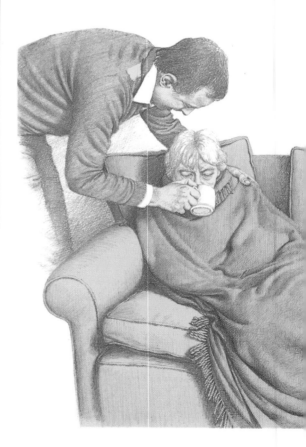

With old people, hypothermia usually results from inadequate food, clothing and heating in winter. Their resistance to cold will also be lessened if they are taking drugs or alcohol.

What you should do

If you suspect that someone is suffering from hypothermia, feel his or her skin. It will be abnormally cold to the touch if the condition has set in. You must take action to prevent the condition from getting worse, and you must call an ambulance to get the victim to hospital.

• If a blanket or rug is readily available, wrap it around the victim, covering the body but not the face.

• Lay him down. If he is unconscious, put him in the recovery position (see page 136).

• If possible, increase the temperature of the room, or move the victim to a warmer room.

• Telephone 999 and ask for an ambulance.

• While waiting for the ambulance, give the victim – if conscious – hot, sweet drinks such as milk or hot chocolate. Do not give alcohol.

• Do not massage the victim's limbs or suggest that he takes exercise. This will only take blood away from the body's vital organs.

• If the ambulance is delayed, wrap a hot-water bottle in a towel or cloth and put it on the victim's trunk, not on the arms or legs.

Hysteria

A fit of hysterics is usually caused by an emotional upset or mental stress. The attack may resemble an epileptic fit, but is more dramatised and is 'staged' to gain sympathy and attention. It will continue as long as there is an audience.

In an adult, hysterics take longer to develop than an epileptic fit and may vary from temporary loss of control, when the person shouts or screams, to a noisy display or arm waving, tearing at clothes and hair, and rolling on the ground in an apparent frenzy.

Although genuinely distressed, sufferers take care not to hurt themselves. They may, for example, 'collapse' into a fairly safe position. They may also move weakly to suggest illness.

What you should do

• Be gentle but firm. Reassure and try to calm the person.

• Ask relatives and onlookers to leave the area.

• Do not slap a hysterical person on the face as it may cause psychological harm. In the case of a person with a weak heart, the shock could even be fatal.

• When the attack has subsided, suggest that the person sees a doctor.

TREATING AN ELDERLY VICTIM OF HYPOTHERMIA
An elderly person living alone may become a victim of hypothermia because she has run out of fuel during winter. So it may not be possible to take quick action to heat the room. First, call an ambulance, as it is imperative to get her to hospital quickly. Then wrap her in a blanket and – if she is conscious – give her a hot drink. A hot-water bottle, wrapped in a towel, could also be placed against her trunk. Do not place it against her limbs, because it will draw blood away from the body's vital organs in the torso.

Insect stings and bites

Stings and bites from bees, wasps and ants can be painful but are not usually dangerous. It is only an allergic reaction, or a sting or bite in the throat or mouth, that can endanger life.

If the victim has been stung by a bee, the sting will probably be left embedded in the skin. Remove it with a pair of tweezers. Alternatively, gently scrape the sting out with a knife blade or needle that has been sterilised in a flame.

Wasps and ants do not leave stings behind.

Dealing with an allergic reaction

A massive allergic reaction to a sting (or to a drug such as cocaine) is known as anaphylactic shock. It occurs within a few seconds or minutes, and the casualty will become very weak and feel sick. His chest will feel tight and he will have difficulty breathing. He may be sneezing and his face may swell up. Less often, he may become unconscious, and may stop breathing.
• Telephone 999 and ask for an ambulance.
• Reassure the casualty that help is on the way.
• Lay him on his back. Raise the feet on a cushion or folded coat. Keep his head low and turn it to one side in case he vomits.
• Keep the casualty warm with a blanket or rug.
• Loosen tight clothing around the neck and waist to help with breathing.
• Do not give the casualty anything to eat or drink. Do not allow him to smoke, either – it may make breathing more difficult.
• If the casualty becomes unconscious, or vomiting seems likely, or breathing becomes very difficult, put him in the recovery position (see page 136).

Stings to the mouth or throat

A sting to the mouth or throat can cause the throat to swell rapidly, blocking the airway.
• Give the victim an ice cube or some ice cream to suck, or cold water to drink, to lessen the swelling.
• If breathing stops, start artificial respiration immediately (see page 50).
• Telephone 999 and ask for an ambulance or take the victim at once to the Accident and Emergency Department of a hospital.

Blood-sucking ticks

Ticks are spider-like creatures which suck the blood of animals and humans by clinging to the skin with beak-like mouths. They are active in spring and summer, and may attach themselves to farmworkers or children who play in woods and grassy areas. Their bodies swell up to hold the blood they feed on.

Do not try to pull a tick out. Touch it with a lit cigarette or match and it will fall off. Alternatively, cover it with machine oil or cooking oil to close its breathing pores. It may fall off at once; if not, leave the oil for half an hour and then remove the tick carefully with tweezers.

Wash the area with soap and water and apply antihistamine cream.

TREATING BEE, WASP OR ANT STINGS

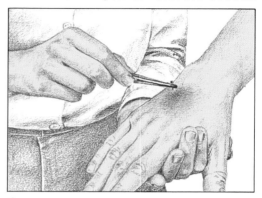

1 *Remove a bee sting with tweezers, but take care not to squeeze the poison bag, because that will just pump more poison into the skin. Wasps and ants do not leave stings behind.*

2 *Apply antihistamine cream to any sting. Or use a solution of 1 teaspoon of bicarbonate of soda in a tumbler of water for bee stings, a weak ammonia solution for wasps and ants.*

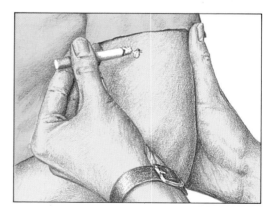

TREATING TICK BITES
Apply the glowing end of a cigarette, or a burning match, to the tick's body; this will make the tick fall off. Do not pull it out, as it may leave its head behind, causing infection.

Measles

The most obvious symptom of measles is the rash of brownish-pink, slightly raised spots which starts behind the ears and spreads in blotches over the whole body.

But before the rash breaks out, a dry, irritating cough generally occurs and the patient develops a high temperature. The cough can occur up to four days before the rash starts. The eyes can also be sore and red, or 'heavy', for a few days before the rash.

What you should do

• Put the patient – usually a child – to bed and give cool drinks to bring the temperature down. It does not matter if the child does not want to eat, as long as plenty of fluids are taken.
• Notify your doctor.
• Keep the child quiet and resting while there is a high temperature and illness. Many children prefer the room darkened because their eyes feel sore.
• If necessary, give temperature-reducing drugs, such as paracetamol, in the recommended doses.
• The disease is likely to last five to seven days after the rash first appears.

Complications that can occur

Most victims of measles recover completely, but there can be serious complications of the ears, lungs and brain.

Consequently the doctor may check the child for otitis media (an ear infection which can cause severe earache and deafness), pneumonia and encephalitis (a rare disease of the brain which causes headache, confusion or unconsciousness, an aching neck and fever).

If one of these diseases occurs, a course of antibiotics will probably be prescribed. Because measles is caused by a virus, antibiotics are of no use against the measles itself.

Because of the serious complications of measles, attempts are being made to eradicate the disease by immunisation. Children should be immunised between 12 and 18 months of age. Although the campaign has greatly reduced the number of cases and the complications, measles is still one of the commonest diseases in the world.

Someone who has had the disease cannot catch it a second time.

Miscarriage

At the first sign of a miscarriage the woman should go to bed immediately. Rest is essential if the pregnancy is to be saved.

Three warning signs occur in succession if the miscarriage takes its full course.
• In the early stages the commonest symptom is loss of blood from the vagina. If the embryo has not been dislodged, this stage is known medically as a 'threatened abortion', and the pregnancy may still be saved.
• If the condition becomes worse, pains like small labour pains may come and go at regular intervals. This is a sign that the threatened miscarriage may have become inevitable.
• The bleeding may also increase at this stage.

What can be done

• Notify the doctor at the first signs and put the patient to bed.
• If the miscarriage passes into the inevitable stage, the doctor may send the patient to hospital.
• In hospital she may have an evacuation of the uterus, under anaesthetic, to remove any placenta or membrane left behind after the embryo has been lost.

How common are miscarriages?

Medical research has shown that probably about one-third of all pregnancies miscarry within four weeks of conception. In many cases the woman never knows that she has been pregnant; the miscarriage occurs about four weeks after her last menstrual period, and so passes unrecognised. In other cases miscarriages may occur a week or so later, and she just thinks that she has had a late period.

Miscarriages may be nature's way of ending a pregnancy that is in some way likely to be unsatisfactory.

Avoiding a miscarriage

Once a woman has become aware that she is pregnant, she should avoid unnecessary fatigue and sporting activities, especially if there is a risk of injury.

It is also a sensible precaution to avoid sexual intercourse during the time when periods would normally be due.

First aid and medical emergencies

111

Moving an injured person

Injured people should be moved only if they are in immediate danger, or if they have to be taken to where medical help is available. This may occur if you have to move a casualty off a busy road, get him out of a burning house, or carry him to safety after a climbing accident.

Otherwise, leave the casualty undisturbed and carry out first aid while someone else calls for an ambulance.

If moving is essential, take care not to injure yourself. Back injuries are easily suffered when moving heavy weights, so keep your backbone straight, your head up, and use the stronger parts of your body to do the lifting – the thigh muscles, the hip and the shoulder. Keep the weight as close as possible to your body.

If other people are on the scene, ask someone to help you. It is always easier for two people to lift a weight than one.

It is usually best for an accident victim to be taken to hospital in an ambulance, but if he is suffering from only minor injuries to the arms or hands, he can be taken in a car.

Moving a casualty by yourself

If the person is only slightly injured and is able to stand, get him to put one arm around your shoulder. Supported in this way, he can be moved fairly easily. This is a useful method of moving a person with a sprained ankle.

An unconscious person can be dragged to safety in one of two ways. You can hold him under the shoulders and drag him backwards in a crouching or squatting position. Or you can tie his wrists together, put your head through the arms and crawl on all fours, dragging him

with you. Either of these methods could be used to drag an unconscious person from a burning building or a gas-filled room.

When you have someone to help you

One of the simplest ways for two people to move a casualty is to carry him on a chair, with one person holding the back of the chair and the other holding the front legs.

This is a useful way of carrying an injured person down a flight of stairs. But first make sure that the staircase and passage are clear of obstructions, or any hazards such as loose rugs or children's toys.

A disabled person in a wheelchair can be carried in a similar way. First, put the wheel-

HELPING A CONSCIOUS PERSON
Stand close to the casualty on the injured side, unless the wound is to the hand, arm or shoulder. In that case, support from the uninjured side. Put your arm around her waist and grip the clothing at the hip. Get her to put her arm around your neck and grasp her hand. Take her weight with your body and move forwards with slow, short steps.

chair's brakes on, and get the casualty to sit well back in the chair. Then stand to one side of the chair, with your helper on the other side facing you. Lift the chair together, holding the fixed parts. Do not hold the wheels, as they might turn, and be careful of the arm rests and side supports, as they might be removable.

A casualty who cannot walk but can use his hands can be carried by two people using a 'four-handed seat'. The two helpers each grip their left wrist with their right hand, and then grip the other person's right wrist with their free hand. The casualty puts an arm around each helper's neck and sits on the 'seat'. The two helpers stand up straight and start walking with the outside foot.

MOVING AN UNCONSCIOUS PERSON

1 *Use this method if you have a fairly long way to go or if the casualty is heavy. Check the breathing but do not start artificial respiration until you are clear of danger. Turn the casualty face up and cross the arms at the wrists.*

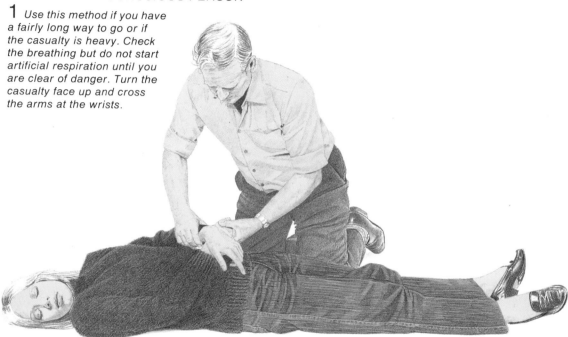

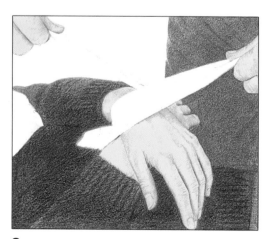

2 *Use a belt, scarf or bandage to tie the wrists together. Wind the material around the wrists tightly, but not so tightly as to impede circulation. Tie the ends with a reef knot, and check quickly with your fingers that the knot is completely secure.*

3 *Kneel astride the casualty and slip your head through the wrists so they are resting on your shoulders at the base of your neck. Push yourself up into a crouch, and work forwards to safety, using your arms to take the weight. Keep the casualty's head off the ground.*

Making an improvised stretcher

Two people can move an injured person a long distance by making an improvised stretcher out of two or more coats with their sleeves turned inside out and a pair of poles, such as broomsticks, pushed through the sleeves.

To get the person onto the stretcher, one of the stretcher bearers should roll the casualty gently onto the uninjured side. While he is doing that, the other bearer should put the open stretcher flat against the casualty's back. Then the stretcher, with the casualty on it, can be rolled back gently onto the ground.

If the casualty is unconscious, put the open stretcher against his front so that he is carried in the recovery position (see page 136).

DRAGGING A LIGHT CASUALTY
It may be possible to drag a very light casualty by simply gripping her under the shoulders. Work your way backwards, letting her head rest on your upper arm. If you have to go down stairs or a steep slope, support the head as much as possible on your thigh. If the casualty is heavier, crouch down into a squat, grasp one of your wrists with the other hand across her chest and then lift (see page 100).

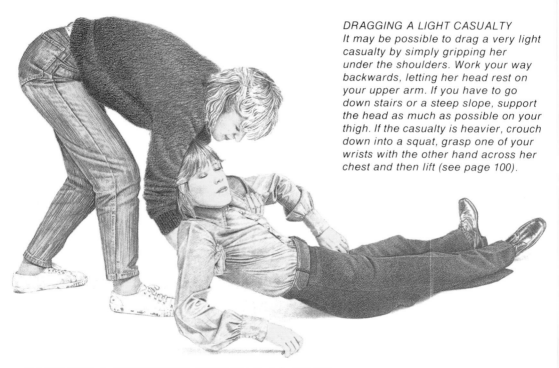

CARRYING A CONSCIOUS PERSON ON A CHAIR

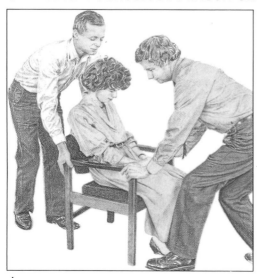

1 *Check that the chair is strong enough to take the weight. Sit the casualty well back in it, and stand in front with the other helper behind. Tilt the chair backwards as you lift it.*

2 *Carry the chair with the casualty facing forwards, so that you go down stairs with the bearer at the front backing down. On wide stairs, the bearers can hold the sides instead.*

First aid
and medical emergencies

IMPROVISING A STRETCHER

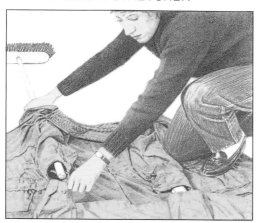

1 Take two or three coats or jackets, and turn the sleeves inside out. Pass a strong pole through one of the sleeves of each jacket, and a second pole through the other sleeves.

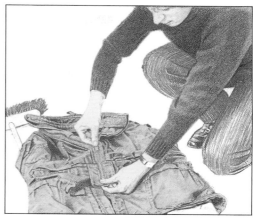

2 Zip or button up the jackets to create the stretcher. If possible, get an uninjured person to lie on the stretcher first, and lift it to make sure that it can take the weight.

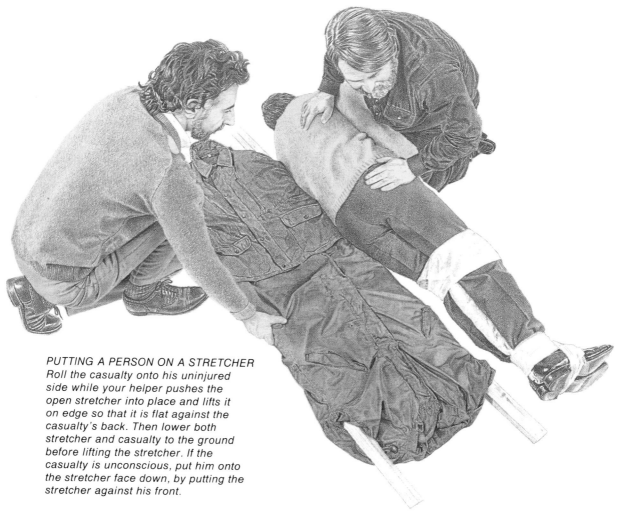

PUTTING A PERSON ON A STRETCHER
Roll the casualty onto his uninjured side while your helper pushes the open stretcher into place and lifts it on edge so that it is flat against the casualty's back. Then lower both stretcher and casualty to the ground before lifting the stretcher. If the casualty is unconscious, put him onto the stretcher face down, by putting the stretcher against his front.

Mumps

The most obvious sign of mumps is a large swelling on one side of the face. It is caused by a saliva-producing gland swelling up in front of the ear and over the angle of the jaw.

A day or two later the gland on the opposite side of the face may also swell. Other saliva-producing glands under the tongue and under the jaw may also be affected.

The patient may also suffer earache and pain when eating.

Mumps is a common infection, mostly affecting children over the age of two, and occurs in epidemics every three or four years. But it can also attack older people, and may cause inflammation of the testicles in men, inflammation of the ovaries in women, and inflammation of the pancreas in both sexes, producing pain in the abdomen.

What you should do
- Keep the patient at rest for a few days.
- If chewing is painful, offer soups and drinks.
- If a testicle is swollen or sore, support the scrotum with a pillow or bandage. A towel beneath the testicles, with the ends draped over the thighs, may help. Leave pyjama trousers off and give a mild painkiller such as paracetamol in recommended doses.

When you should call the doctor
- If the testicles are swollen or sore.
- If there is severe or persistent earache.
- If there is severe or persistent pain in the abdomen – the lower part of the trunk.
- If there is severe headache, with a stiff neck.
- If the patient finds light uncomfortable.

The doctor may examine the patient for an ear infection known as otitis media, for inflammation of the testicles (orchitis), for inflammation of the fluid bathing the brain (meningitis) or, rarely, of the brain itself (encephalitis).

How long is the patient infectious?
Sufferers are infectious for about six days before the glands begin to swell, and remain infectious for a further two weeks. As it is impossible to prevent spread of the disease in the symptomless period, there is no point in isolating the patient once the disease has shown itself.

Someone who has already had the illness cannot catch it again.

Nose injuries

The nose's function as an opening to the body and its prominent position on the face make it subject to a variety of problems.

Nosebleeds
Bleeding from the nose may be the result of blowing too hard, sneezing, picking, air-pressure changes or high blood pressure. Occasionally blood disorders may be the cause, and sometimes there may be no apparent cause for a nosebleed at all.

If blood mixed with a straw-coloured fluid trickles from the nose of an unconscious person, suspect a fracture of the skull (see page 102).

For a normal nosebleed, sit in a chair with your head slightly forward and pinch the nostrils together for at least 10 minutes.

Loosen any tight clothing around the neck.

Spit out any blood that goes down the back of the nose. It is preferable to spit it out as swallowed blood may make you feel sick, so have a bowl close by.

After 10 minutes, release the nostrils gradually. If the bleeding has stopped, sit quietly for a while, and do not blow your nose for at least three hours.

If the bleeding starts up again, squeeze the nostrils for a further 10 minutes.

If the bleeding still continues, see a doctor or go to the Accident and Emergency Department of your local hospital.

You should also see a doctor if you lose so much blood that you become pale or dizzy.

Broken nose
The bones at the bridge of the nose may be broken by an injury, often in a traffic accident. There is then a danger that a deformity of the nose may become permanent, as happens with some boxers.

The symptoms of a broken nose are:
- Severe pain.
- Irregular shape.
- Severe nosebleed.

If a broken nose is suspected, you should take the casualty to a doctor or to the Accident and Emergency Department of your local hospital.

Bleeding can often be stopped with gauze packed into the nostrils.

If there is no deformity causing an obstruction of the nose, treatment is usually unnecessary, apart from an X-ray. The fracture will take about two weeks to heal.

A deformed nose can be corrected by an operation under general anaesthetic.

Foreign body in the nose
Small children often push objects, such as pebbles or beads, into their nostrils. A smooth object may stick harmlessly in the nose, but something jagged can easily cause damage to the inside of the nose and make it bleed.

You should suspect that something is lodged in the nose if:

• A child is playing with its nose.
• One nostril is obstructed, and possibly bleeding.
• The child complains of discomfort or pain in the nose.

Do not try to remove the object yourself; you may make the problem worse.

Take the child to your doctor or to the Accident and Emergency Department of your local hospital, where the object will be removed gently with forceps, or under a general anaesthetic.

STOPPING A NOSEBLEED
Sit down with your head slightly forward to prevent blood running down into your throat. Hold the nostrils together for 10 minutes. If, after that, the bleeding continues, repeat for a further 10 minutes.

Poisoning

Many cases of poisoning occur when a person – often a child – drinks some household or garden chemical.

A child may take bleach, cleaning fluid, rat poison or paint stripper, and gardeners sometimes drink insecticides or weedkillers that they have made up and kept in a soft-drink bottle.

Some plants in Britain are also poisonous. The most common are the seeds and berries of laburnum and deadly or woody nightshade, 'green' potatoes and death cap fungus.

The warning signs
A person who has taken poison is likely to show some of the following symptoms:
• Stomach pain.
• Retching or vomiting.
• Diarrhoea.
• Delirium and convulsions.
• Burns around the mouth if the poison was corrosive, and severe pain in the mouth, gullet and stomach.
• Difficulty in breathing.
• Unconsciousness.

What you should do
• If the victim is conscious, try to find out what he has swallowed. Remember that he may become unconscious at any time.
• Look around for any container or the remains of a poisonous plant that might be a clue.
• Do not try to induce vomiting. It wastes time and may be harmful.
• If the victim is conscious and has swallowed something that burns, such as bleach, give him about a pint of water or milk to drink slowly to dilute the poison in his stomach.
• If the victim is unconscious, place him in the recovery position (see page 136).
• Call an ambulance. Give the ambulance men the container or a sample of vomit to help them to identify the poison.
• If the victim's breathing stops, begin artificial respiration (see page 50). Take care not to get any of the poison on your own mouth. Clean the victim's mouth, or use the mouth-to-nose technique.

How to avoid poisoning
A great number of substances found around the house – in the kitchen, bathroom, workroom and garden shed – are poisonous and may be drunk or eaten by an inquisitive toddler.

Apparently innocent things, including liquid soap, some cosmetics and fire lighters, are poisonous. And others invite a child to pick them up and put them in his mouth; some dangerous medicines look like sweets, and some spot weed-killers can be held and licked like ice cream.

Keep all dangerous chemicals out of the reach of small children, and never store unused weedkillers and insecticides in soft-drink bottles where they may be picked up by either children or unwary adults.

Pulse and breathing

The pulse rate plays an important part in diagnosing some injuries which may have no very obvious symptoms.

A rapid or weak pulse is often associated with shock, internal bleeding and heat exhaustion. Occasionally, a rapid or irregular pulse, occurring while a person is at rest, may be a symptom of serious heart disorder.

A slow pulse can occur if the body cools down to an unnatural degree, as happens to a victim of hypothermia.

The pulse measures the rate at which the heart beats, and this varies throughout life. In a baby's first weeks it may beat 140 times a minute, but by the age of ten the rate will have dropped to an average of 90 a minute. A man, awake but at rest, has a pulse rate between 60 and 80 a minute, with an average of 72. A woman's average rate is slightly higher – 78 to 82 a minute.

An elderly person may have a rate of only 60 a minute, and a sleeping adult of either sex has a rate of 60 to 65.

In times of extreme activity the pulse rate of an adult can go up to 140 a minute.

Each pulse beat is caused by a wave of blood pressure driven along the arteries by the pumping action of the heart. The pulse is most easily detected at two places on the body – the inside of the wrist, just below the thumb joint, and in the hollow of the throat just below the angle of the jaw.

When you take a pulse, note whether it is fast or slow, strong or weak, regular or irregular. Accurate taking of the pulse requires practice, and may be difficult even then. Practise on yourself or a member of your family from time to time so that, if an emergency arises suddenly, you will be able to find the pulse in the wrist or throat without having to hunt for it.

The breathing rate

Respiration – the process of breathing – is closely linked to heartbeat. A person breathes to absorb oxygen from the air into the blood. The oxygen is then circulated to all parts of the

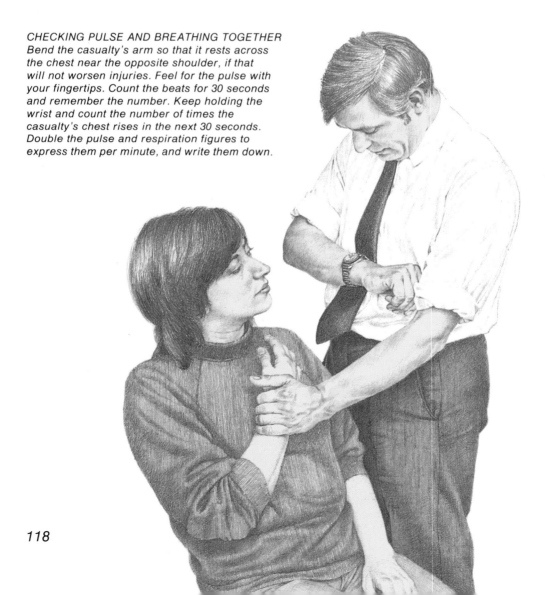

CHECKING PULSE AND BREATHING TOGETHER
Bend the casualty's arm so that it rests across the chest near the opposite shoulder, if that will not worsen injuries. Feel for the pulse with your fingertips. Count the beats for 30 seconds and remember the number. Keep holding the wrist and count the number of times the casualty's chest rises in the next 30 seconds. Double the pulse and respiration figures to express them per minute, and write them down.

body by the regular, pumping action of the heart. Children breathe an average of 20 to 30 times a minute, and adults an average of 12 to 16 times a minute. This increases during exercise and when a person is injured or under stress.

When measuring the breathing rate, count only the number of times the chest rises. Many people unknowingly alter their breathing rate if they are aware it is being checked. So, if the casualty is conscious, measure the rate, without telling him, while you hold his wrist.

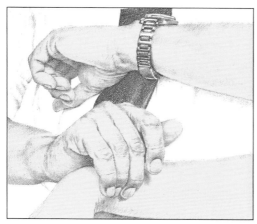

TAKING THE PULSE AT THE WRIST
The wrist pulse can be felt just below the base of the thumb, in the hollow between two bones. Place three fingers on the pulse and press slightly. Do not use your thumb as it has a pulse of its own. Count the beats for half a minute and double the number.

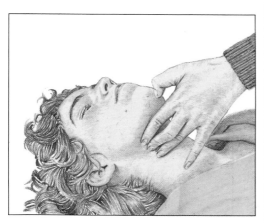

TAKING THE PULSE AT THE THROAT
The throat pulse can be felt in the hollow of the neck, to one side of the Adam's apple and below the angle of the jaw. Place three fingers on the pulse and press slightly. Count the beats for half a minute and double the number. Either side of the throat can be used.

Rabies

Holidaymakers in almost any foreign country run a risk of getting rabies if they are bitten by an animal there.

Rabies is a dangerous infectious disease caused by a virus carried by animals, particularly dogs and foxes. It is also known as hydrophobia (meaning 'fear of water'), because this fear is one of its symptoms.

The virus is transmitted to humans through the bite of an infected animal, and travels from the bite to the brain.

The nearer the bite is to the brain (on the face or neck, for example) the less far the virus has to travel and the quicker the treatment must be to prevent the disease.

The time between the bite and the onset of symptoms can range from ten days to more than a year, but is usually between 20 and 90 days. Before the symptoms begin, the bite usually heals but remains red and inflamed.

Once the symptoms have developed, treatment is ineffective and the patient usually dies within four days.

Rabies occurs in most parts of the world, except Britain, Scandinavia, Australia, Japan and Antarctica, and about 15,000 cases are reported each year.

What you should do
• See a local doctor immediately if you are bitten by an animal in any country where rabies may be present.
• Unless the animal can be proved to be free of rabies by a medical examination, the victim must have a course of injections *before* the symptoms appear.
• If possible, isolate the animal, but take care not to endanger yourself or others. If it escapes, notify the police immediately.

Symptoms of rabies
• Fever, headache, sore throat and muscle pains are followed by pain or numbness at the site of the healed bite.
• One or two days later the patient becomes restless and agitated.
• Confusion and hallucinations develop.
• Muscle spasms, stiffness of the neck and back, convulsions and areas of paralysis may also develop.
• Excess saliva and difficulty in swallowing produce foaming at the mouth.
• Painful throat spasms develop, with a reaction of terror on trying to swallow liquids.

Rib fractures

A hard blow to the chest, or a heavy fall, can fracture a rib, causing a sharp chest pain when the casualty breathes deeply or coughs.

A casualty who has only a simple rib fracture can be taken to hospital in a car, preferably in the back seat.

But there may be a serious chest injury if:
• The casualty is unable to breathe properly, and seems to be suffocating.
• Red frothy blood comes from his mouth.
• He becomes restless and thirsty.

If the casualty shows any of these symptoms, call an ambulance at once (see also *Chest injuries*, page 68).

Recognising a simple rib fracture

A person with a simple rib fracture will feel extremely tender around the site of the injury. The area will swell. Pain will increase with movement, including deep breathing or coughing. And there may be a crackling sound from the ribs.

But he is not likely to feel ill and will have no difficulty in breathing, even though the breaths may be shallow to avoid pain.
• Treat a fractured rib by putting the arm on the injured side in an arm sling (see facing page), and then taking the casualty to the Accident and Emergency Department of your local hospital.

Shock

Some injuries can cause the casualty to become generally weak – or even unconscious – in a condition known as shock, or traumatic shock.

The condition arises because the blood supply, carrying oxygen to all parts of the body, slows down. This may be because the heartbeat has become weak – from extreme pain or distress, say – or because serious bleeding, vomiting, diarrhoea or widespread burns have reduced the amount of body fluid, so that there is not enough blood to supply all the cells.

Shock may be immediate – as when someone receives bad news – or it may develop over two or three hours. And it can kill. It is not the same as the feeling of horror that occurs after an injury or other unpleasant experience, from which the victim may recover quickly.

The warning signs

Faced with the lack of adequate blood supply, the body reacts by concentrating the remaining supply on the vital organs – the heart, brain and kidneys. The less important areas, such as the muscles and skin, go without adequate blood, and the casualty weakens and becomes pale.

The condition also produces other effects:
• Faintness and giddiness.
• A feeling of anxiousness and restlessness.
• Nausea and perhaps vomiting.
• Thirst.
• Sweating.
• Shallow, rapid breathing, with yawning and sighing.
• A weak pulse which is fast and may be irregular.

What you should do

• Lay the casualty down with the head low, and treat any obvious injury or condition which may be causing the shock.
• Comfort and reassure the casualty.
• Loosen clothing at the neck, chest and waist to assist breathing and blood circulation.
• Ask someone to call an ambulance.
• If possible, raise the legs on a folded coat or cushion to direct the blood to the brain.
• Keep the casualty warm with a coat or blanket. But do not use a hot-water bottle, as it will bring the blood to the skin and away from the vital organs.
• If the casualty complains of thirst, moisten his lips, but do not give him anything to drink or eat, as it may cause delay in giving an anaesthetic in hospital.
• Do not move the casualty unnecessarily. It will increase the shock.
• Do not allow the casualty to smoke, as it may hinder breathing.
• If breathing becomes difficult, if the casualty seems about to vomit, or if he becomes unconscious, put him in the recovery position (see page 136).
• If breathing stops, begin artificial respiration immediately (see page 50).

Slings

Once an injury to a hand, arm or chest has been treated, put a sling on the casualty to give the damaged area support.

Slings are normally made from a triangular bandage – a piece of calico that can be bought ready-made from a chemist. But you can make your own with any piece of material about a yard (1m) square, either cut or folded diagonally. Alternatively, there are a number of ways in which you can improvise a sling.

When to use an arm sling

For a wound on the arm, and for some rib injuries, a conventional arm sling is usually used. But it is effective only if the casualty can stand or sit. It supports the forearm across the chest, with the hand slightly higher than the elbow and the fingers exposed.

When to use an elevation sling

A hand that must be raised to control bleeding

MAKING AN ARM SLING

1 *Get the casualty to support the injured arm with his hand. Place an open triangular bandage between the chest and forearm, its point stretching well beyond the elbow. Take the upper end over the shoulder on the uninjured side, around the back of the neck to the front of the injured side.*

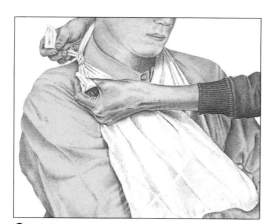

2 *Take the lower end of the bandage up over the hand and forearm and tie it in the hollow just above the collarbone. The tips of the fingers should just protrude from the sling.*

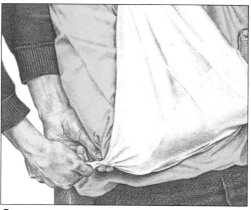

3 *Pin the point near the elbow, or twist and tuck it in. If the arm was bandaged before the sling went on, check that the nail beds are not turning blue. If they are, loosen the bandage.*

can be supported in an elevation sling. This sling is also used for complicated chest injuries or a broken collarbone. And it will support an arm for a casualty who cannot stand or sit.

Improvising a sling

If no triangular bandage is available, and you cannot make one, there are several ways to improvise a sling. Good support can be given, for example, by turning up the bottom edge of

the casualty's jacket and pinning it firmly to the jacket at chest level. The arm will be well supported inside the fold.

Alternatively, suspend the injured arm from a belt, tie or scarf which is tied around the casualty's neck.

The sleeve of the injured arm can be pinned to the front of the jacket, or the casualty's hand can be pushed inside the fastened jacket at chest level, supported by a button or zip.

IMPROVISING A SLING

1 *If you do not have a triangular bandage, improvise a sling from a narrow scarf, tie or roller bandage. Wrap the strip of cloth once around the casualty's wrist on the injured arm, or make a loop round the wrist.*

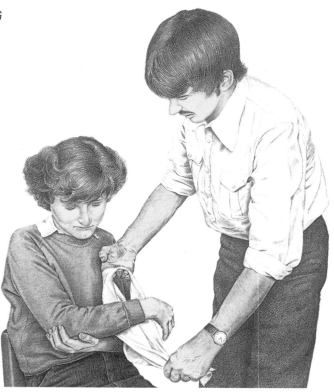

2 *Put one end of the sling over the casualty's shoulder on the uninjured side. Then bring the other end across the chest and around the casualty's neck to the uninjured shoulder.*

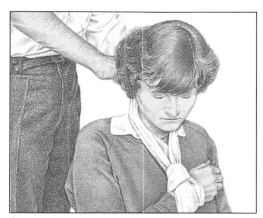

3 *Tie the ends in the hollow above the collarbone on the uninjured side. The hand should normally be just above elbow level, but at shoulder level for hand or forearm wounds.*

MAKING AN ELEVATION SLING

1 *Raise the injured arm –
or the arm on the injured
side, in the case of a chest
injury – so that the hand
rests on the opposite
shoulder. If possible, get the
casualty to hold it in place
while you make the sling.*

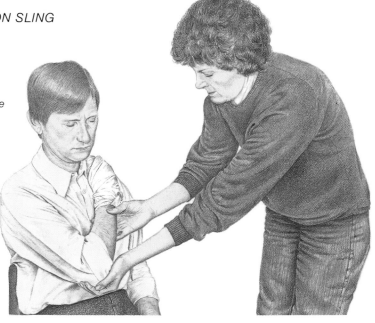

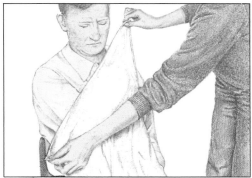

2 *Put one end of the base of the sling over
the casualty's shoulder on the uninjured side,
with the point extended well beyond the elbow.
The sling should then be hanging over the arm.*

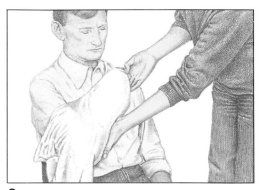

3 *Gently push the base of the sling under the
hand, forearm and elbow of the injured arm,
so that the lower end of the base is hanging
free below the elbow.*

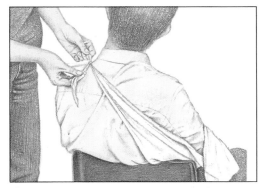

4 *Bring the lower end around the casualty's
back on the injured side. Join the two ends of
the sling together at the shoulder on the
uninjured side, and tie them together.*

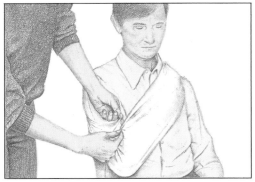

5 *Fold in the point and fasten it with a pin, or
twist and tuck it in. If the arm has been
bandaged, check that the nail beds are not
turning blue. If they are, loosen the bandage.*

Slipped disc

A disc is a shock-absorbing layer between each of the vertebrae in the spine. A slipped disc is caused by the gradual degeneration and softening of these discs after the age of 25.

When a disc slips, its soft core protrudes from its fibrous casing and presses on one of the nerves leading from the spinal cord. This causes pain, which can be severe.

Warning signs

Most slipped discs occur in the lower back and the pain is usually felt there first. The pain may also spread down around the buttocks and hips and along one or both legs.

The pain often starts suddenly just after you have lifted something heavy or have straightened up after bending. But sometimes it comes on gradually or only becomes severe after several mild attacks.

The pain may be made worse by bending, getting up after sitting, coughing or straining. It is easier when lying flat, standing or walking.

The lower leg and the outer foot may also become numb.

What you should do

• Lie down on a firm flat bed which does not sag. If necessary, get somebody to put a wide board the full length of the bed under the mattress. Alternatively, get him to put the mattress on the floor. On no account try to move anything heavy yourself.
• Take painkillers, such as aspirin or paracetamol, in recommended doses.
• A hot-water bottle or heat lamp applied to the painful area may give relief.
• If the pain is not relieved after a day or two of rest, call the doctor. The doctor may confirm the diagnosis with X-rays, and perhaps arrange physiotherapy. Some cases may require immobilisation in a plaster jacket or corset.

Manipulation may help but can be dangerous, and should be considered only after an X-ray and discussion with the doctor.

Many mild attacks get better in a few days and never recur. About 75 per cent of more severe attacks recur within five years, but may then get better.

Avoiding a slipped disc

The risk of a slipped disc can be reduced by keeping the back straight and bending at the knees when lifting, and holding the weight close to you. Particularly avoid lifting and twisting at the same time. These precautions are especially important to people who have already suffered a slipped disc.

Smoke inhalation

If someone is being suffocated by smoke in a burning building, get him out as quickly as possible. But do not go into a burning building without telling someone, or if it will place you in danger.

Protect yourself by tying a towel or piece of thick cloth – preferably wet – around your nose and mouth. As you move through the building, keep low, and reduce the fire risk by closing windows and doors behind you (see *Rescuing someone from a fire*, page 148).

Inhaled smoke can irritate the throat, causing it to contract in a sudden spasm and close the airway. So someone found in a smoke-filled room may be unconscious and his breathing may have stopped.

Smoke from plastic foam in upholstered chairs and sofas is highly poisonous and can kill within two minutes.

What you should do

• Drag the victim away from the smoke (see page 113).
• Once clear of danger, if the victim is unconscious but breathing normally, put him in the recovery position (see page 136).
• If breathing has stopped or is very difficult, begin mouth-to-mouth respiration as soon as possible (see page 50).
• Get someone to telephone 999 and ask for an ambulance.

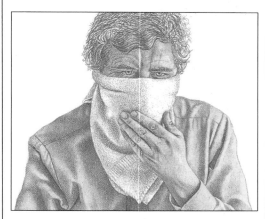

*PROTECTING YOURSELF FROM SMOKE
Cover your mouth and nose with a piece of thick, wet cloth before entering a smoke-filled room. Keep close to the floor where the air should be clear, as hot, smoky air will rise.*

Snakebite

Britain's one venomous snake, the adder, has a bite that is rarely fatal, but needs hospital treatment. Fear induced by the bite can sometimes cause more harm than the bite itself.

The victim of a snakebite should remain still and keep the area of the bite below the level of the heart. Movement will increase the circulation of blood around the body and so speed up the rate at which the venom is absorbed.

The victim should, if possible, be carried to an ambulance or car and taken to hospital.

In hot countries, where there are many venomous snakes, you should try to identify the species by remembering its size, colouring and skin pattern. This will help the doctor to decide if an anti-venom serum should be given. In Britain, a bite may come from a pet snake. The snake's owner should be able to tell the hospital which species it belongs to.

Warning signs

- Sharp pain and swelling around the bite.
- One or two small puncture wounds.
- The victim's vision may become disturbed.
- Nausea and possibly vomiting.
- Breathing may become difficult.

When a serious condition develops

- If the victim becomes unconscious, but is breathing normally, put her in the recovery position (see page 136) until help arrives.
- If breathing stops, begin mouth-to-mouth respiration immediately (see page 50).
- If the victim has been extremely frightened and then becomes weak, with skin that is pale and grey, she may be suffering from shock. Treat as described on page 120.
- Do not try to suck the venom out of the bite or cut the wound to let out blood. Both actions will increase blood circulation around the bite.
- Do not apply a tourniquet. It can cause serious damage to the limb.

TREATING SNAKEBITE

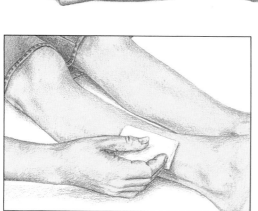

1 Rest the victim in a comfortable position, and reassure her that a snakebite in Britain is unlikely to be serious. Even in tropical countries deaths from snakebite poison are rare. A greater danger comes from fear which may bring on shock.

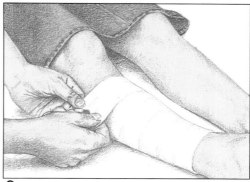

2 Remove venom from around the bite by wiping outwards from the wound. Do not raise the injured limb. Apply a pad or sterile dressing to the wound and keep the limb still.

3 Bandage the wound firmly if possible, with a crepe or two-way stretch bandage. Get someone to call 999 or the local emergency service. Try not to leave the victim alone.

First aid and medical emergencies

125

Splinters

Splinters of wood, metal or glass embedded in the skin can cause infection if they are not carefully, and cleanly, removed.

Do not try to remove a very large splinter, or one that is buried below the surface of the skin. In either case go to your doctor or to the Accident and Emergency Department of your local hospital.

Small, visible splinters can usually be removed with tweezers, but maintain hygienic conditions. If your hands are dirty, wash them before starting. Do not cough or sneeze on the wound, as germs may penetrate and infect it.

Sterilise the tweezers by passing the ends through a flame from a match, cigarette lighter or gas ring. Let them cool for a few moments but do not wipe off any soot, or touch the ends of the tweezers.

Do not probe the wound to get to the splinter. If it is deeply embedded, get medical help. Otherwise you may only push the splinter farther in, making it even harder to remove.

THE RISK OF TETANUS

A piece of splinter left in a wound, or a dirty splinter even if it has been removed, may lead to tetanus. This is a dangerous infection which causes acute muscle contractions, particularly in the jaw, giving the disease its other name of lockjaw.

Puncture wounds, burns, animal bites and road and agricultural accidents all carry a risk of tetanus. So anyone who suffers such a wound and who has not had a tetanus inoculation in the past five years should see a doctor to get a booster injection.

A person who contracts tetanus at first feels unwell and may have stiffness and pain in the jaw, difficulty in swallowing, raised temperature, headache and sweating.

Stiffness of other muscles may occur, in which case there may be painful arching of the back and drawing down of the neck. Sudden muscle contractions may be brought on by noise or by touching the patient.

If you suspect tetanus, take the patient to the Accident and Emergency Department of your local hospital immediately.

Immunisation is the surest prevention for tetanus. Children are given three routine injections in their first year, with boosters on starting and leaving school. A routine booster is recommended every ten years (or five years for people working close to animals or the soil).

REMOVING A SPLINTER

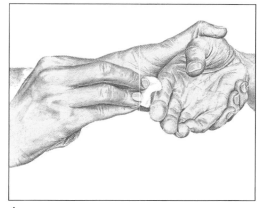

1 *Wash the skin around the splinter with warm, soapy water. Wipe downwards and outwards from the wound to avoid carrying dirt to it. Pat the skin dry with a clean towel.*

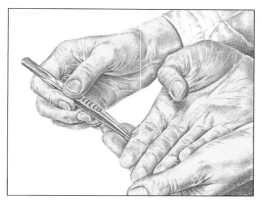

2 *Sterilise a pair of tweezers, then pull out the splinter directly in line with the way it went in. A magnifying glass may help. If it will not come out, get medical help.*

3 *When the splinter has been removed, wash the wound with a mild antiseptic and dry gently. Cover it with a plaster or sterile dressing. If it swells or becomes painful, get medical help.*

Splints

A person with a fractured bone should not be moved unless it is absolutely necessary (see page 112).

But if the ambulance is delayed, or you have to take the person to hospital yourself, the injured limb should be immobilised. The simplest way is to secure it to an uninjured part of the body with bandages – a technique known as body splinting.

To immobilise an arm, put it in a sling and then bandage it against the chest. A broken leg can be bandaged to the other leg, provided that plenty of padding is put between the ankles and knees to prevent chafing.

If the injured person has to be carried to safety, the fractured limb can be given greater support with a rigid splint, such as a tightly rolled blanket, a walking stick or a plank.

Any splint must be long enough to extend well beyond the joints above and below the fracture.

Do not remove clothes to apply a splint, and if possible add extra padding between splint and limb to make the casualty as comfortable as possible.

SECURING A FRACTURED ARM

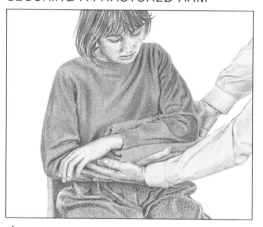

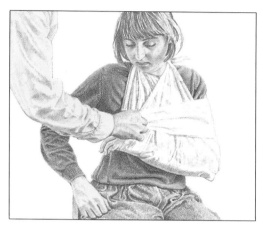

1 *If the arm will bend easily, place it across the chest and put some padding between the site of the fracture and the body. Do not bend the arm by force.*

2 *Put on an arm sling (see page 121), and then strap the arm to the body with a piece of wide material around arm and chest. Tie off the strap on the uninjured side.*

SECURING AN ARM THAT WILL NOT BEND

Lay the casualty down in the most comfortable position. Put padding between the injury and the body, and strap the arm to the body with three pieces of wide material. Avoid the fractured spot.

SPLINTING A FRACTURED ELBOW

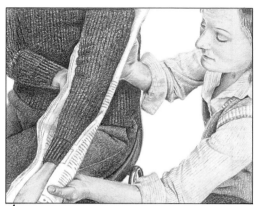

1 *If the elbow has been fractured, sit the casualty down and keep the arm straight. Fold a newspaper and place it along the arm.*

2 *Get the casualty to support the splint, and tie it in place with two bandages, one at the top of the splint and the other at the bottom.*

SECURING A FRACTURED LEG WITH BANDAGES

1 *A broken leg is most easily immobilised by bandaging it to the other leg. Move the uninjured leg to it, and put padding between the legs, especially at the knees and ankles.*

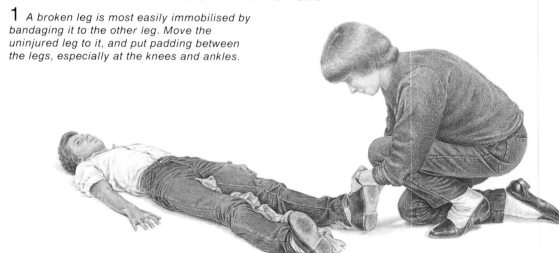

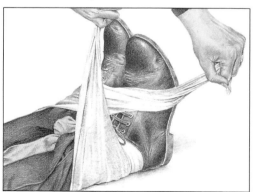

2 *Tie the feet together with a scarf or necktie in a figure of eight. Knot it on the outer edge of the shoe on the uninjured leg.*

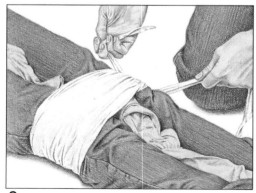

3 *Tie the knees together with a wide piece of material knotted on the uninjured side. Tie extra bandages above and below the fracture.*

A BLANKET SPLINT FOR A FRACTURED LEG

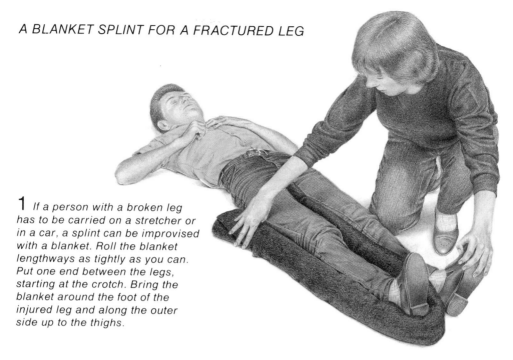

1 *If a person with a broken leg has to be carried on a stretcher or in a car, a splint can be improvised with a blanket. Roll the blanket lengthways as tightly as you can. Put one end between the legs, starting at the crotch. Bring the blanket around the foot of the injured leg and along the outer side up to the thighs.*

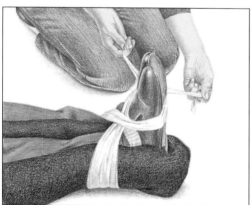

2 *Tie the feet and ankles together with a bandage or other piece of material in a figure of eight. Use a reef knot to tie it off.*

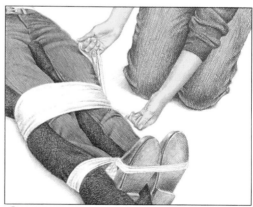

3 *Tie a wide piece of material around the casualty's knees, and knot the ends together on the uninjured side, again using a reef knot.*

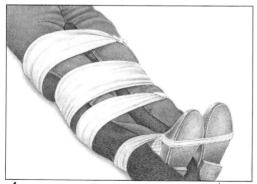

4 *Tie a third and fourth bandage above and below the site of the fracture.*

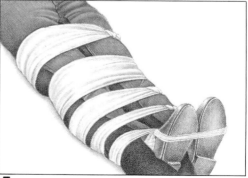

5 *Tie a fifth bandage around the thigh or calf, avoiding the fracture.*

Sports injuries

Two of the most common types of sports injuries are pulled muscles and sprained joints. The damage is similar in each case – tissue in the muscle or joint is torn and internal bleeding occurs, causing swelling and pain.

When one of these injuries occurs you should stop playing immediately, and rest. If you can use the injured part again in five minutes without pain, then it is safe to play on. But if the pain persists, you need treatment.

It is always possible that a bone has been broken, in which case go to the Accident and Emergency Department of the local hospital (see page 98). Suspect a broken bone if:
- The swollen part cannot be used.
- The swelling develops within minutes.
- The pain continues to be severe.

Treating a damaged muscle or joint

If the pain is not too severe and the swelling develops slowly it is usually safe to treat the injury without expert help.
- Put a cold compress on the injured area. Make the compress by putting ice cubes in a plastic bag and crushing them with a hammer or brick. Wrap the bag in a towel before applying it. Alternatively, use a cloth soaked in cold water and wrung out. The cold will cause the blood vessels to narrow and reduce bleeding.
- Bind the compress onto the injured part with a bandage and leave it for 20 to 30 minutes. The pressure also helps to close the blood vessels and slow the bleeding. But take care not to tie the bandage so tight as to cut off the circulation. If the person's fingers or toes become cold or tingle, loosen the bandage.
- At the same time, raise the injured area above the level of the heart for 30 minutes to an hour. This also slows the bleeding. Keep the limb raised as much as possible for the next 24 hours.
- If necessary, take aspirin or paracetamol in recommended doses to reduce pain the first night after an injury. But painkillers should never be used so that you can go on playing. Pain is a valuable warning sign.
- When the injured area has been free of pain for at least ten days, light exercise can be started again.
- If recovery is very slow, or if the problem recurs frequently, see your doctor.

When muscles stiffen up

The reason why muscles stiffen up is not fully understood, but a probable cause is that many small tears occur in the muscles. Also, during exercise pressure builds up inside the blood vessels in the muscles. Some of the fluid in which the blood cells are carried seeps out into the muscle fibres and builds up the pressure there, causing stiffness.

The best treatment is gentle exercise – easy swimming, for example – which helps the fluid to be reabsorbed. Careful warming up reduces stiffness, and so does 'winding down'. After hard exercise do not stop immediately; have a period of gentle exercise. Avoid wallowing in a hot bath after exercise. A quick shower and a brisk rub-down are much better.

Long-lasting injuries from overuse

Regular exercise often involves the repeated use of the same part of the body, and this can lead to the gradual development of painful injuries such as tennis elbow, golfer's shoulder and footballer's ankle.

To begin with, one part of the body aches towards the end of exercise or for a little while afterwards. Then, as the damage increases, the pain lasts longer after exercise and may occur at other times, perhaps when in bed. This type of injury needs expert attention. The first step is a period of rest, but if that does not help, see your doctor. You may be referred to a physiotherapist if you have pain in muscles or joints, or to a chiropodist for aching feet and heels.

How to avoid sports injuries

Many sports injuries can be prevented altogether by careful preparation, which includes proper training for the sport and warming up immediately before a game.

Take lessons to learn the correct way of doing

HOW DANGEROUS IS YOUR SPORT?

The most dangerous sport widely played in Britain is rugby. It has a higher rate of injury than soccer, and a greater number of broken bones and injuries to the face. Soccer injuries usually affect the legs.

In cricket and hockey, a major cause of injury is the hard ball hitting a player on the head. In squash, tennis and badminton, pulled muscles and sprains are the most common injuries, but eye injuries are also common in squash.

Most deaths in sport result from injuries to the head and spine – when being thrown from a motorcycle or falling while rock climbing, for example.

The following list gives the rate of injuries per 100 players each year in 16 sports.

Rugby	4.9	Squash	2.0
Skiing	4.9	Tennis	2.0
Soccer	3.2	Fencing	1.8
Gymnastics	2.9	Badminton	1.4
Hockey	2.9	Cycling	1.4
Cricket	2.4	Basketball	1.4
Judo	2.1	Golf	0.5
Rowing	2.1	Swimming	0.3

things from the very beginning. Faults in technique which may cause injury, such as an awkward golf swing, only get more difficult to eradicate as time goes on. To keep fit and avoid stiffening up, take exercise regularly, not in one burst on a Saturday afternoon.

Using the right kit and equipment also cuts down the risk of injury. This is particularly important in sports such as skiing and rock climbing, but in almost every form of exercise problems can be reduced if you wear the right shoes – broad enough tennis shoes, for example, or jogging shoes with well-padded heels that prevent you from jarring the spine.

DO'S AND DON'TS ABOUT SPORTS INJURIES

An unconscious player	DO roll an unconscious player into the recovery position (page 136). DO remove foreign material (chewing gum, broken dentures, broken teeth, grass) from the mouth to prevent choking.	DON'T lay an unconscious person flat on his face.
Damaged bones	DO support the injured area with padding, a splint or bandage.	DON'T attempt to manipulate a fractured bone or dislocation.
Injuries to the face	DO sit a player upright and press a cold pad to a black eye – which results from bleeding into the soft tissue around the eyeball. DO treat a nosebleed by squeezing the soft part of the nose between finger and thumb and breathing through your mouth for 15 minutes. DO splash water with your hand on your eye if you get dirt or mud in it.	DON'T waste time and money on applying a raw steak to a black eye. This is no more effective than using a cold pad. DON'T continue with the treatment if the nosebleed lasts for more than 30 minutes. Either contact your doctor or go to a hospital. DON'T add antiseptic to the water used on the affected eye.
Cuts and abrasions	DO thoroughly clean and disinfect an abrasion caused by the skin being scraped along a hard surface, such as the ground. DO see a doctor if particles of dirt remain in the abrasion after cleaning. A partly cleaned abrasion can result in an ugly scar – especially if the face is affected.	DON'T forget to protect yourself against tetanus (lockjaw) – which can arise from a simple scratch – with an antitetanus injection. Booster injections should be given every ten years. DON'T use old creams or harsh disinfectants on wounds; they can infect the cut or destroy tissues.
Caring for the feet	DO wash and carefully dry your feet immediately after sport to prevent athlete's foot – a fungus that affects sweaty skin.	DON'T soak your feet in very hot water.
Stiff muscles	DO take a quick warm shower or bath – followed by a cold shower or dip – to ease stiffness. Gentle exercise also helps.	DON'T wallow in hot water after sport or exercise. DON'T sit around 'resting'.

Sprains and strains

Injuries to the joints and muscles – known as sprains and strains – are common and can be extremely painful.

A sprain occurs in a joint when a ligament – the flexible tissue that holds the bones together – is wrenched or torn. A strain occurs when a muscle is overstretched or torn.

Treatment for both injuries includes a cold compress, raising the injured limb and firm bandaging. All three techniques are aimed at restricting internal bleeding from the damaged tissues.

To make a cold compress, put some ice cubes into a plastic bag, knot the opening of the bag and crush the ice with a hammer or brick. Then wrap the bag of ice in a towel and apply it to the injury. Leave it in place for 20 to 30 minutes. If no ice is available, soak a small towel or some other piece of cloth in cold water and squeeze out the excess, then wrap the towel round the injured area. Keep the towel cold by re-wetting it as necessary.

A cold compress works by chilling and constricting the blood vessels around the injury, thus limiting the swelling caused by internal bleeding. To be effective, though, the compress needs to be applied within about 30 minutes.

After about 30 minutes, most of the swelling will already have taken place and the compress will no longer be of much help. In these circumstances raise the limb and bandage it firmly for support instead.

TREATING A SPRAINED ANKLE

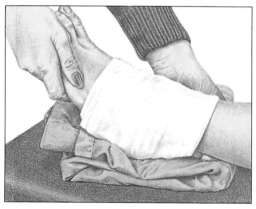

1 *Remove the shoe and raise the foot above the level of the heart. If the sprain has occurred within the past 15 to 30 minutes, apply a cold compress to the injured joint and bandage it in place for 20 to 30 minutes.*

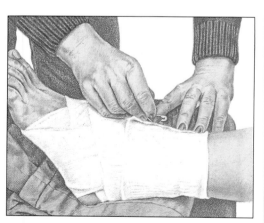

2 *After removing the compress, bandage the joint firmly. For an ankle joint, make one turn around the ankle, then go over the instep, under the foot, back across the instep and around the ankle again several times.*

TREATING A STRAINED MUSCLE

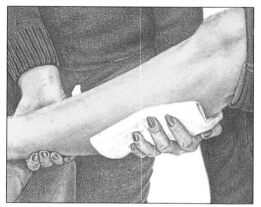

1 *Put the casualty in the most comfortable possible position, with the injured limb above the level of the heart. Apply a cold compress to the strained muscle, and bandage it in place for 20 to 30 minutes.*

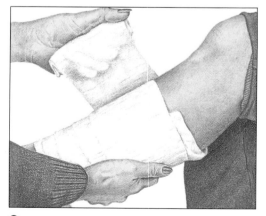

2 *Remove the compress and bandage the area firmly, but not so tightly as to stop circulation. The muscle may swell, causing pain if the bandage is too tight. Support a strained arm in an arm sling (see page 121).*

A sprained joint

The ankle is the joint most often affected by sprains, but the wrist, elbow, knee, hip and shoulder can also suffer.

A severe sprain can be extremely painful and is hard to distinguish from a fractured bone. If you are in any doubt, treat the injury as a fracture and get medical help (see *Fractures*, page 98, and *Splints*, page 127).

An ankle sprain occurs when a foot turns suddenly while walking or running – one of the reasons why boots (which help to support the ankle joints) are recommended for people walking in rough, stony country.

If a wrist, elbow or shoulder is sprained, support it in an arm sling after treatment with both a cold compress and firm bandaging (see *Bandages*, page 56, and *Slings*, page 121).

There are three main symptoms of sprains:
• Pain when moving the joint.
• Swelling of the joint, followed later by discoloration of the skin.
• Tenderness of the area over the torn ligament.

A strained muscle

A muscle may become overstretched or torn by sudden, unaccustomed exertion, perhaps when lifting a heavy weight. It can also be torn during a fall. If the injury occurs while playing sport it is known as a 'pulled muscle', and usually affects the calf or thigh (see page 130).

The main symptoms are:
• Sudden, sharp pain in the muscle.
• Stiffness or cramp developing in the muscle.
• Swelling of the area.
• Possibly discoloration of the skin.

Stab wounds

A nail sticking out of a piece of wood, or any other sharp object such as a bicycle spoke or needle, can cause a potentially serious wound.

On the surface the wound may look so small as not to be worth worrying about, but it may go deep into the flesh, carrying dirt or germs with it. If the wound becomes infected, the infection can spread to other parts of the body, causing serious illness and even death.

A stab wound can also cause serious internal injury to blood vessels and nerves.

Treat all stab wounds as serious. Stop any bleeding, dress the wound and take the casualty to your doctor or to the Accident and Emergency Department of your local hospital.

If the object which caused the wound remains embedded in the flesh, do not try to remove it. It could be helping to plug the wound, and pulling it out could make the bleeding much worse. Instead, cover the object with a ring-pad (see page 58) or the bottom half of a paper cup, so that it will not be forced deeper by the dressing while the casualty is being taken to hospital.

DEALING WITH A STAB WOUND
Stop any bleeding by pressing around the wound with a clean pad, or your bare hands. Do not try to remove any object embedded in the wound. Raise the injured area above the level of the heart to help to stem the bleeding. Bandage the wound and get medical help.

SUPPORTING AN ANKLE IN AN EMERGENCY
If you sprain an ankle during a country walk, leave your shoe and sock on, and bind a figure-of-eight bandage over the shoe or boot. This may give enough support to get you home.

Stroke

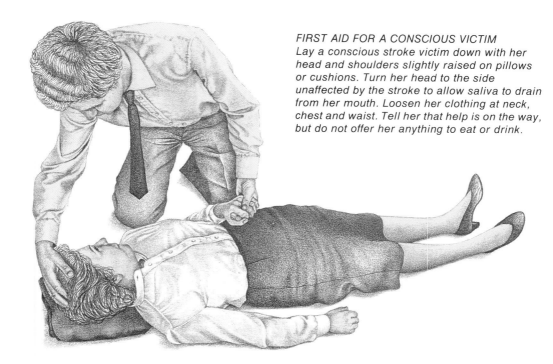

FIRST AID FOR A CONSCIOUS VICTIM
Lay a conscious stroke victim down with her head and shoulders slightly raised on pillows or cushions. Turn her head to the side unaffected by the stroke to allow saliva to drain from her mouth. Loosen her clothing at neck, chest and waist. Tell her that help is on the way, but do not offer her anything to eat or drink.

A person suffering a stroke may become weak or paralysed down one side of the body, including the face, arm and leg.

Alternatively, the victim may have difficulty in speaking or swallowing, with only slight weakness in the limbs.

The victim may also suffer confusion, drowsiness and involuntary urination. The symptoms can resemble drunkenness.

A severe stroke will cause unconsciousness.

What you should do

• If the victim is conscious, lay him or her down, with head and shoulders slightly raised on pillows or cushions.
• Turn her head to one side to allow saliva to drain from the mouth.
• Call the patient's doctor, or telephone 999 and ask for an ambulance.
• Loosen clothing around the patient's neck, chest and waist to help blood circulation and breathing.
• Do not give her anything to eat or drink.
• If the patient becomes unconscious, put her in the recovery position (see page 136).

The after-effects of a stroke

A person who suffers a stroke that paralyses the right side of the body may also be unable to speak, write, read or understand speech.

If the paralysis is on the left, the person may lose the awareness of the left half of the body.

Recovery from a stroke may be complete, with little risk of recurrence; but more usually – especially in elderly patients – the arm and, to a lesser extent, the leg on the affected side of the body will remain disabled.

A massive stroke, particularly in an older patient, is grave; but if the patient survives the first month, a considerable amount of activity can often be restored.

The hospital will arrange a course of physiotherapy aimed at restoring the patient to as much activity as possible so that he or she can return home.

Relatives, with the help of their family doctor, district nurses and hospital out-patient treatment, can make a large contribution to recovery. In the early days they can learn how to exercise the patient's affected limbs to prevent the muscles and joints from becoming stiff.

They can also help by speaking slowly or repeating things that seem not to be understood. They should listen carefully if speech is poor, and spend time talking to the patient, looking at pictures or photographs and encouraging him in his former interests.

Many areas have day hospitals which the patient can attend to ease the burden on relatives and at the same time receive additional therapeutic help.

Hospitals and local authority social services departments can provide aids for use in the home, including special beds, hoists and walking frames. Ask hospital social workers and the local council about which aids are most appropriate. To reduce the risk of further strokes, the patient should stop smoking, watch his or her weight and follow any treatment prescribed for high blood pressure.

Sunburn

If sunburn is very severe and distressing, take the patient to a doctor who may prescribe a cream to give relief.

See a doctor also if the patient has a headache, nausea or a high temperature, because he may be suffering from heat stroke as well as sunburn (see page 106).

If the sunburn is out of all proportion to the time the skin was exposed to the sun, the patient may be suffering from a condition called photosensitivity, which can be brought on by some medicines. The patient should see his doctor, who may prescribe an alternative medicine.

Treating mild sunburn

The symptoms of sunburn can range from skin that turns pink and feels rather hot to skin that becomes red, swollen, blistered and extremely painful.

Reasonably mild sunburn can be treated at home without seeing a doctor.
• Keep the skin cool with calamine lotion or cold compresses. Make the compress by soaking a towel or other cloth in cold water and squeezing out the excess. Or put ice cubes in a plastic bag, knot the opening of the bag and crush the ice with a hammer or brick. Wrap the bag in a cloth before putting it on the skin.
• Antihistamine creams are rarely worth using; they have little effect.
• Leave blistered skin exposed to the air.
• Take aspirin or paracetamol to relieve the pain.
• Avoid clothes that rub the sore area.
• Do not allow further exposure to the sun until the symptoms have disappeared.

How to avoid sunburn

Sunburn is caused by the ultraviolet rays of the sun. Fair-skinned people, who have little pigment in the skin, burn more easily than people with dark skin.
• To prevent sunburn, avoid overexposure to the sun on the first day of a holiday, particularly if you are fair skinned. Expose the skin for only 30 minutes the first day, increasing by 30 minutes each day until you have developed a suntan which will give protection.
• Remember that light cloud does not stop the sun's rays from burning.
• Use a suntan lotion or cream for protection. Most of them wash off easily, so put more on after swimming. Even if you do not swim they need to be renewed every two hours. Filter-type sun-screens may contain substances that cause skin reactions, so follow the instructions on the container.
• Keep small children covered with a shirt for most of the time during the first days of a holiday. Increase their exposure gradually.
• Remember that you can be burnt even while feeling cool in the water.
• Do not expect artificial skin-tanning creams to give protection.

Tooth injuries

All injuries to the teeth should be checked as soon as possible by a dentist or hospital dental department. If there are serious injuries to the mouth, the immediate aim is to ensure that the victim can breathe properly.
• Clear broken teeth and blood from the mouth with your fingers.
• If the casualty is conscious and has no other serious injuries, sit him in a chair with his head tilted forwards over a bowl or basin.
• Telephone 999 and ask for an ambulance, or drive the casualty to your local hospital. He should travel sitting up, leaning over the bowl.
• Never allow a person who is bleeding from the mouth to lie on his back, because he may choke on the blood.

When a tooth has been knocked out

If a tooth is knocked out completely, there may be profuse bleeding from the socket.
• Make a pad slightly larger than the socket from sterile gauze or other clean material. The pad should project slightly above the level of the surrounding teeth.
• Get the casualty to put it over the socket and bite on it firmly for 10 minutes, spitting out any blood that leaks through.
• If the bleeding does not stop, repeat for another 10 minutes.
• If the bleeding still does not stop, telephone your dentist and ask for emergency treatment, or go to your local hospital.

Saving a knocked-out tooth

It is sometimes possible to save a tooth that has been knocked out of its socket.

The roots must be kept moist with saliva, so suck a piece of clean gauze or cloth until it is thoroughly damp, or get the casualty to do so. Wrap the tooth in the gauze and put it in a matchbox or other container to take to the hospital or dentist.

If you get toothache

If you develop toothache at night or during a weekend when you cannot contact your dentist, look in the Yellow Pages of a telephone directory for a dentist who operates an emergency service (though fees for such services can be high). Alternatively, ask the Accident and Emergency department of a hospital if they know a dentist who can help, or ask the nearest police station or chemist.
• While you are waiting for a dentist, relieve the pain by dabbing a little oil of cloves (available from chemists) on the sore area, and by taking painkillers such as aspirin in recommended doses.
• Try also holding in your mouth a mouthful of ice-cold water or a mouthful of hot, salty water (one teaspoon of salt in a glass of water). Hold the water in your mouth for at least five minutes, spitting it out and renewing it as necessary, and repeat the treatment every 2–3 hours.

135

Unconsciousness

A person who has become unconscious is in danger of choking to death if he or she is left lying face up.

Vomit, blood or saliva may block the top of the windpipe, or the base of the tongue may slide back over the windpipe.

Normal reflexes do not work properly when people become unconscious. So they may not cough or turn over if something blocks their airway, as they would do automatically if they were asleep.

If an unconscious person is breathing normally, put her in the recovery position. This is a life-saving technique and takes priority over other treatment. An exception is if you suspect

that the casualty has back or neck injuries, in which case she should not be moved at all (see page 55).

If the casualty is particularly heavy, it may be necessary to get someone else to help you by pushing while you pull.

If an unconscious person has to be carried on a stretcher, or if she is in a confined space, a modified version of the recovery position is used. In this case a rolled blanket is used to prop up one side of the body, rather than a bent arm and leg.

If the unconscious person is not breathing, you must begin artificial respiration immediately (see page 50). In any case get someone

IS THE CASUALTY BREATHING?

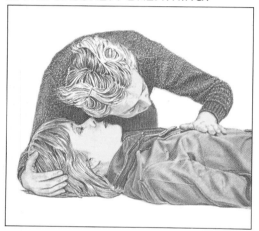

1 *Put your ear to the casualty's nose and mouth and listen for the sound of breathing. Watch the chest to see if it rises and falls, or rest your hand lightly on it to feel for movement.*

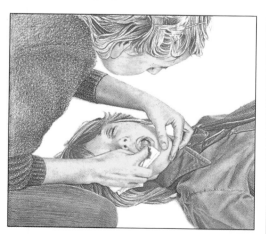

2 *If the casualty is not breathing, start artificial respiration (see page 50). If she is breathing, clear the mouth of foreign matter with your finger. Clean up blood around the mouth.*

THE RECOVERY POSITION

1 *Kneel about a handspan from the casualty. Turn the head towards you. Tuck the near arm under the body, keeping it straight. Put the other arm across the chest, and the far ankle over the near ankle.*

2 *Grip the clothing at the far hip and turn the casualty onto her front by pulling quickly towards you. Cushion her head with one hand as you do so, and support her body with your knees as she rolls over.*

to telephone 999 and ask for an ambulance or, if nobody is available, do it yourself at the first opportunity. Anyone who has been unconscious, even for a short time, should receive immediate medical treatment.

Handle any serious wound gently while arranging the casualty. Once in the recovery position, the casualty can be helped by having clothing at the neck, chest and waist loosened. Injuries can be treated while you wait for expert help to arrive.

Do not leave an unconscious person alone, and do not give her anything to eat or drink, even if she regains consciousness (see also *What to do if someone collapses*, page 207).

Three stages of unconsciousness

Unconsciousness is not always total insensibility. There are three stages, and a person may go through all three or remain in one. The three stages are:

• Drowsiness, in which the victim is easily roused for a few moments, but then passes back into a sleep-like state. She may be able to give reasonably coherent answers to questions you ask her about her condition.

• Stupor, in which the victim does not react to questions easily or does so incoherently, giving the impression of being drunk.

• Coma, in which the victim cannot be roused at all, and is motionless and silent.

WHILE YOU WAIT FOR HELP

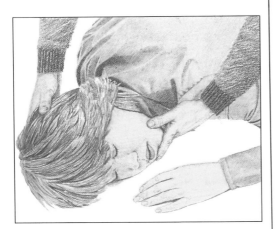

3 *Tilt the casualty's chin backwards to straighten the throat. This will keep the airway open, preventing the tongue from slipping back into the throat, and so will allow her to go on breathing freely.*

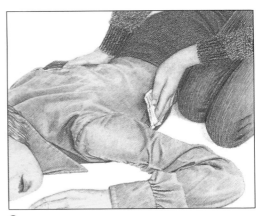

1 *Once the casualty is safely in the recovery position, loosen any tight clothing at the neck, chest and waist to assist breathing and blood circulation. Provide fresh air by opening a window or door.*

4 *Bend the arm nearest to you to prop up the upper body. Bend the leg nearest to you to prop up the lower body. Pull the other arm out from under the body to prevent her from rolling over onto her back. Do not leave her alone.*

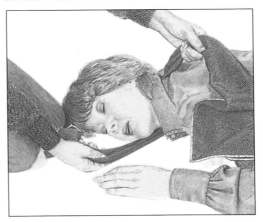

2 *Check for any other injuries and stop any bleeding (see page 60). Get someone to telephone for an ambulance. Then check to see if the casualty is carrying a treatment card – for diabetes, for example.*

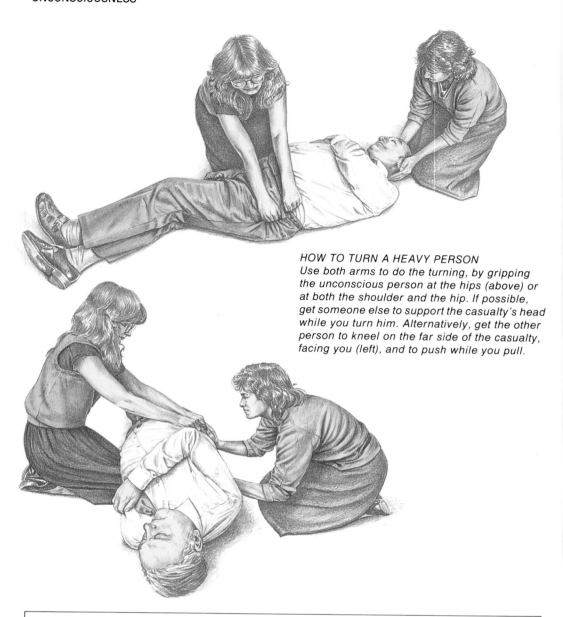

HOW TO TURN A HEAVY PERSON
Use both arms to do the turning, by gripping the unconscious person at the hips (above) or at both the shoulder and the hip. If possible, get someone else to support the casualty's head while you turn him. Alternatively, get the other person to kneel on the far side of the casualty, facing you (left), and to push while you pull.

SUPPORTING AN UNCONSCIOUS PERSON ON A STRETCHER

Use a modified version of the recovery position if you are carrying an unconscious person on a stretcher or if she is in some other confined space. Put a rolled blanket or coat under the side towards which the casualty is facing.

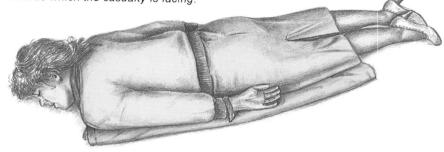

Vertigo

An unpleasant feeling of giddiness, as though the patient's head is moving when it is actually still, usually has a cause related to the ear.

The giddiness may be accompanied by nausea and deafness, and also by flickering of the eyes – a condition called nystagmus.

Vertigo can arise from several different medical conditions.
• An injury to the head.
• Ménière's disease and labyrinthitis, two ailments that disturb the hearing and also the balance of the inner ear.
• High blood pressure.
• A blockage of the blood vessels leading to the brain.
• Travel sickness.
• Overbreathing – a condition in which the patient breathes harder and faster than normal, usually brought on by pain, anxiety or sudden changes of mood.

What you should do
The patient should lie down quietly and rest until the attack ends. The length of an attack can range from seconds to hours.

Consult a doctor if:
• The attacks recur.
• There is severe vomiting.
• Deafness develops.

The doctor may prescribe drugs to relieve the symptoms, but even without treatment a person with recurring vertigo may recover spontaneously after several months.

Some elderly people suffer from vertigo without a treatable cause being found.

Positional vertigo, which is felt when the head is in certain positions, may continue to occur.

Whooping cough

A child who has a cold with a runny nose and bouts of excessive coughing may be in the early stages of whooping cough.

As the disease develops the cough will become worse, mainly at night. A few days after the cold begins, the 'whoop' will start – a sudden noisy intake of breath at the end of a coughing spasm. Vomiting may also occur after the coughing.

What you should do
Whooping cough is a serious disease that can lead to pneumonia and to severe dehydration if fluid loss from the vomiting is not controlled. So notify your doctor as soon as you suspect that a child has the disease.

The doctor may prescribe antibiotics for the patient and also for other children in the family. These do not cure whooping cough, but may prevent it from spreading to other people. In severe cases the patient will be sent to hospital for treatment.

While nursing the patient at home, provide extra drinks to make up for fluid lost by vomiting.

Proprietary cough medicines from the chemist may help the cough.

Do not expose the patient to cigarette smoke – it will make the cough worse.

Whooping cough may last for a period ranging from three weeks to as long as four months.

How to prevent whooping cough
The disease is caused by bacteria which are spread by droplets in the air breathed out by an infected child.

Because whooping cough is more dangerous than the risks of immunisation, all children should have a course of three injections (usually with diphtheria and tetanus vaccine) in the first year of life.

Because of a rare chance of brain damage, however, immunisation may be risky under a number of circumstances:
• If the child has fits or epilepsy.
• If there is a history of epilepsy in brothers, sisters or parents.
• If the child has a disorder of the nervous system or is known to have suffered brain damage at birth.
• If there is a feverish illness at the time of the proposed injection.
• If there has been a severe reaction to a previous dose of the vaccine.

In all these cases – or if you are in any doubt – consult your doctor before the child is immunised.

First aid and medical emergencies

In the home and at work

If you are trapped in a blazing house

Once a fire takes hold, there is only one completely safe place to be – outside. If you are trapped inside, getting out is the priority.

Planning an escape route
If a fire should occur in your home, you have a better chance of escaping quickly if you have worked out the best route from each room beforehand. If you have not done this, take a moment to decide the best way out, unless this is obvious.
• If you cannot get down the stairs, for instance, consider which upstairs room is the easiest to get out of. Which has the largest windows? Which window is closest to the ground, and which has the clearest drop and the softest ground beneath it? Are there any balconies or garage roofs which might make it easier to reach the ground safely?
• Consider, too, which windows can be opened. It is more difficult to climb out through a window you have had to break, and it is more difficult to break a double-glazed window than a single-glazed one.

How to get out
• Try to find a safe way past the blaze to a ground-floor door or window. Firemen follow three cardinal rules when they move through a burning building: test all doors; close doors and windows; and stay low.
• Feel each door before opening it. Do not open it if it is hot, or if smoke is seeping around the edges. In a large or unfamiliar building, you can test doors quickly by touching the knob briefly with the back of your hand. The metal knob conducts heat faster than the panelling.
• Use the back of the hand for safety – heat on the back will make you jerk it away instinctively.
• If the door is cool, stand behind it, open it a crack and glance out before deciding whether to go through. Put your foot against the back of the door to prevent it being opened by pressure from hot gases. If there are flames beyond, flinging the door wide could create a draught and cause a lethal surge in the fire's intensity.
• Close doors behind you and also close any open windows, if possible. This will help to slow the spread of fire. Open doors and windows feed air to the flames and allow them an easier passage from room to room.
• Stay low. Smoke fills a room from the ceiling down. Near the floor the air should be easier to breathe, and it should be easier to see.

When you have got out
• Once you have got outside and are safely clear of the building, check that everyone is accounted for. Stop anyone going back into the building to rescue possessions.
• Send someone to a neighbour's house or a phone box to dial 999 for the fire brigade, if that has not been done already.
• Remember when calling to give the exact

MOVING SAFELY FROM ROOM TO ROOM

1 *As you move through rooms on your way out, test each door for heat by touching the handle or knob briefly. Use the back of the hand for safety – heat on the back will make you jerk it away instinctively, and avoid burns.*

2 *Stand behind the door and brace your foot against the bottom before opening it a crack to peep out into the next room. Your foot will stop the door being forced wide open by the pressure of any hot gases on the other side.*

3 *Once through the door, take the time to close it firmly behind you. This will help to slow the spread of fire, fumes and smoke. Open doors (or windows) create draughts that feed air to the flames, intensifying the blaze.*

KEEP LOW
If there is smoke and fire in a room or corridor, keep as low as possible, and crawl if necessary. Put a handkerchief – wet, if possible – over your mouth and nose as an improvised filter. Smoke and flames fill a room from the ceiling downwards, so that air near the floor should be easier to breathe, and visibility will be better.

address and location of the blaze – in a moment of stress it is easy to forget such vital details, and that could delay the arrival of help.

If the exit is blocked

• Try to reach a window or balcony. Open the window. If there is a balcony get onto it and close the window behind you.

• If you are on the ground floor, jump out.

• If you are not on the ground floor and the drop is not too far and onto soft ground – a flowerbed, for example – hang out of the window with fully outstretched arms to lessen the distance you have to fall. It may be safer to risk a sprain, or even a broken bone, than to wait for rescue.

• Just before you drop, let go with one hand and use that arm and your legs to push yourself away from the wall as you fall.

• Do not jump out of an upstairs window except as a last resort. Instead, use anything to hand – knotted sheets, for example – to reach the ground or at least get closer to it before dropping. Anchor the rope to a solid piece of furniture inside the room.

• If you have to break a window to get out, use a chair or kick it out. If you have to use your hands, wrap something round your fist to protect it, or use an elbow if you are wearing something with sleeves.

• Knock out jagged pieces of glass around the edge, or throw a blanket or clothing over them, before climbing through.

• If there is no safe way down, shut the door of the room, open the window, then wave and shout to attract attention.

• On a balcony, shut the window behind you.

• If there is no balcony, try to keep the blaze out of the room while waiting for help. A building rarely collapses in a fire, so if you succeed you stand a good chance of surviving.

• Douse the walls and door between you and

GET OUT ONTO A BALCONY
If you are trapped by fire on an upstairs floor and you can get out onto a balcony, do so. Close the door into the room before you go. Once outside, shut the window firmly behind you and shout for help. Try to remain calm while you are waiting to be rescued.

WHEN YOU ARE TRAPPED IN AN UPSTAIRS ROOM

1 *If you cannot get onto a balcony, try to keep the blaze out of the room. If you can reach a tap, douse the walls and door with buckets of water. If you do not have a bucket, improvise with a saucepan, vase or any large container.*

2 *Stop smoke and fumes from entering the room by stuffing the cracks between the door and door frame with cloths – curtains, if necessary. Wet them first, if possible, and put a rolled-up carpet or blanket against the bottom.*

*IF YOUR CLOTHES
CATCH FIRE*
Do not panic and run if your clothes catch fire. You will only fan the flames. Drop to the floor at once and smother the flames by rolling slowly – not quickly – over and over. Wrap yourself in a blanket or carpet, if you can.

the flames with water. This will delay or prevent the spread of fire.

• Stuff cloths – wet, if possible – into the cracks around the door to stop smoke and fumes getting in. Smoke is a far bigger killer than the flames themselves – for every two people burnt to death in fires, five lose their lives through being asphyxiated by smoke or toxic fumes.

Escaping from a high-rise building

Just as you should plan in advance your escape route from a house fire, you should also know what to do to escape a fire in a block of flats or hotel.

• Never use a lift in a fire – you could be trapped if the power fails, or the doors could open on the floor that is ablaze, killing all inside.

• In many hotels a fire escape map is displayed in each room or corridor. Make a point of studying it when you arrive – there may not be time in an emergency.

• Make a mental picture of the halls and stairs between your room and the exit.

• Try the stairway door – if it is locked, have it opened.

• If a fire starts, make your way out as quickly as possible, testing each door before opening it and closing it behind you. Most doors take about half an hour to burn through, and make excellent fire shields.

• Always take your key with you, in case you are forced back into your room.

• As you go, alert others by banging on doors and shouting 'Fire!' Set off a fire alarm if there is one.

• If the stairway is blocked by flames or smoke, do not try to run through. Return to your room, or try to reach a floor which is not affected by the blaze. If necessary, walk up to the roof, then stand on the windward side of the building, with any smoke or flames being blown away from you, until firemen reach you.

• If you get trapped in your room and are too high to shout for help, wave a sheet, pillowcase or towel from the window to attract attention on the ground.

• If there is a telephone in your room, use it to call for help – the line may be open even if the fire has cut off the building's power supply.

When clothing catches fire

Clothing set ablaze through standing too near an unguarded fire or radiant heater is a common cause of serious burns – especially to children.

• Act instantly to smother the flames.

• If the clothing is your own, cross your arms over your chest, so that your hands touch your shoulders. This helps to keep the flames away from your face.

• Drop to the floor and roll over and over slowly.

• If possible, wrap yourself in a rug, wool blanket, coat or heavy curtains.

• If someone else's clothing is alight, get the victim onto the floor – trip him if necessary.

SIGNALLING FOR HELP
If you are trapped in a high-rise building too far from the ground for your voice to be heard, attract attention by waving something from the window. Use the largest and most brightly coloured piece of cloth you can find – a towel, say, a sheet, a rug or a curtain. Keep waving it until you are spotted by someone on the ground. You are unlikely to have to wait long for rescue. High-rise buildings are almost always in densely populated areas where a fire is likely to be noticed quickly and a fire station is likely to be within a few minutes' drive.

• Smother the fire with a fire blanket, rug, wool blanket, coat or heavy curtains.

• Throw water over the victim to help to cool him as well as extinguish the flames. Avoid using a fire extinguisher because it will not cool him, and any chemicals in it could cause difficulties when the burns are treated.

• When the fire is out, do not try to pull clothing away from the victim's skin.

• Call for medical help (dial 999 if necessary) and treat the victim for shock (see page 120).

Using a rope ladder

In a house, a rope ladder stored on an upper floor is a valuable (and relatively cheap) piece of safety equipment.

Ideally it should have built-in stanchions so

that it stands away from the wall in use, leaving room for hands and toes.

A traditional rope ladder is difficult to use if you try to climb up or down it as you would a rigid ladder – facing the rungs.

Used that way, the ladder will hug the wall of the building unless there is someone at the bottom to hold it away.

However, if it is the only type available there is a simple, effective technique used by sailors and mountaineers.

• Climb down the *side* rope of the ladder, placing one foot across the rung at the front of the ladder, and the other foot across the next rung at the back, splaying your feet with your toes pointing outwards.

• Your shoulder and hip will hold the ladder away from the wall, allowing plenty of room for hands and feet to grip.

CLIMB DOWN THE SIDE
It is difficult to climb down a rope ladder against a wall without grazing your knuckles and knees – if you face the rungs. Instead, climb down the side rope, so that your shoulder keeps the ladder away from the wall and gives you room to grip. If possible, ask someone on the ground to pull the ladder taut to stop it swinging.

FIRE IN THE HOME: THE DANGER POINTS

Every year in Britain, more than 51,000 homes are damaged in fires that are started by accident.

Each year more than 600 people die in fires in the home, and another 5600 are burnt – many seriously.

More than 44,000 of these fires – almost 90 per cent – can be traced to one of ten major causes:

COOKERS are the largest single cause of domestic fires – nearly 20,000, or 40 per cent of the total – and the fires are often started by blazing chip pans.

Electric cookers are involved in around 14,400 blazes each year, gas cookers in another 5400.

HEATERS cause more than 5000 blazes a year, usually because they are knocked over accidentally or are left too close to furniture.

Electric heaters account for about 1500 of these fires, gas heaters for 1100, solid-fuel burners for 1300, paraffin for 600 and liquefied petroleum gas (LPG) for 500.

SMOKERS leaving lighted cigarettes around start 4800 fires a year. Particularly dangerous is the fire started by a cigarette left on an upholstered chair or settee. It can roll down the back or side of the seat and the upholstery can smoulder slowly, giving off poisonous fumes while the people in the house are asleep.

MATCHES are involved in starting about 4400 blazes. Often they are left too close to fires or are lit by children who are playing with them.

ELECTRICAL WIRING is the cause of some 3300 fires. The blazes are commonly started by old circuits, incorrect fuses or overloaded power sockets.

ELECTRIC BLANKETS trigger 1700 fires, usually because the insulation around the elements has been cracked by folding the blankets too tightly or creasing them.

BLOW TORCHES AND LAMPS, often those used by home handymen, account for some 1500 fires a year.

TELEVISION SETS are the source of 1300 fires a year, usually when faulty sets have been left plugged in overnight.

CHIMNEY FIRES which spread outside the flue, commonly because of a build-up of soot inside the chimney, set nearly 1300 homes ablaze.

CANDLES and other naked lights such as tapers are the source of around 800 fires each year.

In the home and at work

Rescuing someone from a fire

Getting someone out of a burning building calls for specialised knowledge and equipment and is highly dangerous. Safety experts say it should always be left to the fire brigade.

If, however, you are in a situation where you have to rescue someone – a child, say – who has been trapped or overcome by smoke, there are just two priorities: do not add yourself to the casualty list; and act quickly. Get the victim outside as fast as possible, regardless of his or her injuries.

- Always call the fire brigade (by dialling 999) before attempting any rescue yourself.
- Do not go into a building that is burning fiercely or in danger of collapse.
- Do not go into a building which you suspect may be filled with poisonous fumes. Some modern furniture gives off deadly gases when it burns. If some of this furniture is likely to be in the building, wait for firemen to arrive with breathing equipment.
- Before you go in, tie a rope round your waist and get somebody outside the building to hold it. If you get lost in the smoke you will be able to retrace your steps by following the rope, or if you are overcome by fumes you can be pulled to safety.
- Arrange a system of signals with the person outside. It is usually best to establish that you will keep a tension on the rope all the time by pulling it gently. If the rope slackens you will be pulled out.
- Tie a wet handkerchief or scarf over your mouth and nose. This will keep out the smoke but cannot protect you from poisonous fumes.
- If you have a blanket or coat to hand, carry it with you or drape it round your shoulders. It may be useful for wrapping up the casualty or for protecting both of you from heat.
- As you go into and through the building, test each door before you go through it by touching the knob with the back of your hand. If the knob is hot, do not enter.
- Do not go forward if there is any danger of your escape route being cut off.
- If the door is cool, hold the handle firmly when opening it so that the door cannot be sucked wide open by any hot gases inside. If it opens outwards, stand behind it and put your foot against the back to stop it bursting open.
- Take several deep breaths. Open the door a crack and wait for any hot air to be released, then go in (see *If you are trapped in a blazing house*, page 142).

HOW TO DO A FIREMAN'S LIFT

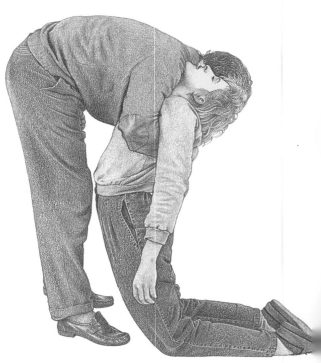

1 *Get the casualty onto her feet. If she is unconscious, lay her face down with her head at your feet. With your arms under her armpits, raise her to her knees, then to her feet.*

HANGING ON – 60 FEET UP
The ability to improvise is vital even for professional rescuers, who have specialised equipment to cope with most situations. On February 27, 1983, it saved the life of a teenage girl.

In the early hours of that morning, Leading Fireman Jeff Yates hung head-down out of a flat window, 60ft (18m) above ground, supported only by his colleague Keith Summerfield who was clinging to Jeff's legs. Hanging by her hands from a narrow ledge outside the next window in the Sheffield block of flats was 19-year-old Dawn Lipscombe. She had been trapped by flames but was beyond the reach of the firemen's ladders. Jeff's improvised trapeze act was the only way to get to her.

Suddenly, as Jeff was trying to reach Dawn, her window exploded. Glass splinters and flames sprayed outwards. Dawn let go of her ledge and flung herself sideways through the air. Jeff grabbed for her arms – and held on. For a few seconds the pair swung in the air until Keith finally managed to pull them both to safety. The unorthodox rescue technique had worked. Dawn was shocked but unhurt.

• Keep low as you go into a smoke-filled room. If necessary, crawl along the floor.
• Once you find the casualty, drag or carry her to safety as quickly as possible. Do not give first aid until you are both out of danger (see *Moving an injured person*, page 112).

Fireman's lift

If you have to negotiate stairs or manage many doors, you may find it easier to carry a casualty with the fireman's lift shown below, which leaves you with one hand free, than to drag her.
• Get the casualty onto her feet, facing you.
• Then put her across your shoulder.
• If you have to go down stairs while you are carrying someone in a fireman's lift, look down them first to see if there are any hazards, then go down backwards.

BUS-STOP RESCUE
Thick smoke and flames blocked the Glassford family's escape from their first-floor flat in Hamilton, Strathclyde. The fire had started at 6am on March 11, 1983, when a frying pan flared up as 17-year-old Thomas was cooking breakfast. It swiftly took hold, trapping Thomas, his parents and his six brothers and sisters.

But just in time, bus driver Jim Beaton saw the children screaming from the windows. He drove his bus up to the building, and he and a passenger helped the family out onto the bus roof.

A fire officer later said that Jim had 'almost certainly saved nine lives' by his quick thinking – and by his use of the bus as an improvised rescue platform.

In the home and at work

2 *Once she is on her feet, hold her right wrist with your left hand. Bend down, with knees bent, and put your head beside her right hip. Let her fall across your right shoulder.*

3 *Stand up carefully, keeping your back as straight as possible. Transfer her right wrist to your right hand, so leaving your left hand free to open doors and hold banisters.*

149

Fighting a fire

If fire breaks out, whatever the cause, the first thing to do is to make sure that nobody is in danger. Only then should you consider attempting to put out a small fire, such as a hearth-rug blaze. If the fire is large, fierce or spreading – or if it looks as though it might become so – do not try to fight it at all. Get out of the house and call the fire brigade at once by dialling 999.

Smoke is often more dangerous than the flames themselves. Many of the 600 people who die in fires each year in British homes are killed by smoke, not by flames.

• Do not put yourself at risk.

• Stand well back from the flames. Keep out of the smoke.

• Stand on the side of the fire nearest to your escape route so that you cannot be cut off.

• Do not try to drag burning objects away from the fire. This will only spread the flames.

• Work from the outside of the fire towards the centre. Use water, sand, heavy blankets and rugs to smother the flames, or use a fire extinguisher. (See *Protecting your home against fire*, page 152.)

• These general guidelines apply to all fires. In addition, however, safety experts recommend specific courses of action to deal with particular types of fire.

Chip pan

Fires in chip pans start when the cooking oil gets too hot and bursts into flame. If you see smoke coming off the oil, it means that the oil is about to ignite.

• Turn off the heat immediately.

• Do not move the pan. If you try to rush it out of the house, the air will cause the flames to flare up fiercely.

• Do not use water on the flames. It will spread the fire explosively.

• Smother the flames. Do not go looking for something; pick up whatever is to hand. Use a special fire blanket if you have one, or any thick cloth (wet if possible). A lid, plate or chopping board will also do as long as it is larger than the top of the pan.

• Hold the cloth or lid in front of you to shield your face as you place it over the chip pan.

• Once the fire is out, keep the pan covered until the oil is quite cool (wait at least 30 minutes). Otherwise it might burst into flames again.

• If you are unable to put the fire out, close all doors and windows, get out of the room and call the fire brigade.

Hearth rug

• If the flames are small, try to stamp them out or smother them with a wet cloth or mat.

• Otherwise, throw water over the flames.

Sofa or armchair

Most modern furniture, upholstered with foam, plastic or other synthetic materials, burns very quickly, giving off thick smoke and poisonous

HOW TO PUT OUT A BLAZING CHIP PAN
Leave the pan where it is. Turn off the heat and cover it with a fire blanket. Hold the blanket up to guard your face as you approach.

fumes which can overcome you in one minute, and kill you in less than two.

• Do not try to put out the fire.

• Get everybody out of the room immediately.

• Close the door.

• Call the fire brigade – even if the fire appears to be out.

• Do not try to take a burning piece of furniture (of any kind) outside – even if it is only smouldering. The fresh air could cause it to flare up.

Television set or computer

Parts of a television set can get very hot. As a result, a fire can break out even after the set has been switched off and unplugged. If a set burns it gives off fierce flames and poisonous fumes. The tube behind the screen may also explode. The same risks apply to home computers. Fires in TV sets and computers should be handled in the same way.

• If a peculiar smell, like burning rubber or plastic, comes from the set or the computer, or you see even a trace of smoke, unplug it immediately. Do not use it again until a specialist engineer has examined it.

In the home and at work

HOW TO SMOTHER A TV FIRE
Throw a fire blanket over a TV or computer
that bursts into flame. Approach the set from
behind in case the screen explodes in the heat.

HOW TO DAMP DOWN A CHIMNEY FIRE
Cut off the heat that has set the flue ablaze
by putting out the fire in the grate. One quick
way to do this is to shovel on garden soil.

• If smoke or flames begin to pour out, unplug the set at once or switch off at the mains. Then cover the machine with a fire blanket, or a wet rug or towel. This will help to contain the flames and fumes, and will protect you from flying glass if the screen explodes.
• Call the fire brigade.
• Do not throw water on a TV set or computer, or use a fire extinguisher of any kind – even after the machine has been switched off. The sudden cooling could cause the tube to burst. There may also be residual electricity remaining in the machine, and throwing water on it could give you an electric shock.
• Do not look under the blanket. Keep well away until the fire brigade has dealt with it.

Chimney
Chimneys – even those serving some central-heating systems – can catch fire if soot and dirt are allowed to collect in them over a period of years. And fires in them can, if unchecked, threaten the rest of the house.
• Call the fire brigade. The fire may penetrate cracks in the flue and spread to other parts of

the building. Move carpets and furniture away from the fireplace.
• Close doors and windows in the room.
• Shovel earth from the garden onto the grate or pour soapy water over the fire. Detergent in the water helps it to cling to the coals and smother the flames. The resulting steam will also help to put out the fire in the chimney.
• Once the fire in the grate is out, put a wire-mesh spark guard in front to prevent hot soot falling out of the flue into the room.
• Check other rooms through which the chimney passes. If the walls against the chimney are very hot, move the furniture away from them.
• When the fire has been extinguished, have the chimney swept. Regular sweeping – at least once a year – is the best precaution against chimney fires.

Electric blanket
• Unplug the blanket. But do not lift off the bedclothes – this will let air in and may turn a smouldering bed into a blaze.
• Call the fire brigade.
• Drench the bed with water.

151

PROTECTING YOUR HOME AGAINST FIRE

• Unplug electric appliances such as TV sets and heaters when they are not in use. This is safer than just switching them off.

• Before leaving the house or going to bed, close all doors and windows in empty rooms.

• Provide deep ashtrays in all rooms where people might smoke. (See *Fire in the home: the danger points*, page 147.)

• Keep matches well away from children, preferably in a locked cupboard.

• Do not air or dry clothes round a convector heater or against a radiant fire, or put them on a storage heater.

• Keep furniture, curtains and bedding well away from fires and heaters.

• Keep paraffin heaters away from doors. They could get knocked over. Never move or fill a paraffin heater while it is alight.

• Surround open fires with a fireguard. The guard should cover the entire fireplace, not just the fire.

• Do not put a mirror over the fireplace. It tends to encourage people to get too close to the fire.

• Never overfill chip pans. Oil and fat expand when heated, and they could overflow onto the burner and catch fire (see also *Danger points – room by room*, page 164).

Fire extinguishers

The simplest and most useful firefighting equipment for the home is a fire blanket and a bucket of water, kept in the kitchen. A portable fire extinguisher can be useful as long as it can be reached quickly by someone who knows how to use it properly. Some safety experts discourage fire extinguishers in the home, however, because they feel that the presence of an extinguisher may give a false sense of security and may make people careless about fire precautions.

If you are in doubt about what size of extinguisher to buy, choose one larger than you think you might need. The smallest useful extinguisher for home use is one with a capacity of about 3lb (1.5kg). And even this is sufficient only for a small fire. Aerosol extinguishers do not usually last long enough to put out more than a very small fire.

The most suitable general-purpose extinguisher for the home is the dry-powder type. It is the least dangerous to use, but makes a mess.

There are five different types of fire extinguisher. Each type is marked by a special colour. The extinguisher may be of one colour only or may be mostly red with the coding colour clearly displayed. The five types are: water (red); dry powder (blue); carbon dioxide (black); foam (cream, buff or white); and a vaporising-liquid type containing chemicals known as halon or BCF (green).

• WATER Use on burning wood, paper or cloth. Do not use on electrical fires where the apparatus is still switched on, or on flammable liquids such as petrol, spirits, oil or cooking fat. Do not use on a TV fire, even if the set has been switched off.

• DRY POWDER Use on flammable liquids or electrical equipment.

• CARBON DIOXIDE Use on almost all types of large fire, including electrical fires. But it is not suitable for oil-burning stoves or small fires.

• FOAM Use on flammable liquids.

• VAPORISING LIQUID Use on all large fires including electrical fires. But it should not be used in confined spaces because it gives off poisonous fumes.

If you have to tackle a fire with an extinguisher, make sure it is suitable for the fire concerned. Switch off the current if electrical equipment is involved. Crouch to keep clear of the smoke, and move the extinguisher from side to side with a sweeping movement. Aim it at the base of the flames and work steadily in from the edge.

Foam extinguishers should be aimed so that the foam drops onto burning liquid. If the foam is directed straight into the liquid under pressure it will be driven beneath the surface and be ineffective.

Learn how to use the extinguisher in advance. Otherwise, when fire breaks out, you could waste valuable minutes reading the instructions.

Keep extinguishers regularly maintained, otherwise they will deteriorate. The supplier will be able to advise you on how often your extinguisher needs checking.

Fire alarms

Domestic fire alarm systems should carry the British Standards Institution kitemark and the code number BS 5446.

Most systems are battery-powered, so that they will still work even if the mains electricity is cut off by a fire.

If you buy a battery-powered system, check that it is fitted with a device to warn when the battery is running low.

Get expert advice from the local fire brigade about where to place the detectors that trigger the alarm system, and about how many you need for your particular home.

If you smell gas or suspect a leak

Natural gas is not poisonous. But it can be dangerous because, when mixed with air in a proportion of between 5 per cent and 15 per cent, it is explosive. The gas has no smell of its own. But a smell is added to it deliberately, before it is piped to homes, to alert householders to leaks.

• If you smell gas or suspect (even with no smell) that gas is leaking from an appliance such as a cooker, put out cigarettes and any naked flames – a candle, say – at once.

• Turn off any electric fire in the room. But do not turn any other electric lights or appliances either on *or off*.

• Do not even allow the doorbell to be used. Operating a switch in either direction is likely to cause a spark which could ignite the gas.

• Open doors and windows to let the gas out, and leave them open until the leak has been stopped.

• Check that no gas taps have been left on accidentally, and that no pilot light has gone out. If no gas appliances are on, there is probably a leak. Turn the supply off at the meter at once.

• Telephone the Gas Region's emergency service. The number is listed in telephone directories under 'Gas'. If there is no directory available, dial 999 and ask for the police.

• Do not attempt to repair any appliances or pipes, or allow anyone else to do so. Repairs must by law be left to a trained gas engineer – such as one authorised by British Gas or the Confederation for the Registration of Gas Installers (CORGI).

• Stay out of the house until the source of the leak has been found and cured, and the smell of gas has cleared.

• If you smell gas in the street, report it to the nearest Gas Region Office at once.

When the gas has cleared

Simple gas escape repairs carried out by British Gas staff are usually free because British Gas make no charge for the first 30 minutes of work, nor for parts and materials up to about £2.50. The repairs of parts of the system belonging to British Gas – those which are on the supply side of the gas meter in your home – are paid for by British Gas.

• Once gasmen have repaired the leak, make sure that all gas taps on appliances are off.

• Then relight any pilot lights, unless gasmen have already done this for you.

If the gas supply fails

The gas supply may be affected by causes outside the home – a burst gas main, say, or a sharp drop in pressure.

• If the gas pressure does drop sharply (so that the flames on a gas cooker or gas fire become much smaller than usual), or the supply stops altogether so that the flames go out, turn off all gas appliances, turn off the supply at the meter or emergency control and notify the Gas Region Office at once.

• Do not attempt to use the supply again until someone from the Gas Region has advised you that it is safe to do so.

If you think the meter is faulty

If you suspect that your gas meter is at fault – if, for example, it appears to be running when no gas is being used – ask the local gas service centre to test it.

• If the gas engineer discovers a meter fault, there is no fee for the test, and any payments the fault has affected will be adjusted.

• If, however, the meter is found to be accurate, you will be charged a test fee – probably in the region of £15.

Living safely with gas

On average, there are some 80 serious gas explosions every year in Britain and about ten people a year die in such explosions. Nearly half of these accidents happen because people have interfered with appliances – either deliber-

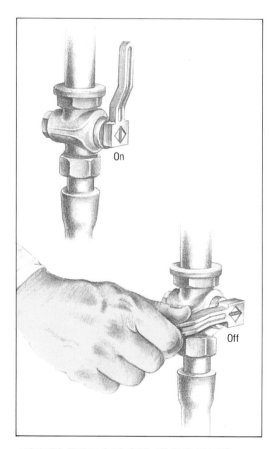

HOW TO TURN GAS OFF AT THE MAINS
Some main gas valves have built-in handles, others detachable handles. On either type, the supply is on when the mark on the pivot points along the pipe, off when it points across.

ately (such as by tampering with the meter), or by accident, or when attempting a repair that they were not competent to carry out.

Around 15 of the explosions are caused by gas leaks in the home.

• Make sure you know where the main gas tap is in your home, and how to turn it off. If the tap is stiff to turn, do not force it. Call your local gas service centre; they will loosen it free of charge.

• More than half the accidents caused by faulty appliances involve secondhand equipment. If you buy such equipment, get it installed by a qualified gas fitter.

• Get all gas appliances serviced regularly – central heating, water heaters and fires at least once a year, other appliances at least once every two years.

• If you know, or are warned, that a gas appliance or installation in your home is faulty, you must get it repaired. Failure to do so is not only dangerous; it could lead to prosecution and a fine of up to £2000.

• Never block ventilators in a room where there are gas appliances. Gas needs a supply of fresh air while it is burning.

• Watch out for signs that fumes of carbon monoxide – a poisonous gas which is given off when gas burns – are entering a room where there is a gas appliance. This could happen if a chimney or flue becomes blocked, cutting off the necessary air supply. Danger signs are staining, soot or discoloration around the fire or water heater, and the appliance may burn with a yellow or orange flame. If you notice any of these danger signs, or if sitting in the room gives you a headache or makes you feel sick, weak or tired, turn off the appliance at once and get it checked. (Modern appliances often have built-in ventilation – they must be fitted to an outside wall, and they take in fresh air from outside. These are known as 'balanced-flue' or 'roomsealed' types.)

• If you use an older style of water heater (not a balanced-flue type), open the bathroom window while you run the water, turn the heater off before you get into the bath, and do not run more hot water while you are in the bath.

• Do not run an unflued sink water heater for more than five minutes at a time – it is not designed to fill a bath or washing machine, or to provide hot water for a shower.

• If you move house, get the gas service to disconnect your appliances. It is against the law to leave unsealed or improperly capped gas points. Leave the instructions for any appliances you are not taking with you, for whoever is moving in.

• Authorised British Gas employees have a legal right of entry to any premises supplied with gas in order to inspect installations and appliances in the interests of safety. All such employees carry an identity card giving their name, photograph and signature, and will willingly show the card on request.

USING BOTTLED GAS

Bottled gas – the fuel sold in canisters for use by campers, in caravans, on boats, in heated greenhouses and in the home – is usually either propane (sold in red canisters) or butane (sold in blue or green canisters). Both fuels are forms of liquefied petroleum gas (LPG).

In use, both gases are effectively the same. But because they operate at different pressures, it is important to use the correct regulator valve for each fuel. Never switch from one gas to the other without also changing the regulator.

• Unlike natural gas, both gases are heavier than air. For this reason, canisters should always be stored outside, above ground level and away from drains if they are to be left for any length of time. This applies whether they are full or empty.

• Keep the canister upright, with the valve uppermost, whether it is in use or not.

• If a canister has to be left in a confined space – a caravan or boat, say – ventilate the area thoroughly before turning it on, before lighting any naked flame (even a cigarette) and before switching on any electrical equipment (because a spark could ignite leaked gas and cause an explosion).

• In particular, make sure that you ventilate thoroughly the bottom of the space – the bilges on a boat, say, or a cellar – to get rid of any gas that has collected there.

• Check gas hoses regularly for leaks by rubbing soapy water over them. Any leaks will be marked by erupting bubbles. Never use a naked flame to check for leaks.

• If you find any leaks, or if the hose is becoming worn, replace it. Do not try to repair it.

• When fitting connections, tighten them with a spanner. Finger pressure is not enough to ensure a gas-tight seal.

• Change canisters well away from any open flame or intense heat, preferably outdoors.

• Open the valve slowly when you want to turn the gas on.

• Ventilate any room where gas-burning appliances are in use.

Using electricity safely

The two major electrical hazards are shocks and fire. Any electrical wire gets warm in use. The thinner the wire, or the greater the amount of current it is carrying, the hotter it gets. Fuses are designed to cut off the power long before this heat builds up to the point where insulation could melt or a fire could start.

By following the guidelines suggested here, you can minimise the risks of starting a fire or suffering an electric shock (for details of first aid treatment, see page 93). You can also save yourself the inconvenience of being plunged into darkness by a blown fuse.

• When connecting an appliance to a plug, check that each wire goes to the correct terminal. Electric cables always contain two or three separate wires. There is always a live and a neutral wire, and often an earth wire as well. The three wires may be coloured in any of the following combinations.

Live	Neutral	Earth
Brown	Blue	Yellow/green
Red	Black	Copper (bare metal)
Red	Black	Green

• Do not use multiplugs (two or three-way plugs) as a regular practice. Have extra sockets fitted if you need them.
• Never put wires directly into a socket – always fit a plug. Never pull a plug out by the cable; you could pull the wires loose.
• Do not overload a socket. For example, a three-bar fire and a 1kW electric iron together take more than 16 amps – which is too much for a standard 13 amp household socket. Turn

HOW TO PROTECT THE FLEX ON AN IRON
A lead-holder attached to the flex of an iron and secured to the ironing board will prevent the flex from chafing against the board and thus wearing through more quickly.

at least one bar of the fire off if you have to use the same socket for the iron.
• If you have more than one appliance on a socket, check the total load by adding up the current each appliance uses. A two-bar fire, for instance, rated at 2kW (8 amps) and a television rated at 500 watts (2 amps) will – if they are both on together – use 10 amps, safely inside the 13 amp capacity of a standard household socket (see *Facts about fuses*, page 156).
• Check leads and connectors regularly, especially where the appliance is moved or gets hot, such as a kettle. Terminal screws (in the back of a kettle, for instance) can work loose with heat.
• Check regularly plugs and leads which are in constant use, such as those to refrigerators, freezers, washing machines and dishwashers.
• Drop leads to ceiling lights become hot in use and the insulation tends to become brittle with age and may crack. Change the leads if they become brittle.
• Switch the lights off at the mains before checking the leads and before cleaning with a damp cloth. Otherwise water could seep into the cracks and give you a severe shock.
• Do not plug any appliance into a lighting point. It could overload the circuit or blow a fuse.
• The cord-grip in a plug – usually a piece of hard rubber just inside the hole where the wire goes into the plug – must grip the outer sheath of the wire securely. If you can see the inner wires, the grip needs to be refitted.
• Always unplug appliances before working on them or making any adjustments, and after use. Unplug a light, too, before replacing a bulb.
• Unplug an electric kettle before you fill it.
• Never take a hair drier, heater or any appliance operated by the mains into the bathroom.
• Fit rubber plugs to appliances that receive hard wear. They chip and crack less easily than plastic plugs.
• Use a connector to join cables together, or, ideally, buy a longer length. Never join wires by twisting them together and insulating them with tape.
• Have the general house wiring checked every five years. Electricity Boards do the testing for a payment.
• Remember that altering the main wiring of your house is a long job calling for skill, care, and inspection afterwards by the Electricity Board.
• Use an orange cable on appliances which are used outdoors. The colour is easier to see.
• Never use an extension lead which is thinner than the lead attached to the appliance. A thinner lead will probably overheat.
• When using an extension lead fitted to a reel, pull out the entire length when it is in use. Wire warms up when current passes through it – the smaller the wire or the larger the appliance, the more heat is generated. If the wire is left on the

reel, the heat cannot escape so easily, and it can build up to a point where the insulation melts, causing a short circuit.

Facts about fuses

The vast majority of houses built or rewired since 1947 are wired on a ring-main system, with each circuit supplying a number of plug sockets. Each circuit has its own fuse in the fuse box, and each plug is also fused. Modern plugs always have rectangular pins; round-pin plugs are almost invariably part of an older, pre-1947 'radial' wiring system, in which each plug socket has its own separate circuit.

The box on this page (see *Fuse ratings*) shows what fuse you should fit in the plug for each of the named appliances. Using a much larger fuse

than necessary carries the risk of causing a whole ring-main circuit to fail rather than a single appliance. There is also an increased risk of fire if the lead to the appliance becomes overloaded.

To calculate the appropriate fuse for any electrical appliance, look for the manufacturer's plate or label – usually on the back or bottom of the appliance.

The plate will show how much power the appliance uses, expressed in watts (W) or kilowatts (kW). One kilowatt equals 1000 watts. Divide the figure, in watts, by 250 and the result is the minimum size of fuse necessary in amps. An appliance using 1.5kW (1500 watts), for instance, needs at least a 6 amp fuse (1500 ÷ 250) – or, in practice, a 10 or 13 amp fuse.

FUSE RATINGS

Appliance	Rating
Cooker 6kW shower	30 amps
3kW immersion heater Storage heater	15 amps
Appliances rated at 720 watts and above including: Dishwasher 3kW fire Freezer Kettle Refrigerator Spin/tumble drier Television (colour) Toaster Vacuum cleaner Washing machine	13 amps
Appliances rated at under 720 watts including: Electric blanket Clock Extractor fan Food processor/mixer/blender Hair drier Hi-fi stereo system/radio Home computer Iron Shaver Standard or table lamp Tape recorder Television (black and white)	3 amps

THREE TYPES OF FUSE

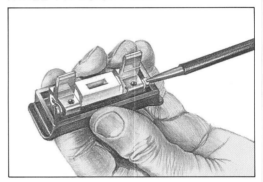

1 *Older types of fuse box are commonly fitted with fuses containing a length of wire attached to screw terminals. Always replace a burnt-out fuse with wire of the same rating.*

HOW TO FIT A PLUG

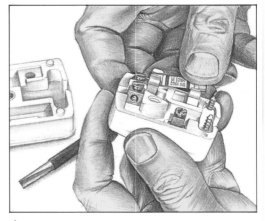

1 *Check that the fuse is the correct rating for the appliance (most plugs are sold with 13 amp fuses). Remove 2in (50mm) of the lead's outer sheath, and bare about ¼in (6mm) of each wire.*

How to change a fuse in a fuse box

• Turn off the mains supply at the main switch.
• Open the fuse box. Pull out fuses until you find the one that has blown. Look for loose wires or signs of scorching. It is a good idea to mark the fuses so that you know which one controls which circuit.
• If fuse wire is used, remove the old wire. Wind new wire of the same rating around one screw and tighten the screw. Take the wire across the bridge (or through the channel in an enclosed fuse) and twist it clockwise round the second screw, leaving a little slack. Tighten this screw and cut off the surplus wire.
• Always fit the correct fuse wire for the circuit. If in doubt, consult the Electricity Board.
• If the fuses are cartridge types, check each one with a circuit-tester. There may be no visible marks on the failed fuse. Alternatively, take the base off a metal-cased torch, turn on the torch and hold the fuse so that it touches the base of the battery and the metal case. If the torch bulb does not light, the fuse is broken. Replace it with a cartridge of the correct amperage.
• If your fuse box has trip-switches, which are designed to turn themselves off automatically when the circuit becomes overloaded, there is no need to repair or replace anything. Switch off some of the appliances on the circuit, then reset the trip (usually by button or switch).
• If a fuse blows repeatedly, or if a trip-switch will not stay on when you reset it, telephone an electrical contractor or the Electricity Board's emergency service for help.

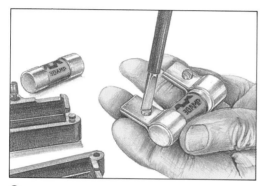

2 *Fuse-box cartridge fuses are coded by size and colour. White (the smallest) are for 5 amp circuits; then come blue (15 amps), yellow (20 amps), red (30 amps) and green (45 amps).*

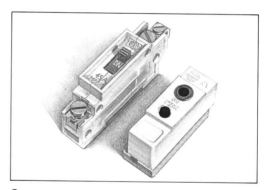

3 *Trip-switch fuses are small circuit-breakers which are fitted to many new fuse boxes. They have a built-in switch or button which turns itself off if the circuit becomes overloaded.*

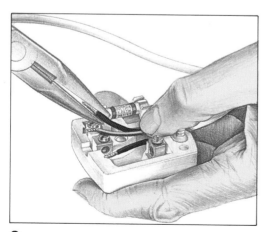

2 *Push the wires under the cord-grip. Use pliers if necessary to manoeuvre them into place. In a modern plug, the earth is the longer top pin; the live wire should go to the fused pin.*

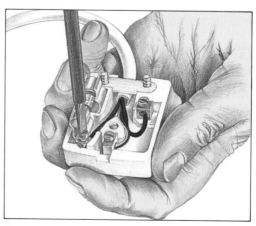

3 *Tighten the terminals with a screwdriver, making sure that there are no loose strands. Tighten the cord-grip screws so that they clamp the outer sheath, and refit the cover.*

When the power supply fails

During industrial disputes and during times of exceptional demand – in the middle of a particularly harsh winter, for instance – power cuts can cause considerable inconvenience, especially if they are unexpected.

But it is possible to minimise the inconvenience, and the risk of accidents during a cut, by taking a few simple precautions.

• Switch off all electrical appliances except those that are normally on all the time, such as clocks, refrigerators and central-heating thermostats. When the power is restored after the cut, there will be an initial surge of current and, if a lot of appliances are on, the surge may be great enough to blow a fuse. More important, appliances such as heaters could become fire hazards if they are left on and forgotten, and the power comes back on late at night.

• As an extra precaution, make a point of unplugging the appliances at the sockets. Move the leads out of the way as well so that nobody can trip over them in the dark.

• Leave at least one light switched on so that you know when power is restored.

• Avoid opening a freezer, even a chest type. Food will generally keep safely for at least 12 hours with the power off. The fuller the freezer, the longer it will stay cold – up to 48 hours in safety, for instance, for a completely full freezer that is left unopened.

• Pack blankets and crumpled newspaper under and around the freezer's base to prevent heat rising into the appliance.

• No special action is needed for central heating – most systems are electrically controlled and will just not operate during a power cut.

• Use hot water carefully during a power cut. Although the water should stay hot for some time if the tank is well lagged, cold water is fed into the tank every time you draw off some of the hot.

• Use vacuum flasks to store spare water for hot drinks.

• If the failure is unexpected, telephone the local Electricity Board to tell them the power is off – it helps the board to identify an affected area quickly. The telephone has its own power supply and will not be affected by the cut.

When power is restored

• Reset electric clocks and timers, including the central-heating timeswitch, after the cut.

• Remove any insulation that you have put round the base of your refrigerator or freezer. Make sure, particularly, that you uncover the vent or grille (normally on the back or side) through which surplus heat is discharged.

• Check that food in a freezer has not started to thaw. If it has, raw food can be cooked and refrozen (do not refreeze it raw). Precooked food that has begun to thaw should be reheated and eaten at once, or thrown away.

• After checking the freezer, do not reopen it for six hours after a long power cut, to give time for the temperature inside to be lowered to a safe level again.

• If further cuts are expected, set freezer and refrigerator controls to maximum to extend the time that food will stay safely frozen.

Preparing for a power cut

Often there is some warning – either through a notice from the local Electricity Board or via newspapers, radio and TV – of impending power cuts. If there is, try to be ready for a cut well ahead of time.

• Keep a small torch by your bed, and a larger electric lantern in the kitchen.

• Fit these lamps with long-life batteries, and check them regularly.

• If you have to use candles, keep them away from anything that might catch fire, such as curtains. Stand candles in holders that cannot be easily knocked over.

• Try to set up alternative heating in at least one room: a gas fire, for example, a paraffin heater, a coal fire or a wood-burning stove.

• In an all-electric house, consider buying a camping stove for emergency cooking and heating during power cuts.

• Set freezer and fridge controls to maximum 24 hours before the power goes off – the colder they are, the longer the food will keep.

• Consider taking out insurance against the loss of food in your freezer – if you add it to your ordinary household policy, it will cost about £4-£5 a year for £100 worth of food.

HEATER SAFETY IN A POWER CUT
If your power supply fails, turn off all electric fires and heaters. Pull all the plugs out at the sockets. Then tidy the flexes away so that you cannot trip over them in the dark.

Plumbing: emergency repairs

A flood in the home – from a blocked drain or a burst pipe – can be controlled or stopped before it does serious damage without waiting for a plumber to arrive.

But taking effective action calls for a cool head, speed and some preparation. It is therefore important to think ahead.

You need to know where to find stopcocks and shut-off valves inside and outside the house. If you do not know, find them and note their position for when an emergency arises. They are usually in or near the positions shown in the diagram below, but there are considerable variations even in modern houses. Once you

In the home and at work

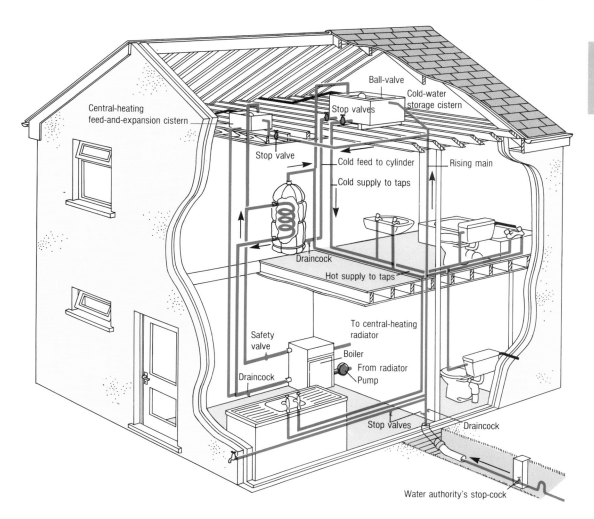

Ball-valve
Cold-water storage cistern
Central-heating feed-and-expansion cistern
Stop valves
Stop valve
Cold feed to cylinder
Rising main
Cold supply to taps
Draincock
Hot supply to taps
To central-heating radiator
Safety valve
Boiler
From radiator
Pump
Draincock
Stop valves
Draincock
Water authority's stop-cock

HOW THE WATER PIPES ARE LAID OUT IN A MODERN HOUSE

This is a typical modern plumbing layout. Exactly where the pipes run varies from house to house. But the principles are the same in all houses of any age. The supply enters the house via the rising main, which carries the water to a cistern in the loft. Only the kitchen cold tap, and sometimes a garden tap or a washing machine, are fed directly from the main. Lavatories, other cold taps and the hot-water cylinder are fed from the cistern.

A spiral tube inside the cylinder (often backed up by an electric immersion heater) heats the water. The tube is kept hot by water circulating through it from the boiler. The water inside the tube, like the water in any central-

heating radiators, is quite separate from the water which comes out of the taps, so that tap water cannot be contaminated by any anti-corrosion chemicals in the heating system.

To stop a leak from a cold-water or hot-water pipe, turn off the stop valve on the rising main (usually in the kitchen) and turn on all the taps. To shut off a leak from a hot-water pipe alone, turn off the valve on the pipe leading from the loft cistern to the hot-water cylinder.

In some flats, there is no cold-water cistern. Instead, lavatories and all cold taps are fed directly from the rising main; hot taps are fed from a mains-fed heater. Stop leaks by turning off the rising main and running the taps.

HOW TO DEAL WITH A LEAK

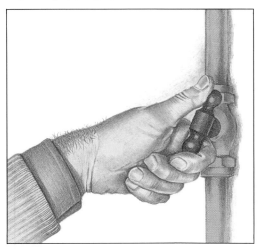

1 *Turn off the valve at the rising main. The valve is usually in the kitchen. Turn on all the taps and flush the lavatories. Do not waste time at this stage looking for the leak.*

2 *If the leaking water has collected above a ceiling, forming a bulge in the plaster, put a bucket or any container below the bulge, and pierce the bulge with a large screwdriver.*

have identified the valves, it might be helpful to label each one so that you can be sure of identifying them quickly in an emergency.

If any valves are stuck, free them with a penetrating lubricant. Check them regularly.

Never leave any tap or valve full on for too long – it can easily become jammed. Once you have opened it fully, turn it back about half a turn and leave it in that position.

Emergency repairs will also be quicker and simpler if you keep the following items in the house: proprietary pipe repair tape; glass fibre tape and epoxy resin putty; plumber's tape (used to seal threaded pipe joints); a drain plunger; and a tin of radiator seal.

If water leaks through a ceiling
If water starts to drip through a ceiling, the most probable cause (other than a leaking roof) is a burst pipe or tank in the loft.
• The priority is to reduce the amount of water in the tank as quickly as possible to stop water flooding the house. Do not waste time at this stage looking for the cause.
• Turn off the main stop valve on the rising main in the house – the valve is usually under the kitchen sink or in the larder.
• Flush all lavatories and turn on all taps in the house except the kitchen cold tap, which is fed directly from the rising main.
• Leave the taps running and keep flushing the lavatories until the pipes and tank are empty, and the taps dry up.
• If you see a distinct bulge in the ceiling at the site of the leak, it means that a pool of water has collected over the spot.
• To stop the weight of water bringing down the ceiling, puncture the centre of the bulge with a large screwdriver and let the water drain out

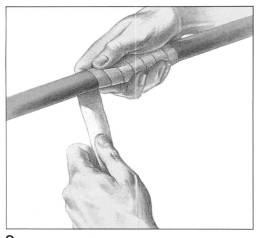

3 *Track down the source of the leak, which will probably be in the loft. When you find it, wait until it stops dripping, then bind the hole with pipe repair tape. Call a plumber.*

into a bucket or any other available container.
• Once water stops flowing from the leak, go up into the loft and find the source of the leak. Take care to step only on the joists if the loft floor is not boarded – otherwise your foot will almost certainly go through the plaster ceiling and you could be seriously hurt.
• Repair the pipe or tank temporarily with glass fibre tape and epoxy resin putty, or with pipe repair tape. You will then be able to turn the water on again. If you cannot repair the leak, leave the water off.
• Call a plumber (consult the Yellow Pages of a telephone directory) to make permanent repairs.
• If the leak is through a hole in the roof, make a temporary repair with a sheet of plastic (see *Storms and high winds*, page 172).

If a pipe bursts

Water expands when it freezes, and if the water is trapped inside a pipe, the expansion can be strong enough to burst the pipe.

If you find a burst and frozen pipe, aim to make a temporary repair *before* it thaws out and the leak causes damage.
• Bind the damaged section of pipe with pipe repair tape, following the maker's instructions on the packet. Properly used, repair tape will withstand mains pressure.
• Alternatively, repair the break with glass fibre tape and epoxy resin putty.
• Once the seal is in place, thaw out the pipe with gentle heat – use a hot-water bottle or a piece of rag soaked in hot water.
• Have the pipe repaired later by a plumber.
• If the damaged pipe has already thawed and water is pouring out, try to cut off the water supply to the pipe.
• Turn off the nearest stop valve, if there is one, or run the taps that are fed by the pipe to reduce water pressure inside.
• When the leak stops or slows, bind the damaged section with pipe repair tape or repair the damage with glass fibre tape and epoxy resin putty.
• If the damage is extensive, it may be necessary to turn off the water supply to the house completely by shutting off the rising main. Wrap the pipe with a towel to confine the water and lead it into a bucket. Call a plumber.

If a joint leaks

If a pipe leaks at a joint, the repair needed depends on the type of joint. There are two types: compression joints and capillary joints.
• Compression joints, where the pipes are threaded and held together by nuts, can be made watertight by tightening the nut slightly with a spanner.
• Alternatively, shut off the water supply to the pipes, unscrew the nuts and wrap the threaded areas with several turns of plumber's tape. Then reassemble the joint.

• Capillary joints, where the pipes are sealed by a sleeve of metal soldered to them, may have to be remade by a plumber.
• On either type of joint you can also make a temporary repair.
• Turn off the nearest stop valve and run taps to reduce the water pressure inside.
• Bind the joint with pipe repair tape or seal it with epoxy resin putty.

If a radiator leaks

A large leak from a radiator can often be cured by draining the radiator and plugging the hole with epoxy resin putty.

But a pinhole leak which allows water to weep out slowly is best dealt with by a proprietary liquid radiator seal.
• Add the seal to the small central-heating cistern in the loft – you should recognise it from the instructions given with the seal.
• Again following the instructions, open the draincock near the boiler so that water in this feed-and-expansion cistern flows into the system. The seal will then find its own way to the leak, on the same principle as the sealants used to mend car radiators.
• Either type of leak often means that the radiator is heavily corroded inside – and that other radiators in the system are also affected. So the only long-term answer is to drain the whole central-heating system and install a corrosion inhibitor. Consult a central-heating firm (local ones will be listed in the Yellow Pages).

If a central-heating pipe leaks

• If possible, put a container under the leak to catch as much of the water as possible.
• Switch off the central heating at the control panel. Shovel out the coal from a solid-fuel boiler so that the boiler pipes do not overheat when they are drained.
• Tie up the ball valve in the central-heating

IF WATER REACHES ELECTRICAL WIRING

Water conducts electricity so there is danger of shocks, short circuits and possibly fire if water from a leak runs along electrical wiring.

If this happens, or there is a risk of it, switch off the main electricity supply at once. The switch is usually near the main fuse box.

Alternatively, isolate the circuit concerned by removing the relevant fuse.

If any wiring or electrical components have become wet, make sure they are thoroughly dry before switching on again.

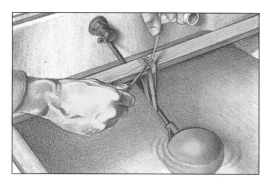

HOW TO SHUT OFF A BALL VALVE
To stop a central-heating tank filling up when you drain the system, lay a board across the tank and tie the valve's float arm up to it. You can use the same technique to stop a cold-water storage cistern filling up if you cannot find the stop valve on the rising main, or if the valve is stuck and you cannot turn it off.

cistern. It is probably in the loft, and is the smaller of the two cold-water storage tanks.
• Attach a garden hose to the draincock, which is usually beside the boiler.
• Run the hose to a nearby sink, or push it out of the kitchen door. Open the draincock with a spanner or pliers, and let the water run out of the central-heating circuit until water stops flowing from the leak. When the leak stops, close the draincock.
• Call a plumber or the people who service your central heating to repair the leak.

How to stop a cistern dripping
If a lavatory cistern drips water, particularly in cold weather, the problem is probably condensation – not a leak.

Moisture in the air is condensing on the cold outer surface of the cistern and dripping onto the floor, or trickling down the flush pipe between cistern and lavatory.
• The best cure is to keep the lavatory slightly warmer. Leave the door open so that warmer air from other parts of the house enters, or install a small radiator or tubular electric heater along the wall.

If water leaks under the bath
The commonest sources of bath leaks are the overflow outlet and the plughole.
• Try replacing the rubber gasket between the waste pipe and bath.
• Alternatively, try tightening the securing nut on the plughole joint very slightly – over-tightening can make the leak worse.

If a basin overflows
Floods in bathrooms and bedrooms are most often caused by leaving the plug in a basin with a tap running.
• If the overflow outlet is blocked, fill the sink so that the overflow outlet is underwater, then try to force out the obstruction with a drain plunger.
• Alternatively, push a curtain wire down the outlet and try to clear the blockage.
• Once the water starts to drain away, flush more water down the outlet – with caustic soda or a proprietary drain cleaner if necessary – to clear any remaining debris.

If a drain or pipe is blocked
• Turn off any taps that drain into the blocked section.
• Feel with your hand at the upper opening of the drain or waste pipe, and clear any obstructions you find. Outside drains, for example, can become choked with fallen leaves or silt.

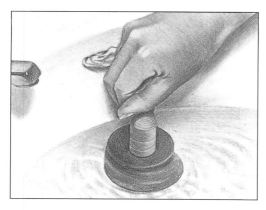

HOW TO CLEAR A BLOCKED DRAIN
Partly fill the sink, and use a drain plunger to free the blockage. Stuff a wet cloth in the overflow outlet if necessary to stop water spurting out of it while you pump the plunger.

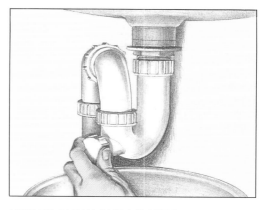

HOW TO CLEAN OUT A U-TUBE
If plunging does not work on a blocked sink or basin, put a bucket under the U-tube. Undo the drain valve, or take the whole U-tube apart and clean it out thoroughly by hand.

• On a waste pipe from a sink or basin, if there is no obvious obstruction, seal the overflow with a wet rag and use a drain plunger to try to force the blockage free.

• Once the water starts to flow, flush more water through to clear any remaining debris.

• If plunging fails on a kitchen sink or basin, put a bucket under the U-bend beneath the sink, disconnect the U-tube trap and clean it out. On modern plastic fittings, finger pressure may be enough to unscrew the trap. If you use a wrench, be gentle with it.

• If none of these methods works, it means that the obstruction is lodged farther along the pipe.

• Shift the obstruction with a plumber's snake – a stiff but flexible wire – if the pipe itself is blocked. If the drain is blocked, use drain rods. Both items of equipment can usually be rented from tool hire shops.

• If this does not work, or if you cannot get hold of the equipment, call a plumber.

If the lavatory will not flush

• If the mechanism in a lavatory cistern goes wrong for some reason, it is usually a job for a plumber.

• You can, nevertheless, go on using the lavatory until the plumber comes. Fill a bucket and pour the water into the lavatory pan – not the cistern – after each use. It will have the same effect as if the flush was working.

If a lavatory or drain is blocked

• Do not use or flush a lavatory if the pan or the sewage pipe beyond is blocked. You could create a health hazard if the sewage overflows, and you will certainly make the job of clearing it more difficult.

• Try first to clear the blockage with a large drain plunger. Do not, however, use the plunger with too much force or you could crack the lavatory pan.

• If plunging does not work, try to find the site of the blockage.

• Lift each drain manhole in turn. If there is stagnant water under the manhole, it means the blockage is farther down the pipe. If there is no water under the manhole, it means that the blockage is farther up the pipe.

• When you find the area of the blockage, explore the drain with a long stick. You may be able to dislodge the obstruction.

• If you cannot reach or shift the blockage with a stick, consider borrowing or hiring a set of drain rods or a plumber's snake (both are usually available from hire shops).

• If you use drain rods, be careful to twist the rods only in a clockwise direction as you work the rods into – and out of – the drain. If you twist them in the other direction, you are likely to unscrew the rods and leave the head deep inside the drain.

• Once the backed-up water begins to flow again, flush hot water or a chemical drain cleaner through the pipes to clear away any remaining debris. If you cannot clear the blockage yourself, call a plumber.

If your pipes are noisy

If water pipes start to make a banging or hammering noise, it may mean that there is an airlock somewhere in the plumbing system. Clearing such an airlock is a job for a plumber.

More commonly, however, the noise is caused by vibration in the ball valve which keeps your cold-water storage cistern topped up. And this can be put right without the expense of calling in a plumber.

• Check the cause of the noise by examining the cistern at the top of the house (it is usually the larger of the two tanks in the loft).

• If the ball valve is bouncing up and down on the surface of the water, releasing intermittent jets of water and creating the noise, try to slow down its movement by fitting a brake or damper of some sort.

• Hardware shops and plumbers' merchants sell an L-shaped piece which clips onto the arm of the valve and hangs underwater, acting like a brake on the arm.

• Alternatively, you can improvise a simple brake yourself with some stiff galvanised wire (such as a wire coat hanger) and a plastic cup.

• Make a loop in one end of the wire, big enough to hold the cup firmly. If necessary, pierce the wire through the side of the cup to anchor it.

• Wind the other end of the wire around the valve arm so that the cup is held upright underwater. The cup will then act as a brake, damping down the vibration and stopping the noise.

HOW TO QUIETEN NOISY PIPES
A damper made out of a plastic cup and wire will stop the vibrations on a ball valve which are often the cause of banging pipes. Hang the cup underwater below the float arm.

Danger points – room by room

Your own home is the most dangerous place on earth. More accidents happen there than anywhere else. Each year in Britain, around 6000 people are killed in accidents at home – at least as many as die on the roads – and another 3 million are hurt badly enough to need some form of medical treatment. Most accidents happen in the evenings or at weekends when people are usually at home. And there are 40 per cent more accidents in summer than in winter. The extra accidents almost all happen outdoors in the garden or in the garage. Nearly half of all home accidents happen in the kitchen, the living room and dining room (often the same), and the garden.

Despite the grim statistics, there is much you can do to make your home safer, and so reduce the risks to yourself and your family. A room-by-room check of the accident black spots shown on these pages could prevent a hazard becoming a tragedy. Special additional precautions are needed if there are young children or elderly people in the house.

There are also safety devices on the market, such as smoke-detector kits, which can be installed by any home handyman. The smoke detectors will warn of fire before it gets out of control, giving valuable time in which to fight the blaze or to escape.

Kitchen

Of the 3 million or so accidents in British homes each year – and this figure does not include those minor accidents whose victims treat their injuries themselves – about one in ten happen in the kitchen.
• Keep the shelving in your kitchen within easy reach, or have a sturdy stepladder to reach high shelves.
• Store dangerous liquids, such as bleach and disinfectant, well out of reach of children and preferably in a locked cupboard. Do not keep dangerous liquids in food containers or store them with food.
• Keep knives out of reach of children.
• Turn pan handles away from the edge of the stove when cooking. You – or a child – could catch them and tip them over.
• If there is a toddler in the house, do not use tablecloths which hang over the edge of the table. He might pull it, and whatever is on it, onto his head.
• Never leave chip pans or other deep-fry pans

Ways to keep a cooker safe
Consider fitting a guard rail to your cooker, especially if there are young children about. Turn pan handles away from the edge, too.

USING A MICROWAVE OVEN

Modern microwave ovens are very safe in use. Early fears that they might be dangerous to cooks have been shown to have no foundation. The ovens are designed so that they cannot function unless the door is closed. All activity stops instantly when the door opens. If any microwaves were to leak, the strongest effect would be within 2in (50mm) of the oven. At arm's length the effect would be reduced to one hundredth of the strength. Microwaves are not like X-rays; the effect of many small doses is not cumulative or dangerous.

If your oven suddenly begins to take longer than usual to cook food, the door seal may be damaged, and microwaves may be leaking.

A simple way to check this is to use a circuit-testing screwdriver – one with a neon tube in the handle. Move the blade of the screwdriver round the outside of the door seal while the door is closed and the oven on. If there is a significant leakage of microwaves, the neon will glow faintly.

If in doubt, ask your local Electricity Board or an electrical shop to test the oven for you.

Get a microwave oven serviced regularly. Do not attempt to do any repairs yourself.

unattended, and do not fill them more than a third full with fat or oil.

• When using a deep-fry pan, have the lid, a fire blanket, a baking tray or a large damp towel handy to smother any fire. Never try to douse the flames with water (see *Fighting a fire*, page 150). Consider using chips that can be cooked in the oven to remove the need for deep-fry cooking altogether.

• When using a pressure cooker, follow the maker's instructions about how much water to put in, and time the cooking carefully so that the cooker does not boil dry.

• Wipe up any grease that spills on the floor immediately. Glue down the edges of any floor tiles that lift, to stop people tripping over them.

• Never use a thin or wet oven cloth.

• Make sure that all burners in a gas oven are alight before closing the door. If you have turned the heat right down, close the door slowly so as not to blow the flame out.

• Do not hang cloths or plastic bags above gas burners.

• Do not set burners so high that the flames come up the sides of cooking pans. The extra heat is wasted, and the flames may melt the handles or make them painfully hot.

• Keep plastic carrier bags and food bags away from young children. Pulled over the head in play, they can suffocate.

• Keep the doors of wall-mounted kitchen units closed whenever possible. Their sharp corners can be dangerous, particularly if they are near eye level.

• Lock potential hiding places for young children such as the freezer, broom cupboard, washing machine or tumble drier. A toddler could get trapped inside.

• Put a baby's bouncing chair on the floor – never on a work-top or table. It may shift as the baby bounces, and topple off the edge.

• Before removing the connector from a kettle

Putting a play-pen in the kitchen
Keep toddlers and babies out of danger in the kitchen, but in sight, by putting them in a play-pen while meals are being cooked. Keep older children occupied safely by giving them empty saucepans or dough to play with.

or other appliance with a removable lead, switch off or unplug at the wall socket. If a 'live' connector falls into a liquid – washing-up water, say – the resultant short circuit may cause the plug fuse to explode, often with sufficient violence to blow the plug to pieces.

• If a live connector does fall into water, turn off the power and unplug it before pulling it out of the water by the cord. If you put your hands in the water while the power is still on, you could get a severe electric shock.

• If a plug, lead or connector becomes wet, turn off the power and dry the plug thoroughly before attempting to use it.

• Turn the iron off if you are called away when ironing. When you have finished with it, leave it to cool out of reach of young children.

Bathroom and lavatory

About one accident in 50 in British homes happens in the bathroom – and one of the largest single causes is people falling in the bath.

• If your bath or the base of your shower is smooth, use an internal bath mat which grips with suction cups. This will prevent you slipping.

THE CURE THAT KILLED

Drinking water is a valuable on-the-spot first aid treatment for anyone who swallows a poisonous substance of any kind – a household cleaner, for instance, such as bleach. The water helps to dilute the poison and thus lessen its effects. The patient should drink as much water as he comfortably can without making himself sick. For an average adult, this may be 2-4 pints (about 1-2 litres). For a child, it could be less than 1 pint (about half a litre).

Drunk quickly in very large quantities, however, water can itself be poisonous.

In October 1982, a 40-year-old housewife from Hayes, London, accidentally swallowed some bleach that had been left in a cup to remove a stain. A hospital she rang advised her by telephone to drink water to minimise any risk, but in panic she took the remedy too far.

She drank water in enormous quantities, gulping it from a plastic bucket. 'She literally drank gallons,' a coroner later reported, 'and, despite making herself sick, continued to drink.'

Eventually the woman had a fit, collapsed and died from brain damage caused by water intoxication. At the inquest, doctors reported that the bleach had done her no harm at all.

• Fit a grab handle on the wall above the bath. This is particularly valuable for older people or for anyone who feels dizzy when getting up from a hot bath.

• If you have a shower unit, fit a thermostat to it to guard against scalding. Or consider buying

Cold water before hot
Always run the cold water into a bath first, then add the hot, in case a child falls in accidentally. Children can die from being scalded in very hot baths.

can condense inside the casing and make it 'live' – exposing you to a severe shock if you touch it. A battery-powered radio is, however, safe, because the voltage it uses is not high enough to be dangerous.

• Mop up water that spills on the floor to avoid the risk of you – or someone else – slipping on it. For the same reason, if you use a bath mat on the floor, make sure it has a non-slip backing.

• Never leave young children alone in the bath. If you have to leave the room, take them with you, wrapped in a towel to keep them warm.

• If you put a bolt on the inside of your bathroom or lavatory door, fit it high enough so that young children cannot reach it and lock themselves in. Remove the keys for the same reason.

• Never mix bleach or any bleach-based cleaner with other lavatory cleaners. The mixture can give off a poisonous gas.

• Store medicines well out of reach of children in a cabinet that can be locked.

• Do not transfer medicines from child-proof containers to ordinary ones.

• Dispose of old medicines safely. Either flush them down the lavatory, or return them to the chemist. Do not throw them away with the household rubbish.

Living room and dining area
More than one in ten accidents happen in the living room or dining room – making these the most dangerous places indoors.

• Make sure that power points are not overloaded. If you have more appliances than you have points for, have extra sockets fitted.

• Check that flexes for lamps and other

Put door knobs out of reach
Fit handles high up to stop toddlers letting themselves out of the house or into a cupboard with medicines or chemicals. Add a higher bolt to stop them reaching the handle from a chair.

a shower head which has a thermostat built in for the purpose.

• By law, bathroom lights, heaters and any other electrical appliances must be controlled either by switches outside the bathroom, or by a cord-operated ceiling switch, so that it is impossible to touch water and the switch simultaneously. Electric shaver points are the only exception, because they use a special socket with an isolating transformer.

• Do not use mains electric appliances, such as a mains radio, in the bathroom. Water vapour

Cover plug sockets
Fit plastic safety plugs to power sockets when they are not in use, to cover up the holes and stop small children electrocuting themselves.

Fix a fireguard round every fire

Sturdy guards should be fixed around all radiant electric and gas fires, and around open fires, and attached to the wall with fastenings' that a child cannot undo. They should cover the whole fireplace, not just the fire, and stand far enough away from the fire to stop a child reaching it with bits of paper poked through the wire.

appliances do not trail across the floor where people could trip over them. Do not run flexes under the carpet – they may overheat and you will not be able to see if they become worn.

• Fix rugs to the floor. Repair worn rugs or carpets. Use non-slip polish on wooden floors.

• Do not balance ashtrays on armchairs or sofas. A lot of modern upholstered furniture contains foam plastic which gives off toxic fumes and dense smoke if it catches fire. The smoke and fumes, which can kill, are often more dangerous than the flames themselves.

• Before going out or to bed, make sure that cigarette ends are out and that fires are damped down or thoroughly contained behind a fireguard.

• Unplug electrical appliances at the wall at night – especially the television set. Exceptions to this are clocks, timers and video recorders, which are designed for continuous operation.

• Ensure that all electrical appliances are protected by appropriate fuses – see the table on page 156.

Bedroom

About one accident in 20 happens in a bedroom. Many involve poisoning, falls from bunk beds or burns from sun lamps.

No pillows for a baby

Babies under 12 months old should never be given a pillow. Because they cannot easily turn over, they could suffocate on it. If you decide to give an older baby a pillow, in or out of a cot, consider using a safety pillow which has air holes built into it. Pillows of this type are available from baby equipment shops – as are safety mattresses, which are designed on the same lines.

• Have your electric blanket checked for safety every year, and check its lead for brittleness and cracks every few months.

• Do not leave an electric underblanket switched on when the bed is occupied. It can overheat and set fire to the mattress and bedding. If the blanket is very badly worn, it could electrocute you.

• Make sure that the bulb in your bedside light is within the wattage range of the shade – too powerful a bulb can overheat the shade and create a fire hazard.

• Do not cover a shade with cloth or paper to cut down the brightness – this too can be a fire risk. Use a weaker bulb or a darker shade, or fit a dimmer switch.

• Moving about in the dark can be dangerous: keep a small torch, fitted with long-life batteries, by your bedside. Make sure that there are no trailing flexes or furniture for you to trip over.

• For the same reason, consider having a telephone socket fitted beside your bed, and plugging your phone in there at night. This is particularly valuable for elderly people who – if they become ill or have an accident – may not be able to reach the phone downstairs.

• Do not smoke in bed.

• Fit safety locks to windows in rooms for children. Do not position furniture that a child could climb on under a window.

Loft

• Fit some form of sturdy floorboarding between the hatch and water tank, so that you can stand safely.

• If the loft is unfloored, tread only on the joists – the ceiling between the joists will not bear the lightest foot.

• Make sure that the joists are strong enough if you plan to make any regular use of the loft – for storage, for example. A rough rule is to measure the unsupported length of the joists in feet, halve it and add 1, and that gives you the depth in inches the joists should be. A joist across a span of 12ft needs to be at least 7in deep if it is to be used in this way. If in doubt, get professional advice from an architect or a reliable local builder.

• If you plan to make any extensive use of your loft, bear in mind that you must have adequate ventilation and light, and the floor may need to be strengthened. Local council planning departments can advise on the detailed building regulations, which can vary from place to place.

• Fit a lighting point near the water tank so that you can see what you are doing if you have to work there.

• Make sure that all tanks and pipes are fully insulated to guard against the risk of their freezing up and bursting during a cold winter. If the loft floor is itself insulated, run the insulation

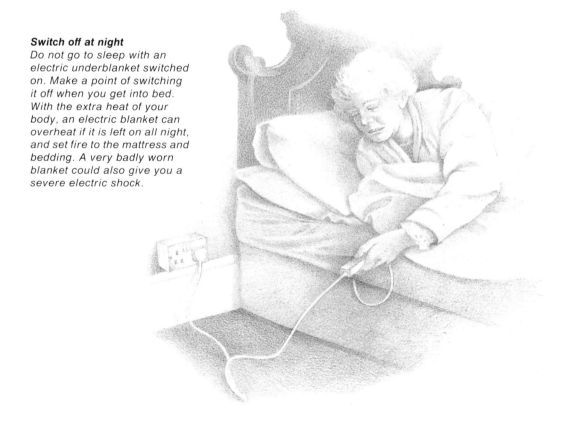

Switch off at night
Do not go to sleep with an electric underblanket switched on. Make a point of switching it off when you get into bed. With the extra heat of your body, an electric blanket can overheat if it is left on all night, and set fire to the mattress and bedding. A very badly worn blanket could also give you a severe electric shock.

over the top of the tank and leave a gap in the insulation underneath to allow some warmth to rise from the house.

• Use either a properly fitted loft ladder or extending steps to gain access to the loft. Do not try to jump up from the top of an ordinary pair of steps.

Stairs and landings

One in ten home accidents are falls from stairs – and about a third of these falls involve children under five.

• Stair and landing carpets should be in good condition and firmly fastened – people may trip on loose or worn carpet.

• There should be at least one firm, continuous handrail on the staircase. If there are old people in the house, fit one on each side. Ensure that stairs are well lit, with two-way switches so that lights can be put on from either floor.

• Replace horizontal rails on a staircase or banister with vertical rails (close together so

that a child cannot stick his head through them) or board them over.

• Consider fitting boards to the back of each tread on an open-riser staircase so that the gap is too narrow for a child to put his head through.

• Fit safety gates at the top and bottom of the staircase to prevent toddlers falling down the stairs or climbing them without supervision.

• Do not put a glass door at the bottom of a staircase – anyone falling into it could break it and suffer cuts on top of other injuries.

• Never put or leave loose objects on the stairs – if you tread on them you will almost certainly stumble, and may fall.

Garden

Gardens and other areas outside, such as garages, are the most dangerous places of all. They account for more than 420,000 accidents a year in Britain – about one in seven of the total.

• Keep the garden path in good repair. Ensure that there are no loose or uneven stones on which people may trip.

• Do not leave tools such as rakes lying about.

• If you have young children, enclose or cover any garden pond or water butt. A child can drown in even a very shallow pool.

• Do not let a child use a lawn mower. If you are using a mower, keep children away.

• Never light a bonfire with paraffin or petrol. Keep a bonfire under control.

• If children are likely to play in your garden, check that there are no poisonous trees or

Making stairs safe
Old people should have two firm, continuous handrails to help them on the stairs. Keep the stairs well lit; dark areas can cause an elderly person to misjudge a step – and fall. The very young are also at risk on stairs. Every year, about 100,000 toddlers in Britain are injured on them – and some die. To cut this risk, fit safety gates top and bottom. Teach toddlers to climb down backwards, on all fours.

plants such as laburnum, deadly nightshade, yew or privet. The berries of all these plants can be dangerous to children.

• Keep garden gates locked or bolted high up so that young children cannot open them and run out into the street.

Doors

• When the house is unoccupied, or at night, keep all internal doors closed. In the event of fire breaking out, this will help to slow the spread of the flames.

• Fit safety locks on external doors so that young children cannot run outside.

• Glass doors should be fitted with safety glass – either toughened or laminated. Ordinary glass can shatter into lethal shards. If this is not possible, cover the glass with clear plastic film, available from DIY shops; it will prevent the glass from shattering if it breaks.

• If the glass in a door is clear, stick coloured tape or transfers onto the glass so that it is clearly visible when the door is closed.

Where to store poisonous substances
Many DIY and household products, including turpentine, some glues, and oven cleaners, are poisonous. Lock them away out of reach of children. Do not leave them under the sink.

Take steps to be safe
Use a stepladder if you have to climb when working around the house. Even to change a bulb, take the time to set up a ladder. Do not be tempted to take shortcuts by standing on a chair or stool. They are less stable than a stepladder, and you have nothing to hold onto if you lose your balance.

Storms and high winds

Strong winds – even those well below hurricane force – can cause considerable damage, ripping tiles from roofs, dislodging chimney stacks and tearing down power cables and telephone wires. However, most well-constructed houses in good repair suffer little damage until winds reach speeds of about 47mph (75km/h).

On the Beaufort Scale this is Force 9 – a strong gale. Television weather maps usually show predicted wind direction and speed. The direction is shown by a black arrow with the speed marked in miles per hour.

Preparing for a storm

• Move indoors anything outside – such as garden tools or toys – that might blow about. This includes children's slides, unless they are very securely fixed.
• Secure dustbin lids and the lids of fuel bunkers with rope or wire. Make sure cloches, cold-frame lids and greenhouse windows are securely fastened.
• Close windows and doors tightly, especially those on the side facing the wind. If the storm is likely to be particularly severe, consider reinforcing the inside of windows with boards or heavy furniture. If the windows have external shutters, close them.
• Put candles, matches and torches close to hand in case the electricity is cut off. If you have camping equipment – a stove, say, or a gas lamp – get it out and keep it handy.
• Have buckets ready in case the roof starts to leak, and boarding, hammer and nails to shore up any window that is blown in.
• If you are expecting a thunderstorm, unplug electrical appliances where possible, including standard or table lamps. If you have an outside or attic TV aerial, unplug it at the wall socket if there is one, or else at the back of the set.
• If your home is prone to flooding in heavy rain, improvise sandbags – strong plastic bags, for instance, filled with any sand, soil or gravel to hand. Use the bags to line the bottoms of doors and low windows (see *What to do if you are caught in a flood*, page 331).

If a window is blown in

Wind and rain can wreak havoc in a room with a broken window.
• Move valuable objects, and anything else that can be shifted, to another room.
• Block the window with boarding or heavy furniture.
• Do not touch any electrical switches or appliances if you are wet or standing in water.

If tiles are blown off the roof

• Do not go outside to inspect the damage until the storm has eased. More tiles may come spinning off the roof onto you.
• If water starts coming through the roof, move everything from rooms likely to be flooded.
• Put buckets or bowls under the drips.

• If you can get access to the attic directly beneath the leaking area, place the buckets there. Set them on joists or on boards across the joists – not on the ceiling itself. Otherwise, the weight of the water or water splashing over the edge of the bucket may weaken the plaster and bring the ceiling down.

Leaks from outside

If a leak through the ceiling becomes apparent during heavy rain, it is probably coming through from outside. Remember, though, that the point from which the water drips is unlikely to be directly below where it is getting in.
• Go up into the loft and find the source by tracking the path the water has taken to its highest point.
• If the leak is through damaged or missing tiles or slates, or through a hole in the roofing felt, call a roofing specialist or builder (consult *Yellow Pages*) and have the tiles, slates or roofing felt replaced.
• If there is a delay, you can make a temporary repair with a sheet of strong plastic.
• Return to the loft and slide the top edge of the sheet of plastic up as far as possible under the tiles above the hole. Tuck it up tightly.
• Tuck the sides of the sheet tightly under the edges of the tiles on either side of the hole.
• Push the bottom edge of the sheet out through the hole and over the tiles below the hole, so that water is directed farther down the roof, where the tiles are sound.
• Try to allow at least 12in (300mm) overlap beyond the damaged area on all four edges of the sheet, and fix the sheet in place with

PATCHING A HOLE IN THE ROOF

1 *Cut a sheet of plastic at least 12in (300mm) larger than the hole on all four sides. Slide the top edge between the roof battens and the tiles.*

HOW TO AVOID STORM DAMAGE

- Check that guttering and drains are kept clear of leaves and debris.
- Have a builder check tiles, aerial fixings and chimney pointing regularly. Make sure that windows and doors fit properly, and that the catches and locks are not loose.
- If you live in an exposed position, consider having a lightning conductor fitted.
- If there are any large old trees in your garden that could fall on the house, have them looked over by a tree surgeon.
- Cut back any branches on trees or shrubs that might flap against windows in a storm.
- Check that neighbours' trees are safe, too. If any appear to be dangerous, report their condition to the owner in writing. This will strengthen your position later if a tree does fall and you want to claim compensation from the neighbour or his insurance company.
- After a storm, check around the house for any signs of damage – loose or fallen tiles, for instance – and get them repaired.
- After a snowstorm, make a point also of checking in your attic to see whether snow has been driven in under the tiles or slates.
- If snow has got in, dig it out while it is still frozen, and take it outside at once. Otherwise, when it melts it could cause considerable damage in the house – even bringing down an entire ceiling, for example.

waterproof tape, or by tying its corners to the rafters with wire, or by tacking it to rafters.
- If the hole is large, the plastic may also need to be supported from below by a length of wood nailed to the rafters.
- Catch any remaining drips in a bucket and have the roof repaired properly later.

If a chimney pot is blown off
Rubble and tiles may come down the chimney if a chimney pot is blown off. The falling pot will probably damage the roof as well on its way down, letting water into the attic.

- Put out any fires caused by the scattering of a fire in the grate.
- Prevent debris from pouring down the chimney onto the carpet by blocking the fireplace with boards or the fireguard.
- When the debris has stopped falling, seal the base of the chimney with cardboard, bits of wood and newspaper to keep out the rain.
- Do the same in other rooms with fireplaces served by the same chimney stack in case other pots on the stack have been weakened.
- Check in the attic for leaks.
- Call a builder after the storm ends.

2 *Tuck the sheet's sides between battens and tiles on either side and then push the bottom out through the hole and over the tiles below.*

3 *Fix the sheet in place with tape, wire or nails. Nail a length of wood if necessary to the battens above and below to support it.*

COPING WITH THE COLD

Draught-proofing and insulation are the two most effective ways of keeping a house warmer during severe winters. Most DIY shops stock strips of metal and foam with which doors and windows can be lined to cut down the loss of heat through draughts.

Insulating a house – through double glazing, or by filling the cavities in the walls with a material such as plastic foam – is a more expensive and specialised job, best done during the summer when the specialist firms involved are likely to be less busy.

Walking on snow and ice

Falling over on hard ice or snow can be extremely dangerous, particularly for young children (who have less strength in their necks and so are more likely to damage their heads if they fall) and for the elderly (because their bones are more brittle).

It is possible, though, to cut the risk of falling by adopting some of the techniques used by skiers and mountaineers.
• Wear shoes or boots with a deep tread to improve your grip.
• On the flat, walk with your legs more apart than usual – rather like the gait of a sailor – and take smaller steps than usual.
• Avoid walking on icy patches at all, if possible. But if you cannot avoid a patch of ice, try to find a handhold to help you across – a garden wall, say.
• On slopes, walk with your toes pointing inwards. On each step, stamp your foot down firmly and at a slight angle so that the outside edge of your shoe digs into the snow and forms a small step.
• On steep downward slopes, bend your knees as well. It helps to improve your grip.

How to cut heating costs

Elderly people, particularly, need to keep warm in winter to avoid the risk of hypothermia (a potentially fatal loss of body heat). Each winter, more than 350 pensioners in Britain die of hypothermia. More than 30,000 other elderly people die each winter of diseases such as pneumonia, chronic bronchitis and flu – all diseases to which the body is much more vulnerable in the cold.

To help pensioners on a tight budget, welfare organisations recommend these tips on how to keep warm economically:
• Wear several layers of clothing. Several thin layers are warmer than one thick one.
• Wear a night cap at night – and gloves and socks too, if necessary.
• Buy a small thermometer to hang on the wall, and keep an eye on it; elderly people often do not realise how cold they are. The ideal temperature for an elderly person's living room is 21°C (70°F).
• Stick kitchen foil, shiny side out, to the wall behind radiators to reflect heat into the room. This is particularly valuable where the radiator is against an outside wall.
• Fix small shelves above radiators to push warm air towards the centre of the room.
• Hang a heavy curtain inside the front door to make the hall warmer, and a small piece of carpet over the letter box.
• As an economical substitute for double glazing, attach plastic sheeting to the inside of windows. Fix it with masking tape, double-sided tape, a wooden frame or magnetic strips. But make sure the sheeting is easily detachable in case of fire.
• Try to cook complete meals in the oven all at once to save on fuel bills. Use a bowl instead of running hot water for washing your hands or dishes. Rinse dishes in cold water.
• Eating properly helps the body to keep itself warmer. Have a bowl of hot porridge for breakfast to give yourself a warm start to the day; and try to eat fish, eggs, cheese, meat, potatoes and green vegetables regularly. Eat at least one good meal a day.

Getting financial help

Nearly a million pensioners in Britain do not claim all the government and council benefits they are entitled to. Councils sometimes offer grants to help to pay for loft insulation, for instance, and for lagging water tanks. Gas and electricity boards have budget schemes to help to spread the cost of fuel bills through the year, and financial help with heating bills is available to pensioners who qualify for supplementary benefit from the Department of Health and Social Security.

To check on what you – or an elderly relative or neighbour – are entitled to, contact your local Citizens Advice Bureau (listed in the phone book under 'C') or your nearest Age Concern Group (listed in the phone book either under 'A' or under 'Old People's Welfare'). If no local group is listed, write to the organisation's national headquarters: Age Concern England, 60 Pitcairn Road, Mitcham, Surrey CR4 3LL.

Alternatively, contact your local council, your gas and electricity boards, and the DHSS direct. Even if you have applied for these grants and benefits before, and been turned down, check again because the qualifying thresholds change frequently.

Working at a height

At least 18,000 accidents a year in British homes involve ladders of various kinds, or scaffolding.

The safest way to work at a height in any situation – up a ladder, say, or in a tree – is to follow the 'three holds' principle used by mountaineers and rock climbers. Always make sure that you have at least three secure holds: two foot-holds and one hand-hold, or one foot-hold and two hand-holds. Do not leave any of the holds until your free hand or foot is secure on a hold to replace it.

• Check ladders or steps before use for cracked or rotten rungs or loose joints. If a stepladder or extension ladder has ropes, make sure they are in good condition.

• Varnish wooden ladders to protect them, but do not paint them. Paint could conceal developing cracks or weak spots in the wood.

• When you use a ladder, set it up so that its base is between a quarter and one-third of its height away from the object it rests against. The base of a 20ft (6m) ladder should be 5-7ft (1.5-2m) away from the wall or tree it is propped on. Any closer, and you risk pulling the ladder over backwards when you climb it; any farther, and you risk the base sliding outwards.

• On soft ground, rest the foot of the ladder on a wide board. Nail a batten firmly to the board to stop the ladder slipping off.

• On hard ground, lay something heavy – bricks or a bag of cement – against the foot. If possible, have someone hold the foot of the ladder steady as well.

• Do not hang out sideways to reach the work – when painting, for example. Move the ladder to suit the work.

• Make sure the top of the ladder is at least three rungs higher than the highest point you want to reach, so that the top is always within reach of your hands.

THE SAFE WAY TO CARRY A LADDER
Carry a ladder vertically to avoid accidentally hitting anyone behind you. Bend your knees slightly and, with one hand, grip the rung just below waist level. With the other hand, grip the rung at eye level. Rest the ladder against your shoulder and straighten up. Keep the ladder steady with the upper hand.

HOW TO RAISE AN EXTENDED LADDER
Extend the ladder while it is still on the ground and wedge its foot against the wall. Lift the top over your head and push the ladder up by moving forwards and working your hands down it. When the top is against the wall, pull the bottom out until it is at least a quarter of the ladder's length away from the wall.

175

• Do not climb a ladder while carrying a heavy load in one hand. Tie the load to a rope, carry the end of the rope up the ladder, then haul the load up once you are in position.

• For roof work, use a roofing ladder or crawling board which hooks over the ridge. Never rely on the gutter for support; it may break.

• Do not lean any ladder against guttering either – use a stay to hold it clear.

• For jobs requiring a lot of sideways movement, such as replacing gutters or pointing, hire a scaffold platform or use two stepladders with one or more planks laid across their rungs.

• Use the rungs rather than the top to improve the platform's stability and to give you something to grab hold of if you lose your balance. For extra security, you can suspend two handrails – made, for example, from thin bits of metal piping – between higher rungs or the tops of the ladders.

• Lash the planks to the rungs and to one side of the ladders to stop them slipping.

• If the planks have not been used for some time, test each one's strength at ground level first by putting a large block under each end and standing in the middle. Jump up and down on the plank. If it sags worryingly or creaks, do not use it.

THREE WAYS TO STEADY A LADDER

1 Secure the foot of a ladder by tying it to stakes. On uneven ground, level the ladder up by putting a wide board with a batten nailed to it under one side of the ladder. On soft ground, put the board under both sides.

SAFETY ON A LADDER
Hold onto the ladder's rungs, not the sides; if you slip, you are less likely to lose your grip. While you work, hook your paint can or tool bag onto a rung so that you always have one hand free to hold on. Never hang out sideways to work. Move the ladder instead.

WHEN TO USE A ROOFING LADDER
Never rely on guttering to support you for roof work; it is not strong enough. A roofing ladder, though – available from most DIY hire shops – will bear your weight. Push the ladder up the roof on the wheels at its top. Then turn it over and hook it over the ridge.

2 *Another way to hold a ladder steady is to anchor it by passing some rope around a rung and tying it to a wooden batten secured behind a window frame or letterbox. Nail pieces of wood to the batten to stop it sliding sideways.*

3 *If you have to lean a ladder against a window, lash a strong wooden batten, longer than the window is wide, to the top of the ladder. When you put the ladder up, rest the batten on the wall on either side of the window.*

IMPROVISING A PLATFORM
If you have to move sideways a lot while working, make a platform by suspending one or more planks between stepladders. Lash the plank both to the rungs at each end and to one side of each ladder to stop it from shifting around either lengthways or sideways.

Do's and don'ts of using tools

Tools are safe as long as they are used and stored correctly, and kept in good condition and well out of the reach of children.

Yet about 120,000 people have to get hospital treatment every year in Britain as a result of DIY accidents.

Around 70,000 of these accidents are caused by or involve the use of hand tools, ranging from circular saws and blowtorches to screwdrivers, knives, pliers and hammers.

The other 50,000 or so accidents involve the equipment or materials used with tools or in DIY work generally, such as ladders, vices, machinery, paints, adhesives and solvents.

Anyone who plans to use tools, especially power tools, for DIY work in the home should make himself or herself familiar beforehand with the positions of concealed water pipes and electric cables. The effort required to draw up a detailed plan is much less than the risk involved in cutting a wire accidentally or the trouble of repairing a hidden pipe.

Hand tools

• Keep sharp-edged tools sheathed and out of the reach of children when not in use, preferably under lock and key.
• Keep tools sharp – blunt tools are dangerous because they require more force to use and thus are more likely to slip.
• Protect the sharp ends of tools such as chisels and bradawls when carrying them in a toolbox. Cover them with fitted plastic covers, wrap them with several layers of cloth or push old bottle corks onto the blades or points.
• Similarly, cover the blades of saws, axes and similar tools when carrying them about.
• Make sure hammer heads are firmly attached to their handles. If necessary, replace the wedges.
• The metal head of a cold chisel roughens when the tool is struck, and sharp fragments may fly off in use. Grind or file these rough edges away regularly.
• Make sure that the material you are working on – a piece of wood or metal, say – is firmly held in a vice or by clamps so that both hands are free to manipulate the tools.
• In the garden, never leave a rake or fork lying down with the prongs up. If you tread on the prongs the handle can fly up and strike you in the face.
• Keep sharp-edged garden tools such as shears, secateurs and billhooks well away from your fingers and legs while in use.

Power tools

• Keep power tools unplugged except when in use, so that they cannot be started accidentally.
• For the same reason, unplug power tools before changing accessories, cleaning, adjusting or lubricating.
• With petrol-driven tools, remove the lead from the spark plug before working on them to remove any chance of the motor starting up by accident. Otherwise, a motor mower, for example, may spring into life when the blades are turned by hand.
• Wear protective goggles when sparks or chips are liable to fly – when using a grinding wheel, say, or an electric saw. Wear them too when working on bricks or concrete with a cold chisel or a hammer drill.
• Tie back long hair and avoid wearing loose clothing – both may become caught in revolving machinery.
• Do not defeat the makers' efforts to keep power tools safe by, for example, tying back the guard on a circular saw.
• Do not use electric tools outdoors in the rain – the wet may cause a short circuit and give you a severe shock.
• When using extension leads, plug into the house power socket last so that there are no unguarded live socket ends lying around. For the same reason, disconnect at the house socket

USING AN ELECTRIC LAWN MOWER
Hang an electric mower's cable over one shoulder to keep it behind you, and make sure there is nothing it could catch on. If you are on a slope, mow across it – not up and down.

first when the work is finished. Check cables, extension leads and connectors regularly for signs of wear or cracked insulation.

• Never use taped joints on loose power cables indoors or out – they may pull apart and are not waterproof. Use purpose-made waterproof connectors instead.

• When using a mains-powered hedge trimmer, lawn mower or grass trimmer, keep the cable behind you. Make sure the cable has a clear run so that it does not become snagged while you are working.

• Push a mower away from you – never pull it – and mow across slopes, not up them. That way there is less risk of the mower running over your foot.

• When using mowers and trimmers, always wear stout shoes and trousers. Wear goggles when using trimmers – they can throw up small stones and dust.

• Remember that the blade of an electric mower carries on spinning for several seconds after the power is switched off. Unplug it before clearing debris from around the blade.

• Hold electric mower trigger switches on by hand – never tie them down.

• Consider buying a circuit breaker (one type is called a residual current circuit breaker – RCCB) for use with electrical equipment. Circuit breakers are designed to cut off the mains power if there is a short circuit or the user gets an electric shock.

• Look out for a symbol showing two squares, one inside the other, when buying electrically powered tools. It means that the tool is doubly insulated.

Using a chain saw

• Apply the saw to the top of the work you are cutting. Do not cut from underneath – unless you are cutting a piece of wood supported at both ends. Otherwise the weight of the wood will tend to close the cut, gripping the saw.

• Cut using the part of the saw closest to the motor end. If you use the tip, you may lose control of the saw.

• Do not carry the saw about with the engine running, even if the blade is disengaged.

• Keep the chain at the correct tension, or it may fly off and cause a serious accident.

• Sharpen the teeth frequently, preferably every time you use the saw. Blunt teeth may make you use too much pressure.

• Before refilling the tank of a petrol-driven saw, make sure the engine is cold, or petrol spilt onto it may ignite.

• If you have a can of petrol with you, keep it well away from the saw. The exhaust will occasionally emit sparks.

• Wear sensible clothing: thick trousers and stout shoes (preferably with reinforced toecaps), and no loose sleeves. Wear goggles to protect your eyes against chips and sawdust.

• Always work in a clear area, so that there are

no twigs or brambles to catch the blade or the trigger. Hold the saw with both hands.

• If you have an assistant, make sure he or she keeps at least 10yds (9m) away, out of range of any flying chips.

• Always disconnect the spark-plug lead or mains lead before cleaning or adjusting the saw. Have the saw serviced regularly and the cutting chain checked for signs of wear.

Hiring tools from hire shops

Specialised power tools – such as jack hammers, cultivators, disc cutters and belt sanders – can be hired by the day from hire shops. This is a convenient way of getting the use of expensive tools that you need only occasionally. But do not forget that many of these tools are potentially dangerous.

Do not even attempt to use them unless you know exactly how to handle them. Get the hire shop to give you clear instructions and preferably a demonstration, too.

HOW TO USE A CHAIN SAW
Saw from the top downwards to cut the unsupported end off a log. Cut with the part of the blade closest to the motor. That way it is easier to hold the saw steady.

In the home and at work

How to remove stains

The best way to remove a stain depends on what has been spilt and what it has been spilt on. But one rule applies to any stain anywhere: try to deal with it quickly, before it dries. Once dry, most stains become more difficult to remove.

Remember, too, that many stain-removing agents are poisonous, flammable or both (see chart, this page).

Read carefully any instructions on proprietary preparations. Never store them in unmarked bottles, and keep them out of the reach of children. Work out of doors if possible, or in a well-ventilated place.

• The first step in treating a stain is to blot, lightly scrape or vacuum the material in order to clear as much of the stain as possible before further treatment.

• For grease stains, shake on plenty of talcum powder, powdered starch or a similar absorbent agent. When the worst of the grease has been absorbed, brush clear.

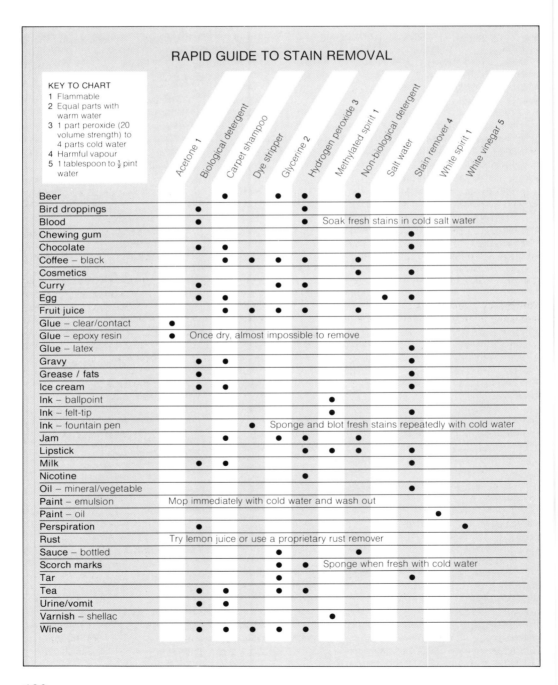

RAPID GUIDE TO STAIN REMOVAL

KEY TO CHART
1 Flammable
2 Equal parts with warm water
3 1 part peroxide (20 volume strength) to 4 parts cold water
4 Harmful vapour
5 1 tablespoon to ½ pint water

	Acetone 1	Biological detergent	Carpet shampoo	Dye stripper	Glycerine 2	Hydrogen peroxide 3	Methylated spirit 1	Non-biological detergent	Salt water	Stain remover 4	White spirit 1	White vinegar 5
Beer		●		●	●			●				
Bird droppings	●					●						
Blood	●					●	Soak fresh stains in cold salt water					
Chewing gum										●		
Chocolate	●	●								●		
Coffee – black			●	●	●	●		●				
Cosmetics								●		●		
Curry	●				●	●						
Egg	●	●							●	●		
Fruit juice		●	●	●	●			●				
Glue – clear/contact	●											
Glue – epoxy resin	●	Once dry, almost impossible to remove										
Glue – latex										●		
Gravy	●	●								●		
Grease / fats	●									●		
Ice cream	●	●								●		
Ink – ballpoint							●					
Ink – felt-tip							●			●		
Ink – fountain pen				●	Sponge and blot fresh stains repeatedly with cold water							
Jam		●		●	●			●				
Lipstick						●	●			●		
Milk	●	●								●		
Nicotine						●						
Oil – mineral/vegetable										●		
Paint – emulsion	Mop immediately with cold water and wash out											
Paint – oil											●	
Perspiration		●										●
Rust	Try lemon juice or use a proprietary rust remover											
Sauce – bottled				●			●					
Scorch marks				●		●	Sponge when fresh with cold water					
Tar				●						●		
Tea	●	●			●	●						
Urine/vomit	●	●										
Varnish – shellac							●					
Wine	●	●	●	●	●							

- For other stains, sponge or rinse through with cold or lukewarm water – never hot water, which could fix the stain.
- Blot carpets or upholstery frequently, while you work on getting out the worst of the stain, to avoid overwetting them.
- What you should do next to complete the job depends upon what caused the stain, and what will dissolve it (see chart).
- Not all stains can be removed. If in doubt, and for delicate and valuable articles, just blot the stain and do not attempt any further treatment at home. Instead, seek advice from a professional cleaning firm.
- In general, stains on suede and leather, waterproof fabrics or rich materials such as velvets should be left to a professional.
- With other fabrics and surfaces, start with the mildest treatment and test first on a hidden area. Some solvents can damage certain materials, such as rayon.
- Use a white absorbent pad for applying solvents. Where possible, work from the underside of the stain, holding another pad on the top side to absorb it.
- Dab at the stain. Rubbing can spread the mark and damage the surface. Work inwards from the edge to avoid spreading the stain.
- If a stain has become dried, try to soften it. Rub in some glycerine solution (equal amounts of glycerine and warm water) and leave it for an hour. Then sponge with cold water.
- Once the substance has been loosened, treat it as a freshly made stain.

Emergency alternatives

If you find in an emergency that you do not have the substances mentioned in the chart, there are other ways, using more common household items, to get rid of some stains.
- If somebody spills wine, for example, on your carpet, flush it out immediately with a soda siphon or by sponging with warm water.
- If you get wine on a washable fabric – a tablecloth, say – immediately sprinkle it with salt to stop the stain spreading. Then, as soon as possible afterwards, stretch the stained area over a bowl and pour hot water through the fabric. If it is red wine, you can also pour white wine over the stain; this will make it easier to remove.
- If a pet or a baby urinates on your carpet, immediately give the area a good squirt with a soda siphon. Blot up the soda water. Then sponge with warm water with a few drops of antiseptic added.
- Use lemon juice for tea and coffee stains on washable fabrics. Rub the juice into the stained area and then wash the fabric in warm soapy water.
- If you get chewing gum on your clothes, put the article of clothing in a plastic bag and leave it in a freezer until the gum has hardened. You will then be able to pick it off easily.

Trapped in a lift

When a lift breaks down with people trapped inside, the greatest danger is from panic.
- Stay calm and try to reassure anyone who shows signs of panic.
- Explain that you and they are not in danger, that help can be summoned in several ways, and that there is no possibility of the lift falling out of control down the shaft.
- Tell the others in the lift that automatic brakes, usually fitted under the floor of the lift, prevent this happening by clamping onto the steel guide rails that run down each side of the lift shaft. The brakes will work even if there is a power cut and the lights go out.
- Use the alarm button or the telephone inside the lift to call for help.
- If there is no alarm system, bang on the doors and shout. Use a shoe to bang with, if your hand hurts.
- Once you contact someone outside, explain what has happened and ask him to get expert help at once.
- If there is no lift engineer immediately available, lift rescues are often handled by the fire brigade. Tell your contact to dial 999. Firemen will usually winch the lift up or down to the nearest floor, then open the doors. Manual overrides enable them to do this even when the power supply has been cut off.
- Never try to escape from the lift without help from an expert outside.
- Do not even try to force the inner lift doors open. Even if you managed to do so, it is most unlikely that you would be able to reach and open the outer doors onto a landing, let alone climb out safely. There is also the danger that you might slip on the oil and grease that accumulates on the outside of a lift. Having shoes with a good grip or bare feet is no guarantee that you would be able to balance steadily.
- Do not be tempted, either, to climb out of any hatch there may be in the lift's ceiling. When a lift hatch is opened, an electrical contact prevents the lift from moving. But if the open hatch falls shut by accident the lift could move without warning, throwing you off balance. In the darkness of the shaft, you could also trip over the lift cables or slip on grease and fall off the roof of the lift.

If you cannot raise the alarm

It is very rare for calls for help to go unanswered for long, particularly in a block of flats where there are other people within earshot. But in an office block late at night or at the start of a weekend, it may happen that nobody passes near the lift for hours – or even days.
- The safest course in this situation is to stay put, stay calm and wait. You may get hungry, thirsty and hot – but you will survive.
- Listen for a caretaker and try to attract his attention. If that fails, wait for the building to open again, then bang on the doors and shout for help.

In the home and at work

Intruders in your home

The vast majority of people who are likely to visit your home are law-abiding citizens. But it is worth being cautious always, just in case the visitor is a thief or a confidence trickster.

If a stranger calls at your door
• Use a peephole to vet anyone who knocks at your door and keep the chain on the door if it is someone you do not know.
• Never let in strangers who call unexpectedly until you have checked their credentials.
• If the caller gives you a telephone number to ring, check it in the directory yourself – it may be that of an accomplice. Ask the caller to wait outside, with the door closed and the chain on, while you make the call.
• If you are still in doubt about the caller's identity, ring the local police station and explain your suspicions. Suspect anybody who protests at your caution.
• Remember that the longer you draw out the process of identification, the better your chances of scaring off a potential wrongdoer.
• If in any doubt, refuse entry politely but firmly.
• Always be fully clothed before opening the door. Close the door on a stranger before going for your purse or to make a phone call.
• If you live in a block of flats, do not automatically 'buzz open' the main door if a stranger calls your apartment on the intercom with a plausible excuse.
• Do not hold the door open for a stranger whose arrival coincides with your departure.

If you return to see signs of a break-in
• If you notice or suspect that somebody is inside your home when you arrive at the gate – you see movement, perhaps, or notice an open door – avoid entering the house at all.
• If you have driven in by car, back out of the drive again and drive off. The intruder may think you were just turning round.

• If you are on foot, walk on down the pavement.
• Go to a neighbour's house at once and call the police. Follow the same drill if you find strangers outside your house.

If you get indoors to find a prowler inside
• Ask the intruder what he wants.
• Do not, the police advise, give any impression that you intend to fight over money or possessions – you may get hurt. Try not to anger or provoke him.
• Memorise the intruder's appearance, and call the police as soon as he has gone.

If you wake up to hear a burglar in the house
• If you wake at night to hear an intruder downstairs – or if you hear someone trying to break in – put all the lights on and make a lot of noise by moving about. Most burglars will choose to flee empty-handed rather than risk coming face to face with their intended victim.
• Do not go downstairs. Dial the police from your bedroom if possible. Find something that

HOW TO IMPROVISE WINDOW LOCKS

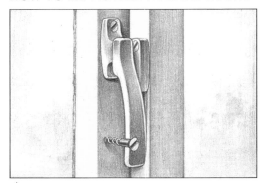

1 *A screw makes an effective lock. Sink it about 1in (25mm) into the wood beside the catch.*

USING A PLASTIC BLOCK-JOINT

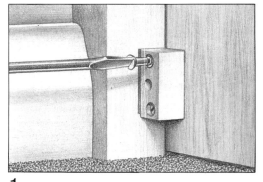

1 *To make an inexpensive lock that can be left in place, fit block-joints in the angle between a door or window, and its frame.*

DOWN A KNOTTED SHEET AT 76
Tied up, gagged and blindfolded by armed, masked burglars, and locked in a first-floor bedroom of their Wiltshire home with the phone wires cut, two elderly ladies seemed helpless on the night of October 23, 1984.

But 76-year-old Miss Dorothy Watson never thought of giving up. Instead, like others who have survived crises, she made use of inner strengths: courage and a cool head.

She managed to untie herself, and knotted sheets into a rope. She then climbed down the sheets to fetch help for her 86-year-old friend, Miss Beatrice Knatchbull. Miss Watson fell when still about 10ft (3m) from the ground and broke her ankle. In spite of the pain, she crawled to a neighbour to raise the alarm. Miss Knatchbull was later rescued unhurt.

Two men were later charged with the robbery.

---

you can use as a weapon – a comb, say, a vase, knitting needle or a bunch of keys – but plan to use it only if you cannot avoid a fight (see *If you are attacked in the street*, page 336).

• If you are on your own, call out loudly to an imaginary male companion: 'Harry, there's someone in the house.'

• Look out of your window after you hear the intruder leave and try to note what he looks like, what direction he heads in and what car, if any, he gets into. Then call the police.

How to give a description to the police

Anyone who contacts the police to report a crime – an intruder, say, or someone behaving suspiciously near his or a neighbour's home – may need to give a description of the person he has seen, or of the person's vehicle. This is a checklist of details useful to police:

• Male/female
• Colour of skin
• Complexion
• Height
• Hair (colour, length, straight/curly, receding)
• Build
• Age
• Eye colour
• Glasses
• Face (long, thin, round, clean-shaven, moustache, beard)
• Marks (scars, tattoos)
• Mouth (narrow/wide)
• Dress (description of clothing)
• Any other distinguishing features (mannerisms, say, such as a limp or a stutter)

If you see a suspicious vehicle, try to note these details:

• Car/van/lorry/motorcycle
• Colour
• Registration number
• Other details (damage marks, any company name on it and so on)
• Make/model
• Body type (saloon/estate car, number of doors, soft top)
• Direction it was travelling

In the home and at work

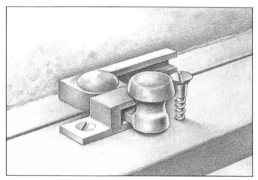

2 On a sash window, put the screw in vertically to prevent the catch being moved from outside.

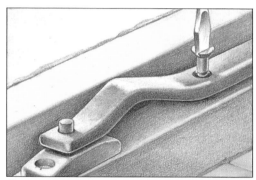

3 For extra security, put another screw through one of the holes in a window stay-bar.

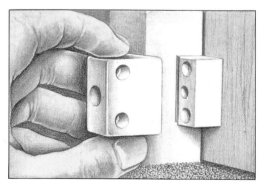

2 Screw one half of the joint to the door, the other half to the door frame. On long windows, use two joints top and bottom.

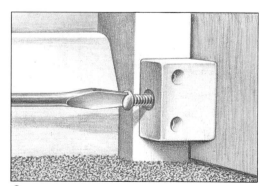

3 Once the two halves are in position, they can be left there. To undo the lock, simply remove the bolt that holds the halves together.

PROTECTING YOUR HOME

If you are going away or leaving the house for a period, the central rule is: do not advertise your absence.

• Cancel deliveries of milk and newspapers.

• Consider hiring a telephone answering service, so that your telephone gives no clue that you are absent. If you have a telephone answering machine, word your announcement as though you were merely away for an hour or two.

• Fit timeswitches (available from DIY shops) to turn your lights on at night.

• Consider using screws to make improvised locks for windows and internal doors (see pictures, pages 182-183). Fit the screws tight up against window catches to stop them being moved. Alternatively, sink the screw into a convenient part of the frame, and tie the catch to it with wire.

• Ask a neighbour to keep an eye on the house – to collect mail and other material left in the letterbox, to mow the lawn, sweep up leaves, leave footprints in the snow and generally make the house look lived in. Offer to do the same for the neighbour.

• If you are going away for only a short period, consider leaving your car locked outside. It may fool a prowling thief into thinking that the house is occupied. But if you will be away for a long holiday, remember that a dusty car may itself become an indication that the house is empty.

• Tell the local police station that you will be away. The police will then make a point of keeping an eye on the property.

How to deter burglars

Each year, around 1,120,000 buildings are burgled in Britain – an average of more than 120 every hour of the day and night. Burglaries of homes make up more than half the total. A skilled professional burglar will always find a way into a house if he wants to – and has the time. But eight out of ten burglaries are committed by unskilled and often young opportunists who are looking for easy pickings. You may deter both kinds of thieves by offering stiff resistance in the form of security devices. If a burglar has to make a lot of noise or spend a lot of time breaking in, he is likely to give up and look for an easier target elsewhere.

• Remember that windows are as vulnerable as doors. So consider fitting window locks to all windows that are on the ground floor or can be reached by an easy climb.

• Make sure that all security devices on doors and windows are fitted with strong screws or bolts. Small ones can be wrenched out of the wood by a firm shove or kick.

• The main value of burglar alarms is to deter amateur thieves. Ask local police for advice about the best type to fit.

• Do not put your name on your key ring. That way if you lose your house keys nobody will know which house they belong to (you can use a post code marking to identify them if they are handed in to the police).

• Keys should not be carried in a handbag. If it is stolen, letters or documents also in the bag could tell the thief your address.

Neighbourhood Watch: how it works

Neighbourhood Watch, Home Watch, Crime Alert and other similar schemes, which now operate in many parts of Britain, were first introduced in 1982 by the police in Cheshire. Their primary aim is to stem the rising tide of burglaries around the country by encouraging people to keep an eye out for suspicious activities near their homes – by being, in other words, good neighbours.

Police say that neighbourhoods which have joined the schemes – and announced the fact publicly by putting up stickers visible from the street – have considerably lower crime rates than similar areas which have not joined.

The schemes do not encourage people to have a go themselves if they see anyone behaving suspiciously. But the schemes do encourage householders to phone the police at once by dialling 999, or to contact their street coordinator.

As a further deterrent to thieves, police also recommend that you should mark anything valuable you own – car, bicycle, furniture, household appliances and so on – with an indelible identification. The identification, they suggest, should show your post code, along with the number of your house or flat or the first two letters of your name.

The marking can be done at home by using a do-it-yourself engraving tool or stamp, or an invisible marker (available from many hardware shops) whose ink shows up only under ultraviolet light. The presence of the marks should be advertised through stickers placed in the windows of your house.

Stickers, leaflets and detailed advice about the police Property Marking scheme, about how to join or set up a local Neighbourhood Watch, and about ways of making your home more secure, are available free of charge from the Crime Prevention Officer at your nearest police station.

Caring for a sick or injured animal

There are more pet dogs and cats in Britain than there are people in the whole of Greater London. Around the country, there are nearly 6 million dogs and about 5.5 million cats – compared with about 8 million people in the capital. In addition, there are some 500,000 domesticated horses, including 100,000 which are involved in racing.

If a pet animal becomes seriously ill or is seriously injured in an accident, the safest course is to take it to a vet as soon as possible. But you can do much to alleviate its distress before you get there by using the first aid advice given here.

In some circumstances, swift action can save the pet's life. When a cat or dog gives birth, on the other hand, the best course is to leave the mother alone, and to call a vet only if the birth seems to be going wrong.

The section that begins on these pages describes the commonest emergencies that arise with a pet dog, cat or horse, and explains how to cope with each. It also explains what to do if a swarm of bees or a colony of wasps invades your home, and how you can help an injured bird or wild animal.

How to handle an injured cat or dog
Any dog or cat which has been injured is almost certain to be in pain. As a result, even the most loving, placid pet is liable to bite or scratch, or to run off, if it is given the chance. The priority, therefore, is to get the animal under control and into a safe, escape-proof place where you can examine its injuries.
• Approach the animal slowly and carefully, talking soothingly as you do.
• If it is a dog, have with you a rope, string or bandage fastened into a noose at one end.
• Drop the noose over the dog's head and draw it tight on the neck. Lead the dog to a safe place.
• If the dog is unable to stand, slide it onto an improvised stretcher – a large blanket or towel. Get someone to help you to lift the blanket by the corners and carry the dog to a safe place.
• In the case of a cat, grasp it by the scruff of

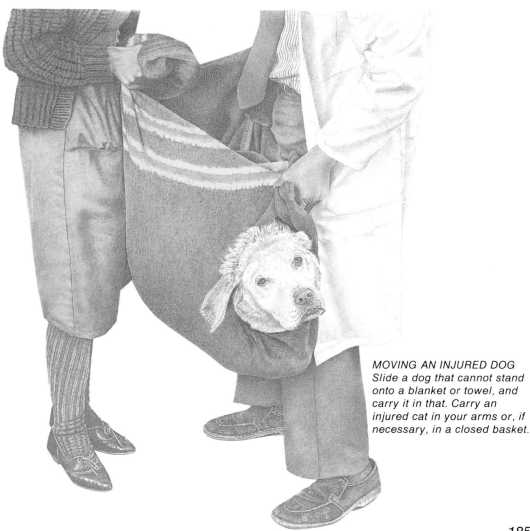

MOVING AN INJURED DOG
Slide a dog that cannot stand onto a blanket or towel, and carry it in that. Carry an injured cat in your arms or, if necessary, in a closed basket.

the neck with one hand and support its bottom with the other.

• Take it – in a closed basket, if necessary – to a safe place.

Preparing for treatment

• Before you start to examine a cat's or dog's injuries, get it onto a smooth surface such as a table or, if it is a heavy dog, on a slippery floor such as lino.

• Get someone else to help you to hold the animal – the slippery surface will stop it getting a grip and lessen its ability to escape.

• Put a collar on the animal to give yourself an easy handhold.

• Grip the animal firmly. Better still, get a helper to hold the animal so that you have both hands free to tend the injury.

• With a dog, tie a handkerchief or bandage firmly round its muzzle as well, so that it cannot open its mouth to bite.

Treating the injury

The principles of giving first aid to animals are much the same as they are for humans. Do what you can to stop the injury getting any worse, and then get professional help. This means taking the animal to a vet as soon as possible.

The commonest serious injuries are bleeding or a broken leg.

How to stop bleeding

• If an animal is bleeding badly, cover the wound with a clean pad – a piece of gauze or a handkerchief – and bind it on firmly with a bandage. If you cannot bandage the wound, hold the pad firmly in place by hand.

• If the wound is on a leg, and pressure does not stop the bleeding, apply a tourniquet above the wound. A bandage tightened by twisting a stick is effective. Tighten the tourniquet only until the bleeding stops, and relax it every 10-15 minutes to avoid the risk of gangrene.

HOW TO PUT ON A TOURNIQUET
To stop bleeding from a bad wound, tie a bandage around the limb above the injury. Slide a stick through the loop and twist it to tighten the bandage until the bleeding stops. You must loosen the tourniquet for at least a minute every 10-15 minutes to avoid the risk of gangrene.

• Get the animal to a vet at once. If possible, have someone phone the surgery to alert the staff that an emergency case is on the way.

How to treat a broken leg

If a leg is lying at an awkward angle, it may mean that a bone is broken.
• Stop any bleeding.
• Ease the leg into as comfortable a position as possible. Warn whoever is holding the animal before you move the leg. The pain may make the animal try to bite or scratch.
• Straighten the leg gently into a more normal position. Then splint it by bandaging it gently but firmly to a piece of wood or hardboard of roughly the same shape as the leg.
• Take the animal to a vet.

Giving medicine to a cat or dog

Whenever you have to give pills or any other kind of medicine to a pet, prepare in much the same way as you would when examining a pet for injuries. Put a cat or small dog on a smooth-topped table. Put a large dog on a smooth floor with its back to a wall. Ask someone else to help you to hold the animal still.

Giving pills

• With a cat, grasp its head from behind with one hand and tilt the head up. Use the other hand to open the mouth by pressing down on the front of the lower jaw. Push the pill to the back of the tongue, then close the mouth and hold it shut until you see the cat swallowing. Rub the throat if necessary to encourage swallowing.
• With a dog, use one hand to hold it across the top of its muzzle just in front of the eyes, and push your thumb into the side of its mouth. Push up on the roof of its mouth. Use the middle

HOW TO GIVE A CAT A PILL
Tilt the cat's head well up with one hand, and with the other press down on the lower jaw to open its mouth. Push the pill to the back of the tongue, then close the mouth. Hold it shut until the cat swallows.

finger of the other hand to hold down the front of the lower jaw while you push the pill to the back of the tongue. Close the mouth and hold the jaws shut until the pill is swallowed. Rub the throat if necessary to encourage this.

HOW TO GIVE A DOG A PILL
Hold the muzzle across the top and slide your thumb into the side of the mouth. Push up with your thumb. Pull the jaw down and put the pill on the back of the tongue, then shut the mouth.

187

Giving liquid medicine
- Buy a disposable plastic syringe without a needle. They are available from vets and most chemists.
- Load the medicine into the syringe.
- Hold the animal firmly and calm it by talking gently to it.
- With a cat, push the nozzle into the side of the mouth behind the large canine teeth and trickle the liquid in slowly. Hold the mouth up while you do this so that the medicine does not dribble out.
- With a dog, push the nozzle in where the lips meet at the side of the mouth. Pull the cheek back with one finger and hold the mouth up while you trickle the liquid in slowly.

Giving eye drops or eye ointment
- With both a cat and a dog, ask someone to hold the animal's head steady, or – if you are confident you will not be clawed or bitten – hold it steady against your body.
- Use two fingers above and below the eye to open the lids, and apply the drop or ointment directly onto the eyeball.

Giving ear drops or ear ointment
- With either pet, hold the ear flap with one hand to expose the ear canal and administer the medicine directly into the ear.
- Once the medicine is in, massage the base of the ear gently to ensure that the medicine gets well down into the ear.

- Never try to clean out the inner part of the ear canal of a cat or dog. You will damage the ear no matter how gentle you are, and the animal will resent the pain you cause.

When an animal has a fit
Fits are not uncommon in dogs; they are rarer in cats. They can have any of a number of causes, including brain tumours and epilepsy. With either animal, the basic principle of treatment is not to interfere more than necessary.
- Make sure the pet is not in danger – from knocking things over, for example.
- Try to keep it quiet and cool. Draw the curtains in the room to reduce the light.
- Get it to a vet as soon as you can, but do not try to move it while it is still convulsing.
- Take care when you do move it. An animal that is ill is more likely to bite or scratch unexpectedly.

If your cat or dog is poisoned
Ordinary vomiting and bad diarrhoea in pets are only rarely signs of poisoning. The usual symptoms of genuine poisoning are persistent vomiting and diarrhoea, often combined with shivering tremors or convulsions, leading later to coma.
- If your pet is already in a coma, get veterinary help at once.
- If your pet is still conscious and you know that it has swallowed a corrosive poison, such as acid or caustic soda, wash the mouth out

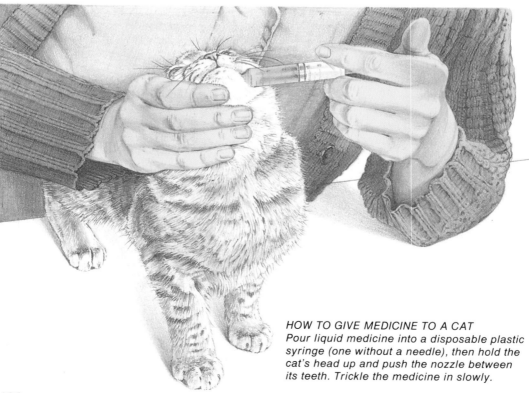

HOW TO GIVE MEDICINE TO A CAT
Pour liquid medicine into a disposable plastic syringe (one without a needle), then hold the cat's head up and push the nozzle between its teeth. Trickle the medicine in slowly.

HOW TO GIVE MEDICINE TO A DOG
Use a syringe for a dog, in much the same way
as for a cat. But instead of pushing the nozzle
between its teeth, slide it alongside the teeth,
so that the medicine trickles into its cheek.

rapidly with milk or water. If you have a syringe handy, use that to wash the mouth out. Otherwise hold the animal's mouth open and pour in the liquid from a jug or cup.
• After washing the mouth out, give the animal plenty of milk or water to drink. The aim is to dilute the poison without causing vomiting – because vomiting up a corrosive poison will burn the mouth and throat for a second time.
• Follow up the drink with a 'stodgy' meal of bread and water or porridge.
• If you are certain that the animal has swallowed a non-corrosive poison, make it vomit as soon as possible.
• The best way to make a pet vomit is to feed it a crystal of washing soda – anything from a hazelnut-sized piece for a cat to a walnut-sized piece for a large dog. Do not dissolve the crystal first. Just give it to the animal in the same way you would give it a pill. The washing soda will make it sick in about five minutes.
• If washing soda is not available, use a solution of 1 part of mustard powder in 20 parts of water.
• With either type of poisoning, take the animal to a vet and take with you labels or samples of the poison.

• If you are not sure what type of poison is involved, treat the animal as if it had swallowed a corrosive poison.

Dealing with a choking animal
The priority in treating a choking animal is the same as for a choking human: speed.
• If there is something tight around the neck, remove it at once.
• If something is lodged in the mouth or throat – a bone, say – hold the animal's mouth open and pull the obstruction out. Use a bar such as a spoon handle to stop the jaws closing while you work. Push the bar to the back of the animal's mouth and between the teeth like a gag.
• If a ball gets stuck in a dog's throat, the obstruction tends to make the dog salivate profusely, which makes the ball slippery and difficult to get hold of.
• Open the mouth wide and try to get a finger behind the ball. Alternatively, put the fingers of both hands on the outside of the dog's cheeks as far back as you can and press forward from behind the ball.
• If the dog is choking on a sharp stick which has pierced its mouth or the back of its throat, pull the stick free.
• Keep the dog warm, do not let it eat or drink and get it to a vet as fast as possible.

Treating a limp
If a cat or dog develops a limp for which there is no obvious cause, examine the injured leg gently (see *How to handle an injured cat or dog*, page 185).
• Feel the limb from the paw upwards, looking for swelling, heat and pain.
• Look for cuts too, especially in the pads of

In the home and at work

CHOKING – AVOIDING RISKS

• If your cat wears a collar, make sure it has an elasticated section.
• Never leave a choke chain on an unattended dog.
• If your dog enjoys chasing a ball, use one that is far too big for it to swallow. Never use a small, solid, hard rubber ball.
• If you throw sticks for a dog, use one with blunt ends. A sharp one can land end-on in the ground and a running dog can impale itself.
• Never give any animal cooked bones to chew. They can splinter and cause the animal to choke or to cut itself severely. Pork and chicken bones are particularly dangerous – even if they have not been cooked. The only safe bones for an animal are raw beef bones.

the feet, and for splinters, grit and thorns. Clean any cuts in cold water.

• Remove any foreign bodies you find, if you can do so easily. If you cannot remove them easily, get veterinary help.

• Bending and straightening the leg may reveal painful areas and help you to find the cause of the problem. But again, if you cannot find the cause easily, take the animal to a vet.

• If a cat or dog develops a limp, particularly if part of the affected leg is swollen, the chances are that it has been bitten in a fight. This is much more likely to happen to a cat than a dog.

• Bathe the swollen area in water which is as hot as your hand can tolerate. Put a little salt or Epsom salts in the water.

• After bathing the area, contact a vet.

• If a septic wound is obvious, apply a warm poultice to reduce inflammation, especially if there is any delay in getting to the vet.

• Make the poultice from hot kaolin paste – available from chemists – spread on a bandage. Or squeeze out cotton wool or a flannel in water as hot as you can stand, then bandage the hot pad over the wound.

Removing a barb from a paw

Barbed objects such as fish-hooks that become embedded in the skin of a cat or dog need special treatment, to avoid making the injury worse when the barb is removed.

• Get the animal to a safe, escape-proof place before you start trying to treat it (see *How to handle an injured cat or dog*, page 185).

• Cut the hook free from any fishing line it is attached to.

• If the hook will not pull out easily, push it through until the barb is exposed.

• Cut off the barb with the wire-cutting section of a pair of pliers.

• Remove the rest of the hook by pulling the shank back out through the original incision.

• Clean the wound, cover it with a clean dressing and consult a vet.

• Do not try to remove a hook that has pierced a particularly sensitive part of the body such as the lips or eyes. Treatment of these areas may require an anaesthetic and is best left to a vet.

If a dog gets heat stroke

Never leave a dog in a car on a hot day. It can quite rapidly become seriously overheated, to the point of collapse.

• If a dog is obviously in distress, get it at once into a cool place and soak it in cold water, using towels or sponges. Wrap cold, wet towels round its head and body as well.

• If possible, put it in a bath or paddling pool – but do not do this if the dog is unconscious.

• If you have small lumps of ice handy, push them up the dog's bottom.

• Get the dog to a vet as soon as possible. Keep it cool on the journey by wrapping it in more wet towels. Use more ice if you have any.

If your cat or dog is bitten

A pet that has been bitten or scratched in a fight may have several small wounds which are not easily visible through the fur.

• Use your fingers to find the site of the injury.

• Clip away the fur around the wound, but do not pull the hair away if it seems to be part of a scab or clot. You may start the wound bleeding again.

• Clean the wound with warm water containing a little salt or Epsom salts.

• Cover and bandage the wound if it looks serious.

• Have the injuries checked by a vet. Bites and scratches suffered in a fight may go septic without treatment.

• With cats particularly, the first evidence of a bite may be an abscess, which often develops behind a tiny wound. You may notice the swelling, or the cat may become listless and off its food. The cat will need antibiotics – get it to a vet for treatment as soon as possible. If there is any delay, bathe the swelling with warm water to reduce the inflammation.

How to stop a dogfight

• Intervene in a dogfight only if it looks serious. Most dogs will, in ordinary circumstances, stop fighting of their own accord fairly quickly.

• If you do decide to intervene, take care not to get bitten yourself.

• Make a loud noise, such as a shrill whistle. Alternatively, throw a bucket of water over both contestants or turn a hose on them.

• If there is someone else available to help, ask the helper to move in behind one of the dogs at the same time as you move in behind the other.

• Grab the dog by the collar, if it is wearing one, or the scruff of the neck.

• Do not pull the dogs apart because this will worsen any wounds – if one has its teeth in the other, say. Instead, hit the dog in the side of the chest to make it let go, then pull it away.

• Once the dogs have been parted, keep a firm grip on them to make sure that they do not start fighting again.

If cats fight

• Stop a cat fight by chasing the combatants and shouting and shooing at them. Cat fights rarely last long.

• Do not try to get hold of a fighting cat – you are very likely to be scratched or bitten.

If a pet is stung

Cats and dogs often chase wasps and bees. So when they are stung, it is often on or around the face.

• If the sting is on the skin, rub on a proprietary cream such as Waspeze. It is as effective on animals as on humans. Do not use a cream of this kind near the eyes or mouth, however.

• If the sting is inside the mouth, get the animal

HOW TO GET A HOOK OUT OF A PAW

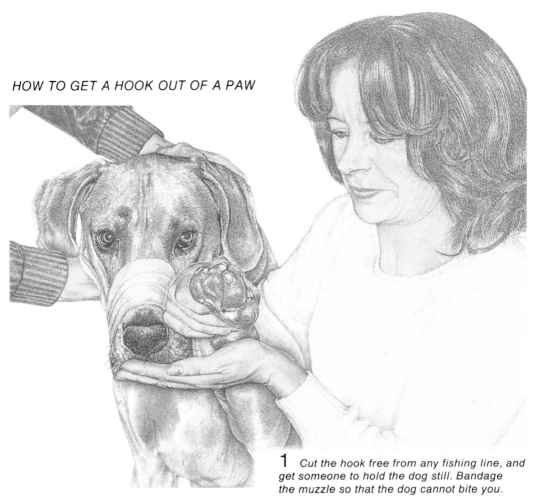

1 Cut the hook free from any fishing line, and get someone to hold the dog still. Bandage the muzzle so that the dog cannot bite you.

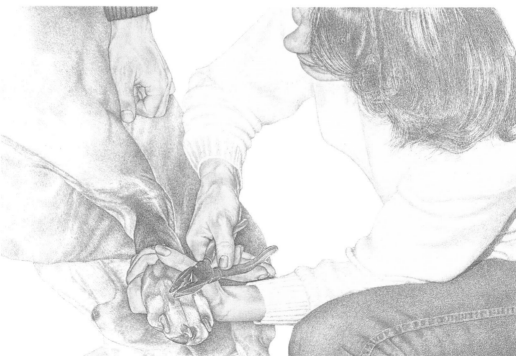

2 If the hook will not pull free easily, push it through until the barb is exposed. Cut the barb off with a pair of pliers, then pull the shank back and out. Dress the wound and see a vet.

191

to a vet at once. A sting in the mouth is much more serious because the swelling could block the animal's airway and choke it.

Coping with wasps or bees

• If your home is invaded by a swarm of bees or a colony of wasps, do not try to hold them back with pesticide sprays.
• Retreat quickly, closing all doors and windows between you and the swarm.
• Get expert help at once.
• If the problem is wasps, telephone the local council's Health Department, which will normally clear the colony free of charge or for a small fee. Alternatively, contact a local pest-control firm, who will usually provide treatment within 24 hours, but will charge a higher fee. Most firms are listed in the Yellow Pages under 'Pest and Vermin Control Services'.
• If the problem is bees, contact the police, the local council or the nearest Citizens Advice Bureau. They will put you in touch with a local beekeeper who will remove the swarm.
• If you are attacked by bees or wasps – and this is likely to happen only if a nearby colony has been disturbed for some reason – the safest course depends on where you are.
• If you are in a garden, retreat indoors quickly but calmly, closing doors and windows behind you. Stay inside until the insects disperse, which they will do within a few minutes.
• If you are in open country away from any building, plunge into the nearest patch of dense undergrowth or bushes. Keep going until you leave the insects behind. This will usually happen within 50yds (45m) because the insects will be disorientated by the moving branches. When you are clear, wait until the insects disperse.
• A swarm of bees on its way to found a new colony will not normally attack a person. If you are in the path of a swarm, move out of its way, or lie flat and cover yourself with a coat in case any bees settle on you.

Caring for an injured bird or wild animal

If you come across an injured bird, a helpless fledgling, or a wild animal such as a rabbit that is obviously hurt, there is little you can do by way of first aid without knowing what the problem is. And that requires expert help.
• If the creature is young and helpless but apparently uninjured, do not interfere unless you are certain it has been abandoned. If the mother is about she will help and feed it, but if you handle it she may be frightened away.
• If you can catch an injured wild creature without hurting it, take it to a vet. You will not usually be expected to pay a fee.
• If you cannot catch it easily, tell the Royal Society for the Prevention of Cruelty to Animals or the police. The nearest RSPCA office will be listed in the telephone directory under 'Royal'. Alternatively, contact the society's head office in West Sussex on Horsham (0403) 64181.

Handling a sick or injured horse

Like any animal in pain, a horse is likely to become vicious and turn on even a person who knows it well. So get it under control first.
• Approach the horse quietly with a halter, talking to it steadily and looking at it all the time. Let it see you coming. Slip the halter on and hold the rope firmly. But do not wind the rope round your hand. If the horse jerks back, it could give you a painful rope burn.
• If further restraint is necessary, use one hand to hold it round the soft tip of its muzzle.
• If someone else is with you, ask him to hold the horse by an uninjured foreleg and bend it to lift it off the ground. This will help to immobilise the animal. Once the horse is under control, examine it for injuries.
• If the horse is standing on three legs, it may mean that it has gone lame or that the leg is broken – if the leg is at an awkward angle or badly swollen, say. Do not move the horse unless it is in danger of further injury (on a road, for example). Get veterinary help at once.
• If the horse is lying down and cannot get up, leave it alone and get veterinary help.
• If the horse is lying down and thrashing about, try to restrain it from causing itself further injury. Get hold of its head and lie on it to hold it still. But stay well away from the forefeet. Get veterinary help at once.

Dealing with a horse that has gone lame

Lameness in a horse usually happens when the lower part of the leg or the foot is damaged in some way and the tissues inside the hoof swell up. The rigid hoof constricts the swollen tissues, causing considerable pain.
• If you are riding a horse that goes lame (you can tell because the animal's gait becomes awkward and lopsided as it tries to guard the painful foot), dismount at once.
• Pick up the foot of the affected leg and examine it for injuries. A nail may have penetrated the sole, or a stone may have caught in the hoof.
• Remove any foreign body you find, then lead the horse home.
• Once you get there, pack a hot poultice round the foot and call a vet. Make the poultice from hot kaolin paste – available from chemists – spread on a bandage; or use a cloth pad that has been squeezed out in hot water.
• If you find nothing in the foot, feel the rest of the leg for areas which feel hot or swollen or which seem to cause the horse pain. Whether or not you can find the source of the trouble, call a vet. Rest the horse until the vet arrives.

If a horse is caught on barbed wire

• Restrain the horse and hold it firmly to stop it tearing itself away from the wire and making its injuries worse.
• Restrict its movement by lifting its foreleg as well, if you can.
• Ease the barbed wire free, making all your

movements slow so as not to startle or hurt the horse. Once the horse is free, clean any cuts with warm water containing a mild antiseptic (the same antiseptics that work on people work on horses, too).

• Ask a vet to come and look the horse over. Horses are highly susceptible to tetanus, and even minor cuts can easily become infected.

Treating a horse for colic

Colic in a horse is abdominal pain usually resulting from it eating or being fed something other than its natural diet of grass and vegetation. The pain can often be violent.

The symptoms of internal pain are: restlessness; pawing and scraping at the ground; looking round at the flanks; getting up and down frequently; rolling; sweating; and rapid breathing. In addition, a horse suffering from colic may strain as it tries to defecate without success, or with very limited success.

• Once you have the horse under control, get it walking gently and try to keep it on the move.

• Try to stop it rolling on the ground. Rolling could lead to the intestines being twisted, and could seriously worsen the horse's condition.

• Call a vet. Keep the horse on its feet and moving until the vet arrives.

If fire breaks out in a stable

• Dial 999 and ask for the fire brigade, or get someone else to make the call.

• Open the stable door and chase the horse out, if you can do so without getting burnt yourself. Do not wait for it to bolt out – it will probably be too terrified to move and may need a prod with a pitchfork.

• Shut the door once the horse is out. A horse panic-stricken by the flames may well try to get back into its stall unless you prevent it by shutting the door.

• Let the horse or horses run free if necessary while you clear the rest of the stable.

• Once all the animals are safe, fight the blaze as best you can until firemen arrive (see *Fighting a fire*, page 150).

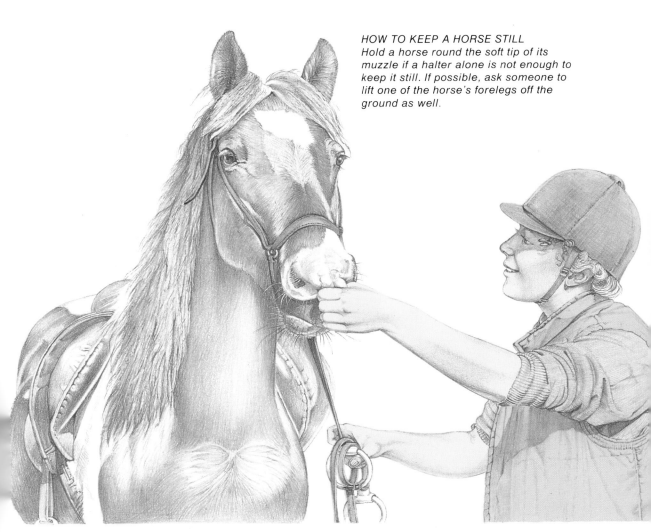

HOW TO KEEP A HORSE STILL
Hold a horse round the soft tip of its muzzle if a halter alone is not enough to keep it still. If possible, ask someone to lift one of the horse's forelegs off the ground as well.

193

Emergencies on the road

At the scene of an accident

WHEN YOU ARRIVE
Park your car well clear of the crashed cars and turn on the hazard warning lights to alert traffic behind you on the road. Take a moment to assess the seriousness of the crash, then act. The most urgent priorities are to protect the scene, and yourself, from other cars, and to send someone to call the emergency services.

If you are the first on the scene of a crash, do not dash headlong from your car to the aid of an injured person – you or your car may be struck by another vehicle and add to the disaster.

For this reason, the first thing to do at the scene of any accident is to protect the area from other traffic.

Once you have warned other traffic, the priorities, in order, are: send for the police; immobilise the crashed vehicles; and help anyone who has been injured.

Warn other traffic
• Park your car well away from the accident – behind it, if possible. Turn on your hazard warning lights. At night, train your headlights on the wrecked vehicles as well.
• Leave your car with its front wheels turned towards the kerb so that if another car runs into yours, your car will be pushed off the road, not into you or the crashed vehicles.
• If one of the crashed vehicles is on fire, keep clear. Its petrol tank could explode without warning.
• Take charge of the accident scene if no one else has done so. If someone is already in charge, make yourself useful to him.
• Warn approaching traffic in both directions. If other traffic is coming up behind you, flag it down, keeping well to the side of the road; at night use a torch or light-coloured scarf. Ask someone to stop traffic coming the other way.
• Put a warning triangle, if one is available, about 100yds (90m) behind the wrecked vehicles, towards the nearside edge of the road. Ideally, put another the same distance in the opposite direction.

WARN OTHER TRAFFIC
Put a red warning triangle about 100 yds (90m) behind the crashed cars, and, ideally, another the same distance ahead. Flag down the first car and send the driver to call the police.

TURN OFF THE IGNITION
Switch off the engines of all the crashed cars to cut the risk of fire, and put the handbrakes on. But leave the keys in the ignition in case the cars have to be moved later.

START SELF-HELP TREATMENT
See if the casualty can help herself, and show her what to do. She can, for instance, stem bleeding by pressing a clean handkerchief over a wound. Tell her that help is on the way.

Send for the police

• Check the number of vehicles involved, and the number of victims, noting whether anyone is trapped.

• Ask a passing driver or anyone living nearby to make a 999 call at the nearest telephone. Tell him how many people are injured or trapped. It does not matter if more than one person makes a call.

• If you make the call yourself on a public or private telephone, dial 999. Do not put any coins in a coin box.

• When the operator answers, ask for the police, who will alert other services.

• Tell the police you are reporting an accident, and give the telephone number in case you are cut off.

• Describe the accident location as exactly as you can. Say how many vehicles are involved, whether any vehicle is on fire, how many people are injured and whether anyone is trapped.

• Answer any other questions, and do not hang up until the operator tells you to.

Immobilise the crashed vehicles

• Switch off the ignition of each vehicle, but leave the key in the ignition in case the steering locks – the vehicle may have to be moved later.

• Check that the handbrake of each car is on. If it is not, put it on.

• Do not smoke, and warn others not to – even away from the cars. There may be petrol running in the gutter or leaking across the road from a ruptured fuel tank.

Help the injured

• Do not move anyone unless he is in immediate danger – if there is a car on fire close by, for example, or if he is lying in leaking petrol which you think might catch fire. If you move an injured person, you risk aggravating his injuries; that risk is worth taking only to protect him from a greater risk.

• Do not attempt to pick out glass from face or body wounds. If the glass is plugging the wound, you could make the bleeding worse by pulling it out.

BREAD OF LIFE
For six days in July 1983, Peter Marsh lay trapped under his crashed motorcycle. His leg was broken, he had no food or water and the standing crop in the Cambridgeshire cornfield where he had landed hid him from passers-by. To obtain some sustenance, he sucked juices from the stalks and grasses around him.

Marsh, who was 42, was discovered when police were called to another accident close by. His broken leg was badly infected, he was covered in insect bites and he was delirious and severely sunburnt. But thanks, in part, to the stalks he had chewed, he was alive.

TRAGEDY OF A CRASH HERO
Hampshire publican John Dodd did not hesitate when he came to the scene of an accident in the winter of 1981. He ran to help. But he overlooked the first rule of rescue on the road: make sure that the area is safe.

He was driving in snow along the Kingston bypass near London when he saw a car that had crashed into the central reservation and was blocking the fast lane. Sitting in the car was a woman driver, who was paralysed by fear and shock. 'I didn't think about it,' Dodd said later. 'I just went to help.'

Although he succeeded in getting the woman out of the car and behind the crash barriers on the central reservation, Dodd was himself hit by another car while he was trying to move the crashed car out of the way.

He suffered a broken leg that left him with a permanent limp, and was unconscious for three days as a result of head injuries. Even after his recovery from the immediate injuries, he suffered from headaches and loss of concentration to the extent that he had to give up the tenancy of his public house in Droxford.

Three years after the accident, in December 1984, he won £65,000 damages in the High Court from the motorist whose vehicle ran into him. But Dodd, by this time working as a weighbridge clerk, commented: 'The money can't give me back what I have lost.'

• Check that each casualty can breathe freely. Loosen tight clothing round the neck.

• Do not give anyone anything to eat or drink. Hot, sweet tea is appropriate only for someone who has had an emotional fright. It should not be given to anyone who has been injured or who is suffering from the serious clinical condition known as shock (see page 120).

• See if the casualty can treat himself and show him what to do. He can stem blood coming from an arm or leg by gripping the wound with his hand, or by pressing on it with a clean handkerchief or tissue.

Treatment priorities

• Treat casualties in any accident – on the road or anywhere else (a bomb blast, say) – in the following order:

1. Unconscious and not breathing (see *Artificial respiration*, page 50).
2. Bleeding severely (see page 60).
3. Unconscious but breathing (see page 136).

• Then search the scene in case someone has left or been thrown from a crashed vehicle and is wandering around in shock – or has collapsed at a distance. Persuade anyone wandering around in a state of shock to lie down.

• Cover each injured person lightly with a rug or coat.

• Reassure them that help is on the way. Tell

them that any missing friend, relative or pet is being taken care of – even if at that stage you are not sure. The priority is to keep each casualty safe and as calm as possible until the emergency services reach the scene.

• If possible, do not leave the casualties alone after you have treated them. Get someone – a passer-by, say, or another motorist – to stay with each casualty until help arrives.

At the scene of a motorway crash

Because of the volume of traffic on motorways, the road can quickly get blocked if motorists stop at the scene of a crash, and the resulting traffic jam can delay the arrival of police and ambulance services.

For this reason, and because of the extra risks for rescuers caused by the speed of traffic, safety experts recommend that motorists should not stop at the scene of a motorway accident unless it is absolutely necessary – if, for example, someone is lying injured in the path of traffic, or struggling to get out of a car on fire.

• Go to the nearest emergency telephone and call for help. Emergency telephones are 1 mile (1.6km) apart, and there are marker posts at intervals by the hard shoulder giving the direction of the nearest.

• To make a call from an emergency telephone on the motorway, simply pick up the handset (there is no dial). This will automatically connect you to the motorway police control room.

• Give the letter and number on the side of the phone box, which pinpoints its location.

• Briefly describe the accident, the number of vehicles involved, and the number injured.

• Do not hang up until told to do so by the police operator. Some older types of phone work in one direction only, so the operator cannot call you back. On newer types he can call you back.

ACCIDENTS: WHERE, WHEN AND WHY THEY HAPPEN

On average, there are about 410,000 accidents on British roads each year. More than 200,000 people are injured in them, and about 6000 people die.

Nearly half of those who are killed or injured are young people of between 15 and 24. About one-third of the accident victims are pedestrians – often children or the elderly. Another fifth are motorcyclists.

Most accidents happen in built-up areas – three times as many as on country roads and more than 20 times as many as on motorways. But motorway accidents and crashes on country roads are more often serious because of the higher speeds involved.

More accidents occur in summer and autumn – when driving conditions are usually good but there is more traffic – than in winter and spring. And two-thirds take place when the weather is good.

Each week, too, there is a regular pattern to the toll on the roads.

The commonest times for an accident are: weekday rush hours; late evenings around pub closing times between Thursday and Sunday; Saturday shopping hours; and Sunday afternoons between 2pm and 4pm, when many people go out for a spin or are coming back from a lunchtime drink.

The accident blackspots

Most accidents need not happen. They are caused by errors of judgment or sheer carelessness much more often than by mechanical failure. These are the ten most common road situations that can turn a car trip into a tragedy.

DRIVING STRAIGHT About 250,000 accidents happen each year when drivers are on a perfectly ordinary stretch of road. The causes are usually careless, dangerous or drunken driving, ignoring traffic signals – or, less commonly, mechanical faults such as defective brakes or steering.

TURNING RIGHT About 50,000 accidents are caused each year by motorists misjudging a right turn or crashing into someone who is turning right.

OVERTAKING About 34,000 accidents are caused by drivers overtaking dangerously.

PARKED CARS Badly parked cars, and people getting out of them carelessly, are responsible for more than 22,000 accidents.

IMPATIENCE Drivers trying to beat a hold-up by, for instance, overtaking on the inside cause about 13,500 accidents.

TURNING LEFT Drivers turning left and swinging too wide as they do so, or turning into the path of a cyclist, cause more than 13,000 accidents each year.

STOPPING Sudden, unexpected stops by a driver cause nearly 12,000 crashes.

MOVING OFF Nearly 6000 accidents happen because a motorist pulls out carelessly into traffic or bumps into the car in front in a slow-moving queue.

U-TURNS They are responsible for almost 3000 accidents a year.

REVERSING Around 2500 accidents a year happen when a driver backs into something or someone.

If you are involved in an accident

A traffic accident may involve only your vehicle and damage to property, such as a lamppost. Or it may involve other vehicles and perhaps injury to people or animals. Whatever the involvement, there are certain steps the law requires you to take and others that are advisable for insurance purposes.

Try to keep cool and note down essential information, even though you will probably be feeling shocked and flustered by the incident.

At the scene

• Stop as soon as you safely can. You must stop even if your vehicle is undamaged but you have been indirectly involved – if, for example, one car collided with another after swerving to avoid you.

• Whatever the circumstances, do not become involved in arguments with other drivers or onlookers about what happened. Particularly, do not make any statement admitting liability. If you think you may have been at fault, it is wisest to say as little as possible.

• If anyone is seriously injured, dial 999 and ask for the police, who will alert other emergency services. Otherwise there is no need to call the police unless there is a serious traffic obstruction.

• Before any vehicles are moved, make a sketch plan or note of their position in the road and in relation to the other vehicles involved. Note, for example, if any car has crossed the central white line. If any car has skidded, make an estimate of the length of skid marks.

• Examine your vehicle and the others involved and make a note of the damage each has sustained. Look, too, at the condition of the other cars. Were all their lights working at the time, for instance, and were their tyres in good condition?

• If anyone has been injured, you must also produce a motor insurance certificate on the spot. If you cannot, report the accident to the police within 24 hours.

• Give your name and address and the registration number of your car to other motorists involved and to anyone else who has reasonable grounds for asking, such as the owners of any damaged property. If you are not the owner of the car you are driving, give the owner's name and address as well.

• Collect the same information from other motorists involved. If anyone refuses, write down his car registration number (the owner can be traced through the number).

• If the police have not been called, try to find an independent witness (not someone travelling in your car) who is willing to make a statement about the incident to your insurance company. Take his name and address.

After the accident

• If the accident involved serious damage to a vehicle or property, or if a traffic sign was damaged, it is advisable, though not legally essential, to report it to the police as soon as possible – certainly within 24 hours.

• If you hit and damage an unoccupied car – in a car park, say – report it to the police. If you fail to do so and are eventually traced, you could face not only a claim for repair of the damage you caused, but also criminal charges as a hit-and-run driver.

• Tell your insurance company of the accident within 24 hours, whether or not you or anyone else will be making a claim on your policy.

• Ask the company at the same time to send you an accident report and claim form on which you can fill in the details.

• Ask a garage to give you a written estimate of the cost of repairs to your car, but do not get any repairs done at once if you plan to claim the cost from an insurance company. The

MAKING A SKETCH OF THE ACCIDENT
A sketch of the accident scene, made on the spot, will be useful in any later court case and for making an insurance claim. Show the road layout and the cars' positions. Mark where any witness was standing. Add the compass points, too (get them from a map if necessary); official reports often refer to them.

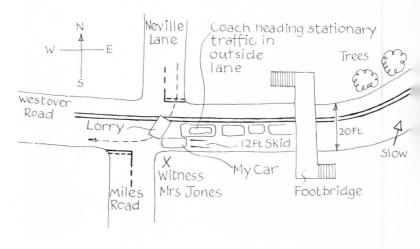

insurers will probably want the damage inspected first by an engineer.

• Send any bills or letters you get from other motorists involved to your insurance company. Do not write to or contact the other motorists or their insurers.

• Let your insurance company know if you receive a Notice of Intended Prosecution from the police. This should arrive within 14 days of the accident unless you were warned at the time that you would be charged.

If you have an accident abroad

The legal requirements about what to do if you are involved in an accident vary in detail from country to country, even within Europe. Nevertheless, if you follow these general guidelines, you will be doing at least as much as the law requires in any country.

• Stop at the scene of the accident.

• Warn approaching traffic of the obstruction by setting up a red warning triangle at least 100 yds (90m) from the scene – ideally use two, one in each direction.

• Call the police, or ask a passing motorist to call them. Even if this is not obligatory under local laws, it is always advisable.

• Help anyone who has been injured (see *At the scene of an accident*, page 196). Call an ambulance if necessary.

• Generally, do not move the car or cars from the positions in which they have come to rest. But if they are seriously obstructing other traffic, mark the positions on the road and get the details confirmed by independent witnesses before moving them.

• Do not leave the scene of the accident until the police arrive, unless there is an overriding reason for doing so. If you think there is such a reason, explain it to the police by telephoning them, and get their permission before leaving.

• Give your name and address, and any other details requested, to others involved in the accident. Collect the same details from them.

• Cooperate with the police when they arrive. Answer their questions as fully as you can, but avoid saying anything which could be construed as an admission of liability.

• Make notes or a sketch plan of the accident to help you fill in your insurance company's accident form later. If you have a camera, back the notes up by taking photographs of the cars and the scene. Try particularly to show any factors which might have helped to cause the accident – a concealed road sign, for instance. Take close-up pictures of the damage, too; they may be useful evidence if you want to claim compensation from the other driver or from your insurance company.

• Report the accident to the insurance company or bureau whose address is given on the back of your Green Card or frontier insurance certificate. Telephone as soon as possible, and follow up your call with a letter – within 24 hours, if possible.

• If you have additional insurance cover through a British company or motoring organisation, report the accident to the British insurer as well. The policy will tell you how soon after the accident you should let the firm know. If the time limit is short, make the first contact by phone and follow it up with a letter.

• Some insurance policies – such as the Automobile Association's Five-Star Service and the Travellers Bond Foreign Touring Service of the Royal Automobile Club – cover the costs of repairs to your car, medical expenses and a variety of other costs which may arise after an accident. If your policy is of this type, ask the insurer about where and how to get the repairs done, and about how medical bills will be settled (see also *Seeing a doctor overseas*, page 288).

Emergencies on the road

HOW TO AVOID A HEAD-ON COLLISION

If you see another vehicle coming towards you on the wrong side of the road, whose driver seems to be either unwilling or unable to get out of your way, you must act quickly and coolly to avoid a head-on collision. Head-on collisions are the most dangerous of all road accidents.

• As soon as you see the hazard, sound your horn or flash your headlights as an early warning of your presence.

• Brake firmly but not violently. Otherwise the car may start to skid and you could lose steering control.

• As you reduce speed, scan the road ahead to see if there is anywhere to get out of the way safely – a verge, say, or a side turning.

• Start to pull left, but do not commit yourself until you see which way the other car is going. There is a danger that both of you could pull onto your nearside verge and collide there.

• As soon as you see which way the other vehicle is swerving, turn away from it – even if this means side-swiping another car on the road. This type of accident is far less likely to kill you and your passengers than a head-on smash.

• If a collision is unavoidable, try to scrape the side of the other vehicle rather than meet it head on.

Defensive driving

The best way to avoid an accident is to be alert to what might cause one – to develop your powers of observation so that you can see danger coming and react to it in time. The principle of the technique known as defensive driving is to be prepared for the unexpected by observation and anticipation. These pages show how to apply the principle in practice.

Other motorists – watch for:

• Taxi ahead – it may slow down and move to the left with little warning. Keep an eye open for someone hailing it from the kerb.

• Learner stopped on a hill – do not get too close. He may roll back when starting off.

• Bus ahead – beware of people running to catch it. If it has a rear platform with people on it, the bus is probably about to stop. Watch out for people jumping off.

• Motorcyclists at a road junction ahead – if you see two ready to come out and one emerges safely, watch for the other. Will he follow?

• Pedal cyclist ahead – if he glances over his

shoulder he is probably preparing to pull out to the right, and may hesitate and wobble. Watch his movements.

• Turning signal on a car ahead – never rely on the driver doing as he has signalled. He may have forgotten to cancel a previous signal, or may change his mind.

• Turning signal on a car to your right – if you are waiting to emerge from a side road onto a main road, never assume that it is safe to pull out just because an oncoming driver is signalling left. Wait until he slows down and is obviously going to turn.

• Brake lights coming on ahead – touch your own to warn traffic behind. There may be an accident or obstruction ahead.

• Headlamp flashed as signal – never assume another driver means: 'You go ahead, I will wait.' He may mean: 'I'm going ahead. You wait.' Such a signal is easily misinterpreted and could lead to an accident. Headlamp-flashing should be used only to let another driver know you are there.

• Siren sounding on police car, ambulance or fire engine – if you do not know where the sound is coming from, slow down and keep to the side of the road. Do not move across a road junction until you are certain you will not be in the path of the emergency vehicle.

• Headlamp dazzle – if a car approaches with headlamps on full beam, do not look at them directly. Look slightly to the nearside. Do not retaliate by switching your own headlamps to full beam. This is offensive rather than defensive driving and could cause an accident.

• Slow vehicle ahead very close behind another – the rear vehicle is probably being towed, even if it is not displaying a towing notice. Be careful about overtaking.

• Moving out from a side road onto a main road – watch for cycles and motorcycles near the kerb as well as for cars. A cyclist or motorcyclist is easy to overlook if you are trying to nose out of a side road in heavy traffic.

Approaching a parked car – watch for:

• People inside – the door may be opened.

• Flashing indicator – the car may pull out into your path.

• Wisps of smoke from the exhaust – the car may be about to move off.

• Feet under vehicles – a child may run into the road.

• An ice-cream van – there are bound to be children around it, and they may dart across the road to or from it without warning.

Roadside signs – watch for:

• Bus stops – people may run across the road from the right.

• School signs – children may run across the road, especially in the morning between 8.30

How to make use of clues
Be alert, as you drive, to clues which can warn of potential danger. There are six such clues in this urban street scene. The slightly open door on the parked car may mean that the driver is about to get out – and he may not have noticed you. The smoke from the exhaust and the lit brake light on the parked car beyond both mean that it may be about to pull out, perhaps without indicating. The cyclist is looking over his shoulder; he may be about to swing across the road. There are feet visible below the van on the right; a child may be about to dash into the street. And the loose dog on the pavement farther down the street may run across your path without warning.

Debris from roadworks
A loose pile of sand or tar by the side of the road (above) may be a warning of roadworks ahead. Look out for workmen and machinery which may be blocking the road around the next corner (right).

Vehicles emerging from a turn
Watch out for cars and buses moving out of a side road. In a town, others could be queuing behind the first, and one or more of them – fed up, perhaps, with waiting – could try to slip out as well, blocking your path.

and 9.30 and in the afternoon between 3.30 and 4.30. But look out for a lone child near the school at any time of day.

• Zebra crossings – scan the pavement on both sides to see if anyone is preparing to cross.

• Garage or pub forecourt – vehicles are likely to pull in and out without signalling, especially late at night.

• Red traffic light – stop. Before starting off again, watch the cross traffic and pedestrians, in case someone tries to rush through at the last minute.

• Amber traffic light – be decisive. Slow down and stop unless you are almost at the lights. If you are almost at the lights, accelerate through; otherwise traffic behind may run into you.

• Green traffic light – do not treat it as an open door; it may change. Reduce speed as you approach, and look right and left to make sure that nothing is coming through.

• Roadworks sign – prepare to slow down or stop; the roadworks may be some distance ahead round a bend, or masked by parked cars.

• Road-narrows sign – get into the continuing lane in good time, and watch for other drivers cutting across.

Making use of clues – watch for:

• Mud or hay on a country road – there may be a slow-moving tractor ahead.

• Droppings on a country road – there may be horses, cattle or sheep ahead.

• Telegraph poles – in country areas, the line of poles ahead of you can sometimes alert you

Farm-produce shops
Slow down whenever you see a sign advertising a farm shop or a roadside stall. Cars ahead may be backed up waiting to get into a narrow turning, or they may be carelessly parked along the verge

Hedge or grass clippings
Freshly mown grass, or a newly trimmed hedge – with or without loose clippings – indicates that a road gang or a hedge-clipping tractor may be working on the road ahead. Slow down until you are sure.

to bends in the road that may be masked by hedges. Do not rely on them, however; the lines sometimes cut across fields, rather than go round them, and so can mislead you.
• County boundary sign – the road surface is likely to change, and at night the street lighting ahead may be different.
• Shop-window reflections – in built-up areas, make full use of reflections in windows and on shiny vehicles. They can help you to see round bends, round corners at awkward junctions, and to see how close you are to the car behind when parking on the street.
• Builders' or rubbish skips (large metal containers) – note their position during the day in case you are returning at night. They may not be lit after dark.

Approaching animals – watch for:
• Dog not on lead – it may wander into the road or run across, especially if there is another dog (or a cat) on the other side.
• Cat crouching on footpath watching traffic – it may be intending to cross the road, and may dash in front of your car, relying on speed to get across.
• Horses ahead – slow down and give them plenty of room as you pass. Do not toot your horn or accelerate hard, or they may shy into your car.
• Herd of cattle or flock of sheep ahead – stop until they have gone round you or off the road. Do not sound your horn or rev your engine. If you startle them, they may blunder into your car and damage it.

What to do if you hit an animal

If you suddenly find an animal in your path – a pet, a straying farm animal or a wild animal – there may be no time to avoid it. In heavy traffic or bad weather, there may be no choice but to hit it rather than to swerve and risk a serious accident.

• Pull over to the side of the road and stop as soon as you can after the impact. Find out whether the animal is dead or injured.

• If it is injured, try to restrain it so that its injuries can be treated (see *Caring for a sick or injured animal*, page 185).

• Whether the animal is dead or injured, and whatever type of animal it is, call the police.

• If the animal is a pet or a farm animal, go to the nearest house or farmhouse as well and try to find the owner.

• If the animal is injured and small enough to handle, consider taking it to a vet at once. Tell the police if you plan to leave the scene of the accident to do this.

• Tell the vet that you have informed the police about the accident. In such a case, the vet will sometimes not charge you for treating the animal, but will instead claim his fee from a fund administered by the police.

PET-OWNERS AND THE LAW

Anyone who owns or looks after a pet has a legal duty to try to make sure that it does not hurt anyone or damage their property. If it does – if it bites someone, for example, or if it runs in front of a car and causes an accident – you could be sued for compensation by the victim.

In ordinary circumstances you will not be liable for the cost of any damage or injury your pet causes, unless it can be shown that you were in some way to blame – if, for instance, you let your dog run loose in a busy street.

If, however, you own or look after what the law calls a dangerous animal – a poisonous snake, for example, or an alligator – then the courts may hold you responsible for any accident it causes, even if you are not, in the ordinary sense, to blame.

This responsibility is known in law as 'strict liability'.

In practice, owners of cats are rarely held to be responsible for damage done by their pets because the law recognises that cats are very difficult to control.

• If your pet has a habit of chasing passers-by, cyclists or cars, keep it well fenced in so that it cannot run into the street.

• Keep your dog on a lead in crowded places and in a field of livestock.

• Train your dog properly. A local vet will probably be able to tell you about nearby training classes. The Kennel Club – whose head office is at 1 Clarges Street, London W1; telephone 01-493 6651 – also has details of training classes around the country.

• Keep children and strangers away from a bitch with a litter. She may be unusually aggressive.

• If your dog has already bitten somebody, take extra care to keep it under control. If it bites somebody again, the courts could order you to have the dog destroyed.

• Consider taking out insurance against your pet doing harm if you do not already have it. Most household insurance policies include such cover as a matter of course.

Motorists and the law on animals

Although it is always advisable to call the police if you hit an animal on the road – because they can help to arrange treatment or for the body to be removed, and can help to trace the owner – it is not always obligatory to do so.

This is because your legal duties as a motorist if you run over an animal on the road depend on what animal it is.

• If you injure a horse, cow, bull, ass, mule, sheep, pig, dog or goat, you must stop at the scene of the accident and give your name and address and the car's registration number to anyone involved in the accident who has reasonable grounds for asking for them – the owner of the animal, for instance.

• If there is no one else present – if you have knocked over a straying animal, for example – you must report the accident to the police within 24 hours.

• You are not legally obliged to stop or to report the accident to police if you run over any other animal – including a cat.

• If you accidentally kill a wild animal it is not an offence – even if the animal is a protected species, such as the otter.

• If you accidentally injure a wild animal – even a protected species – you may keep it, but only until it can fend for itself. Then it must be released.

• Alternatively, if a wild animal is too badly hurt to recover, the law allows you to kill it humanely. In these circumstances, the humane way is the quickest way available.

• The law does not, however, allow an unqualified person to kill a farm animal or pet in these circumstances.

What to do if someone collapses

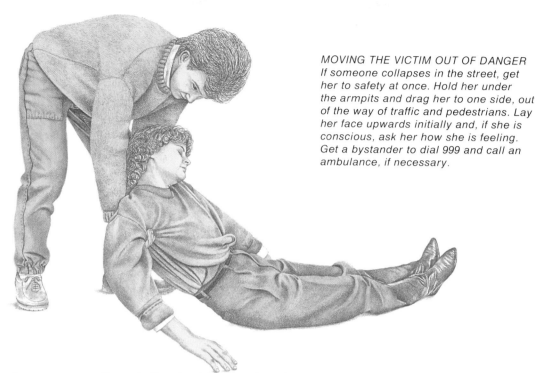

MOVING THE VICTIM OUT OF DANGER
If someone collapses in the street, get her to safety at once. Hold her under the armpits and drag her to one side, out of the way of traffic and pedestrians. Lay her face upwards initially and, if she is conscious, ask her how she is feeling. Get a bystander to dial 999 and call an ambulance, if necessary.

Emergencies on the road

A person may collapse in the street for any of a number of reasons. The most common cause is fainting (see page 96).

Less often the cause may be an epileptic fit (see page 94). More rarely still, it could be a heart attack (see page 105) or a stroke (see page 134).

Whatever the cause, the priority is always the same: move the victim to a safe place out of the way of traffic.
• Watch out for traffic as you approach the victim, and flag down cars if necessary.
• Lift or drag the victim to the side of the road.
• Once out of immediate danger, lay the victim down on his or her back.
• If the victim is conscious, ask her to describe her symptoms. If necessary, call an ambulance, or get a passer-by to do so.
• If she is unconscious, put one hand under her neck, the other on her forehead and tilt her head well back. This will open her airway.
• Check that the victim is breathing. Rest one hand on her chest to feel for movement; watch for movement as well.
• Put your ear near her mouth so that you can hear and feel her breath.

If the victim is breathing
• Someone who is unconscious but is breathing normally should be turned into the recovery position until she comes round (see page 136). Do not make a fainting victim sit up unless she feels she wants to.
• Send a bystander to dial 999 for an ambulance. Ask him to return afterwards to confirm

that he has done so. Anyone who has been unconscious, even for a short time, should have immediate medical treatment.

If the victim is not breathing
• If the victim's breathing stops, use a finger to clear her mouth of any blood or vomit, and give the kiss of life (see page 50).
• Give the two full breaths, then check for a pulse at the carotid (neck) artery.
• If you cannot detect a pulse and the victim's complexion is blue-grey, give chest compression as well if you have been trained in the technique (see page 52).
• Once the casualty is breathing, loosen her clothing at the neck, chest and waist.
• Turn her into the recovery position.
• Stay with her until an ambulance comes. Do not give her anything to eat or drink – you could make hospital treatment more difficult.

Helping the victim of an epileptic fit
• If the victim is having an epileptic fit, do not try to push anything into his or her mouth.
• Simply restrain her gently. Muscle spasms – twitching or convulsing limbs – and the breath-holding often associated with fits rarely last more than a minute.
• Once the fit passes, the victim may fall into a deep sleep. Use a finger to clear any blood, mucus or vomit from her mouth.
• If she is breathing normally, turn her into the recovery position.
• Get someone to call an ambulance. Stay with the casualty until help arrives.

Controlling a skid

A car skids because the tyres lose their grip and begin to slide over the road surface instead of rolling along it. What to do to control a skid depends on which tyres are skidding and whether or not the car has front-wheel drive. The 'natural' reaction – jamming the brakes on hard – is the worst thing you can do.

How to stop a rear-wheel skid

In a rear-wheel skid the back of the car slides sideways and the vehicle begins to swing round back to front. This usually happens when you drive too fast round a bend or corner, but can occur if you brake harshly on an uneven surface or a steeply cambered road. It is most likely to happen in a car with front-wheel drive.

Whether the car has front-wheel or rear-wheel drive, the action to take is the same.
• Take your foot off the accelerator or brake. Do not push in the clutch pedal or grip the steering wheel hard.
• Turn the steering wheel in the direction the back of the car is sliding (turn right if it is sliding to the right, for example). Do not turn it too far or you may start a second skid in the opposite direction.
• When all four wheels are back in line, accelerate gently.

How to stop a front-wheel skid

In a front-wheel skid, the front of the car keeps straight on, even though you have turned the steering wheel to right or left.

Front-wheel skids usually happen when the driver accelerates too harshly round a bend. What to do depends on whether the car has rear-wheel or front-wheel drive.

IN A CAR WITH REAR-WHEEL DRIVE Take your foot off the accelerator. Do not apply the brake or push in the clutch pedal.
• Turn the steering wheel so that the front wheels are straightened – pointing again in the direction the car is moving. Do not turn it too far or you could cause the rear wheels to skid.
• Once the front wheels are gripping again, accelerate gently and steer in the direction you wish to go.

IN A CAR WITH FRONT-WHEEL DRIVE Ease off the accelerator smoothly, but maintain enough pressure on the pedal to keep the car in motion. If you decelerate too fast the rear wheels may skid as well.
• Do not touch the clutch or brake pedals, and do not straighten the steering wheel.
• Continue steering smoothly in the direction you want to turn, but do not turn the wheel violently or too far.
• As the car moves back on course, straighten the wheels and accelerate gently.

How to stop a four-wheel skid

In a four-wheel skid – which usually happens during hard braking – the wheels lock and the car slides forward not seeming to lose speed. It may skid in a more or less straight line, or off to the side if the road is steeply cambered.

STOPPING A REAR-WHEEL SKID
In both rear-wheel and front-wheel-drive cars, correct a rear-wheel skid by taking your feet off all three pedals and steering into the skid until the wheels come back into line.

• To control a four-wheel skid, ease off on the brake pedal until the wheels start to roll again. Do not push in the clutch pedal.
• Once steering control is restored, straighten the wheels.
• Reapply the brakes by repeatedly pushing them on and off with a pumping action – a technique known as cadence braking – to avoid locking the wheels again.

How to avoid skidding
A car is most likely to skid when it is driven too fast for the road conditions and the driver is forced to alter course or speed abruptly. This results in a sudden redistribution of the car's weight – it may be thrown forward or to one side – so that weight is lifted from some of the tyres to the extent that they lose their grip on the road (their area of contact with the road surface is only the size of an average man's shoe). Tyres will also lose their grip if the wheels lock during hard braking, or if the wheels spin during harsh acceleration.

Following a few commonsense rules will cut the chances of your being involved in a skid.
• Make sure your car has good all-round vision before you drive. Misty glass can prevent you from seeing a hazard in good time.
• Drive smoothly and steadily.
• Read the road ahead and adjust speed in good time to avoid hazards (see *Defensive driving*, page 202).
• Make allowances for road conditions. Braking distances are greater in wet weather, and on a slippery or icy surface may be much longer than normal (see box, this page).
• Keep a lookout as you drive for slippery areas such as ice, mud, wet leaves, patches of dry dust or loose gravel.
• Be particularly careful in damp weather after a long dry spell. Oil and rubber-dust deposits on the road surface are extremely slippery when blended with mist or water.
• Try to anticipate the actions of other drivers. Keep well clear of those who appear to be uncertain or rash.
• Make sure your car is in good condition. Worn tyres, worn dampers and badly aligned steering all increase the risk of skidding. The legal minimum tread depth in Britain is 1mm, but for safety it should be at least 2mm, preferably 3mm or more, for at least three-quarters of the width all round the tyre.

Learning to control a skid
About half the vehicles which are involved in serious accidents on snowy or icy roads in Britain were skidding before impact. Drivers may lose control in a skid because they do not recognise what is happening, so do not respond smoothly or quickly enough.

A good way to become familiar with the sensation of different types of skid is to practise skidding deliberately on a skid pan – an area with a surface designed to give minimum tyre grip. The local council or the police should be able to tell you where the nearest skid pan is, and how to join courses which use it.

Emergencies
on the road

HOW LONG IT TAKES TO STOP AT 50MPH

This chart shows how road conditions and tyres can radically affect the distance a car takes to stop from 50mph (80km/h). On a dry or damp road, or on ice, tread depth makes little difference. But in the wet, it is crucial.

At higher speeds, the differences between good and bad tyres become even more marked. At 70mph (110km/h) on a wet road, a tyre with 5mm of tread depth can stop a car in little more than half the distance it takes for a tyre whose tread depth is at the 1mm legal minimum.

Damp roads – such as occur in misty conditions – are even more dangerous than wet roads, largely because light moisture combines with the rubber dust and oil on the road to create a slippery film. Heavy rain washes the film away.

Road condition	Tyre condition	Reaction distance	Braking distance
Dry	Tread depth 1mm or more	50ft (15m)	106ft (32m)
Wet (2mm of water)	Tread depth 5mm	50ft (15m)	120ft (37m)
Wet (2mm of water)	Tread depth 1mm	50ft (15m)	145ft (44m)
Damp	Tread depth 1mm or more	50ft (15m)	172ft (52m)
Black ice	Tread depth 1mm or more	50ft (15m)	625ft (191m)

Brake failure at speed

If the brakes fail when you try to stop a car at speed – perhaps on the approach to a crossroads – your only option is to slow down using the engine and possibly the terrain, such as a steep upward slope or a thick hedge.

• Apply the handbrake smoothly and at the same time pump the footbrake in the hope that brake pressure will be restored.

• Keep a firm grip on the steering wheel while you do this, because using the handbrake at speed may lock the rear wheels and cause a skid (see page 208).

• Do not switch off the engine, because you will then be unable to use its power as a brake by changing down to a lower gear. Moreover, the car will take a long time to roll to a stop from high speed. In addition, on cars with power-assisted brakes, the brakes will not work properly with the engine switched off.

• With manual gears, change down to third gear as the handbrake slows the car, and keep changing down as soon as you can. Attempting to change too quickly will throw the car about. To engage lower gears at speed, try double-declutching (see box, this page).

• With automatic transmission, move the lever into L (low lock) or 2 (second gear) as soon as you are slow enough. In most cars, this is likely to be at about 20mph (30km/h).

• If you cannot slow down or stop fast enough to avoid a collision, try to run the car up a slope or bank.

• Mounting the kerb, if it is safe to do so, and scraping the car along a hedge or fence will also slow it down. You may be able to drive straight into a hedge to stop, but you risk hitting a concealed tree or fence post – or someone unseen on the other side.

If the handbrake fails on a steep hill

If the handbrake fails when you stop on your way up a steep hill, starting off again is difficult in a car with manual gears because, with your left foot on the clutch, you cannot move your right foot from the brake to the accelerator without the car rolling backwards.

• Swivel your right foot so that your toe remains on the footbrake while you place your heel on the accelerator.

• As you release the clutch pedal, ease your right toe off the footbrake and press your heel down on the accelerator. This should allow you to hold the car until you move forwards and can release the brake completely.

• If you cannot stop the car rolling backwards, turn the steering wheel so that the car backs into the kerb and does not crash into any other vehicles behind you.

WHY BRAKES FAIL

Complete brake failure is rare because modern cars have two separate circuits of hydraulic fluid operating the brakes. If one circuit is damaged, the other can operate the brakes on its own, although less effectively. Nevertheless, water, driving habits or inadequate maintenance can all cause brakes to become dangerously unreliable.

Brakes may become temporarily ineffective after driving through floods (see page 220) because the discs or shoes get wet.

They may also fail temporarily on a steep descent or after prolonged use because the fluid gets hot and may partially vaporise; if this happens, the pedal feels spongy when it is depressed.

Repeated pumping of the brakes usually restores pressure in these circumstances. Use a low gear on a long or steep descent and brake gently to lessen the chances of the brakes overheating.

Sometimes hard braking causes the brake pads to get so hot that they temporarily lose their stopping power. When this happens, the pedal does not feel spongy, and the brakes will work again after a short stop to let them cool off.

How to double-declutch

Changing down a gear enables you to use the engine as a brake, but changing down at high speed puts considerable extra strain on the gearbox.

On a manual gearbox, it is possible to minimise this strain and to make changing down at speed easier by using the technique known as double-declutching. Its purpose is to match the speed of the road wheels with the speed of the engine in the new gear and so make it easier for the cogs inside the gearbox to engage. To double-declutch down through the gears:

• Take your foot off the accelerator.
• Press in the clutch pedal.
• Move the gear lever to neutral.
• Release the clutch pedal.
• Give the accelerator a quick burst, then remove your foot.
• Press in the clutch pedal.
• Move the gear lever into the lower gear.
• Gently release the clutch.

With an automatic gearbox, double-declutching is impossible. The only option is to move the gear lever into a lower gear and risk some mechanical damage.

When a tyre bursts

HOW TO STAY IN CONTROL
If a front tyre bursts, counter the pull towards the side of the burst tyre by turning the steering wheel smoothly in the opposite direction. Once you are back on course, slow gently to a halt.

A burst tyre may be caused by a fault in the tyre structure, but it is much more likely to be caused by a puncture.

A punctured tyre does not always burst; it may deflate, giving the driver the impression he is travelling over something bumpy like cobbles, but the steering is affected in the same way as a burst. The main concern is to avoid slewing into other traffic.

If a front tyre bursts or deflates, the car pulls strongly to one side (the side on which the tyre has burst).

If a rear tyre bursts or deflates, the back end of the car may slide to one side.

• If a front tyre bursts, avoid braking if possible – let the car roll to a stop – and turn the steering wheel smoothly and gently to counter the sideways pull and keep the car on course.
• If a rear tyre bursts, brake gently – not suddenly or fiercely – and keep a firm grip on the steering wheel to keep the car on course.
• Do not change gear.
• Signal left, if you can, and steer the car to the side of the road to pull up.
• If you are on the outside lane of a motorway, it may be safer to pull onto the central reservation if possible.
• Try to stop on hard ground rather than a soft verge, because you will need a firm base for changing the wheel.

AVOIDING TYRE TROUBLE

Punctures occur when a sharp object such as a nail or screw lying in the road pierces the tyre wall. They tend to occur more in wet weather, probably because the water lubricates the screw or nail and helps it to penetrate. Many punctures are unavoidable, but some might be prevented by regular checking.
• Check tyres regularly for embedded stones, nails or other objects that might result in a puncture, and remove them.
• If anything is piercing the casing, change the wheel and get the tyre repaired.
• Check also for cuts, cracks or bulges in the sidewalls that might cause tyre failure, and get damaged or worn tyres renewed or repaired. A tyre that develops a bulge affects the car in the same way as a puncture, but there may be more warning that it is failing – such as a repeated slapping sound against the road.
• Always maintain tyres at the pressure recommended by the tyre manufacturer.

Driving through fog

In foggy conditions, being seen − particularly by drivers behind you − is as important as seeing. When fog is forecast, make sure all lamp glass on your car, front and rear, is clean and bright. The film of dust and dirt that collects on a lamp from road spray can cut the light intensity of the beam by half.

• By day or night, drive through fog with dipped headlights. Sidelights are not bright enough and full-beam headlights will reflect from fog particles and may dazzle you.

• Use fog lights if they are fitted. A single fog lamp must be used in conjunction with headlights, otherwise your car may be mistaken for a motorcycle.

• Switch on the windscreen wipers to keep the windscreen clear, and operate the washer as necessary. Use the demister to keep warm air blowing onto the inside of the screen.

• Keep your speed low. You should be able to stop within your range of vision, which could limit you to 5mph (8km/h).

• Drive with your window open. You may hear something coming, or hear a warning toot from a horn, even if you cannot see another vehicle. You need to glean every scrap of information in order to avoid obstacles and other traffic.

• Do not hunch over the wheel and peer forward. You will see better if you sit relaxed in your normal driving position.

• Try to drive in line with the nearside kerb or verge; if you have a passenger, ask him to keep you informed of your distance from the roadside.

• Alternatively, use the reflective studs in the middle of the road as a guide. But do not drive on the central line, or you may collide with vehicles coming the other way.

• Avoid getting too close to the vehicle in front. With vision restricted, you will not be able to anticipate it making an emergency stop. You therefore need more reaction time before braking than in normal conditions.

• Remember that fog makes road surfaces even more slippery than rain. So braking distances will be greater, too (see *How long it takes to stop at 50mph*, page 209).

• Beware of blindly following red lights in front; if the driver ahead gets into trouble, you could follow him into it. Plot your own course.

• Do not overtake unless you are sure it is safe to do so. When you are behind another vehicle, especially a large one, it pushes the fog aside and gives you the impression that the fog is thinner than it actually is.

• If you do have to overtake, or pass a stationary car, give plenty of warning by sounding your horn and flashing your headlights.

• Turn right with extreme care. Signal in plenty of time, and put your head out of the window to look and listen for oncoming traffic before you make the turn.

• If a large vehicle is going in your direction, follow behind it at a safe distance. In a high cab the driver has a better view of the road and may be able to see above the worst of low-lying fog.

• When you have to stop in fog, try to park off the road. If you are forced to stop on the carriageway or a motorway hard shoulder, switch on the car hazard lights.

• For a lengthy stay, put out a warning triangle as well. It should be 100yds (90m) behind the car towards the nearside edge of the road − 150yds (135m) behind the car if you are on a motorway hard shoulder.

THE HAZARDS OF FOG

Most fog occurs in the highly populated lowlands of central England and Wales, where the average amount is from 5 to 20 days a year; air pollution from factories, power stations and domestic heating increases its density. In patchy, swirling fog, the uncertain visibility and the unnatural quietness (fog particles muffle sound) strain a driver's senses and soon bring on fatigue. Sometimes, too, drivers do not slow down in fog, where they would in heavy rain or snow.

Research suggests that with vision restricted and landmarks blotted out, drivers lose all sensation of speed, especially on motorways. In addition, because fog distorts distances, other vehicles may seem to be farther away than they really are. It may also be that the stress of the conditions makes drivers want to forge ahead in the hope that the fog will be thinner farther on.

Many drivers drive too close to the vehicle in front in fog, probably in the belief that it is safest to keep in sight of the tail lights of the vehicle ahead as a guide to direction.

This can be dangerous because it leaves insufficient time for reaction and braking if the car in front stops, and this is what leads to multiple pile-ups.

If, for example, a driver travelling at 50mph (80km/h) sees an obstacle ahead, it might take him as much as three-quarters of a second to react and begin braking. In that time he will have travelled about 55ft (16.5m). If all the drivers travelling behind are driving at the same speed and have the same reaction time, the tenth driver in the chain will travel some 550ft (165m) after the first driver sees the obstacle before reacting. So unless each car is at least 55ft (16.5m) apart − about five car lengths − and has reasonably efficient brakes, a string of collisions is inevitable.

When the windscreen shatters at speed

Most standard windscreens are made of glass which has been toughened so that it does not break easily. If it does shatter, however, it makes a crazed pattern of small pieces that can obscure vision. Zone-toughened screens break so that larger pieces remain 'immediately in front of the driver, giving him enough vision to stop safely.

• If your windscreen shatters, do not follow the natural impulse to punch out an area of the glass with your fist as you drive. You risk cutting your hand or arm badly, or having a splinter blown into your eye.

• Instead, lean forward. It will help you to see more clearly through the shattered glass. Pull in and stop as soon as it is safe to do so.

• Stuff rag or paper tissues into the demister slots on top of the dashboard and spread newspaper or cloth over the car bonnet. Pad your hand with a glove or cloth, get back inside the car and push the glass outwards onto the paper.

• Remove as much of the glass as possible, otherwise it may fall out while you are driving.

• If you have any adhesive tape, such as masking tape, put a strip right round the windscreen so as to cover the grooved rubber flange which held the glass, and thus prevent fragments being blown into your face.

• If you have no tape, wear sunglasses to guard your eyes. Alternatively, pull the rubber flange off the car completely.

• Wrap up the glass in the newspaper. Dust any fragments off the top of the dashboard before removing the stuffing from the slots. Take the glass home to the dustbin – do not leave it at the roadside.

• Fit a temporary windscreen, if you have one.

Emergency screens are usually wrapped round the front door jambs so that they are held in place when the doors are shut.

• If you do not have a temporary screen, drive slowly and carefully to the nearest garage.

• Alternatively, you can get an emergency windscreen fitted at the roadside by a specialist firm (these firms are usually listed in the Yellow Pages of the telephone directory). If you call one, check whether there is an extra charge for attendance; at night this could be expensive.

• If you suspect that glass fragments may have fallen through the heater vents, do not use the demister until the system has been cleaned. You may be able to clear it yourself by uncoupling the hoses and sucking out the bits of glass with a vacuum cleaner.

Cutting the risks

A windscreen usually shatters because it has been hit by a stone flung into the air by the tyre of another car. There is no way of avoiding a stone, but there are ways to cut the risks.

• Consider fitting laminated safety glass to your car. The glass – which is usually tinted – will not shatter, no matter how hard it is hit. It may crack or chip, however, and eventually need replacement.

• On a newly surfaced road with loose chippings, keep your speed low and keep a more generous distance than usual between you and the vehicle in front.

• Consider taking out insurance to cover windscreen damage, if your policy does not already include it. Ideally, the insurance should cover the whole cost of replacement, with no excess and no loss of your no-claim bonus.

HOW TO GET THE GLASS OUT
Once you have stopped, cover the front seats and the bonnet near the windscreen with newspaper or anything else to hand. Block the demister slots as well. If you have no gloves, protect your hand with a cloth. Then push the glass out onto the bonnet.

If you feel drowsy at the wheel

If you find yourself beginning to nod off while driving, you must make an urgent effort to revive yourself until you can stop the car safely and wake yourself up.

Danger signs

Cruising for long periods in a warm car – particularly on a wide straight road such as a motorway – can be more hazardous than negotiating busy urban streets. With little to do, you can be tempted to daydream and let your attention wander dangerously. And the road sliding unvaryingly past the windscreen can exert a hypnotic effect powerful enough to put you into a mental state not unlike a trance.

Since fatigue builds up only gradually, judging – in yourself or someone else – when it has reached a dangerous level can be very difficult. These are the symptoms to watch for. If you notice any of them, take action at once.
• Continual yawning.
• Eyes feel heavy and are difficult to keep open.
• Difficulty in concentrating, especially on a monotonous stretch of road.
• Suddenly realising that you have no recollection of the last few miles you have travelled.
• A spasmodic jerk of the body, recalling you from the brink of sleep.
• The car begins to wander off course and you have to correct the steering hurriedly.

• You have to take rapid action to avoid a hazard you had not noticed.
• You start at a shadow, reacting to an imagined hazard.

Reviving yourself at the wheel

• If you do find yourself becoming drowsy, pull off the road to a safe parking place as soon as possible. Do not stop on a motorway hard shoulder, however – it is only for emergencies such as breakdowns.
• In the meantime, slow down.
• Direct the dashboard air vents onto your face. The blast of cold air will help to wake you up.
• Lick your finger and dampen your forehead and your eyelids – particularly at the inner corner of each eye. Let the air blow onto your face to cool it.
• Take a deep breath, purse your lips, and then breathe out again very slowly.
• Encourage passengers to chat with you.
• Wind down the window if the road is quiet and the weather dry. On a motorway or a busy road, however, let in blasts of fresh air only for short spells, because the extra noise increases fatigue.
• Play the radio or taped music only if it is something you will respond to positively. Some sounds can send you to sleep; others can irritate you and increase tiredness.

HOW TO STAY WIDE AWAKE ON A JOURNEY

• Do not drink alcohol or take drugs shortly before starting.
• Do not eat a heavy meal immediately before a journey; the process of digestion encourages sleep.
• Before a long journey, eat a light meal and take a rest. Do not set off on an empty stomach. You need to be comfortable to concentrate well.
• If you intend to drive through the night, make sure you have at least three hours of sleep first.
• Adjust the seat if necessary to ensure that you have a comfortable driving position before you set off.
• Avoid wearing tight clothes. When you sit for long periods, the stomach and ankles tend to swell up.
• If you are driving in bright sunshine, wear sunglasses. Glare puts extra strain on the eyes, and adds to fatigue. But do not wear night driving glasses or any other tinted glasses after dark; although they help to cut the dazzle of oncoming headlights, they restrict your ability to see dimly lit objects.
• Make sure the car is well ventilated.

• In heavy traffic, take advantage of holdups by exercising your limbs gently. For example, curl your toes, rotate your wrists and stretch your shoulders and neck. This helps the blood circulation and relieves boredom or frustration.
• On a long journey, alternate the driving with someone else, if possible.
• Suck boiled sweets occasionally for refreshment while you are driving.
• Make regular stops on a long run – never drive for more than three hours without a break.
• If you are driving abroad, take breaks more frequently than normal. Driving on the right and interpreting unfamiliar signs demand extra concentration and so will tire you more quickly.
• When you stop for a break, take a short nap if you feel you need it. But always get out of the car and go for a stroll to exercise cramped limbs and pep up circulation. A hot drink is also beneficial.
• On a brief stop, try taking your shoes and socks off for a while. Relaxing and cooling the feet seems to help to clear the head.

Fire in your car

A car fire must be put out very quickly because of the danger of the petrol tank exploding if the petrol vapour should ignite. As with any fire, the way to extinguish it quickly is to cut off its air and fuel supply.

• As soon as you notice smoke or flames, switch off the ignition but leave the key in position to avoid locking the steering.

• If the car is moving, coast to the side of the road if possible and stop.

• Get all passengers out and away from the vehicle.

• Disconnect the battery if you can, by pulling the wires off the terminals. But if the fire is under the bonnet do not open it wide, as air will increase the flames.

• If you do not have a fire extinguisher, try to smother the flames with a blanket, car rug or any thick material.

• If this is not successful, dial 999 and call the fire brigade.

Using a fire extinguisher

• If the fire is under the bonnet, lift the lid just enough to direct the extinguisher through it.

• Direct the extinguisher at the base of the flames and work methodically from side to side and from the edge inwards.

• Do not leave a patch uncovered, otherwise the flames may spring up again.

FITTING A FIRE EXTINGUISHER IN YOUR CAR

Every year, about 20,000 cars in Britain are damaged or destroyed by fire. About one-third of the fires are caused by faults in the wiring, and nearly as many by petrol under the bonnet catching fire. Others result mainly from collisions or are started by cigarettes.

An aerosol extinguisher of at least 3lb (1.4kg) capacity is effective for putting out most car fires. The extinguisher should be either of the type known as dry powder or one containing a liquid gas known as BCF (see *Protecting your home against fire*, page 152). Both can be safely used on electrical equipment. BCF fumes are, however, toxic in a confined space, so the car should be well ventilated once the fire has been put out.

A car fire extinguisher needs to be mounted in an easily accessible place, such as on the dashboard or in the driver's footwell – not in the boot.

Get it checked once a year by the manufacturer to ensure that the filling is kept up to capacity.

Stuck on a level crossing

Your chances of surviving a crash with a train are minimal. If your car stalls or breaks down on a level crossing, therefore, the priority is to protect yourself and your passengers – not the car. Even if the train driver can see you, he is unlikely to be able to stop in time. A train moving at 125mph (200km/h) takes up to a mile (1.6km) to stop.

• Get everyone out of the car and off the crossing as quickly as possible.

• Telephone the signal box immediately. The driver and passengers in an approaching train could be injured in an accident as well – and the sooner you can alert the signalman, the more chance he has of stopping any trains before they reach the crossing. There is an emergency telephone at most level crossings.

• Do not waste time trying to move the car before warning the signalman.

• Try to move the car off the crossing only if the signalman tells you that there is no train approaching.

• If the engine will not start, take off the handbrake, put the gear lever into neutral and try to push the car clear of the tracks.

• In a car with a manual gearbox, you can also use the starter motor to move it. Put the car in first gear with the handbrake off and your foot off the clutch, and turn the ignition key. The car will lurch forward as the starter motor turns.

• If you succeed in moving the car, let the signalman know immediately.

If the barriers come down

• If the alarms start to sound, the lights flash or the barriers come down while the car is still on the crossing, get everyone right away from the tracks. A derailed train or the wreckage from a crash can travel hundreds of yards from the point of impact.

• Abandon the car and everything in it. The train might be at the crossing within a matter of seconds – especially on a modern automatic type of level crossing.

Safety on crossings

There are about 10,000 level crossings in Britain, and each year they are the scene of 50-60 accidents, which cost the lives of between six and ten people. Motoring experts recommend four rules for crossing a railway line safely.

• Approach at a moderate speed.

• At an open level crossing – one with no barriers, attendant or warning lights – treat the crossing as if it were a major road. Stop, look both ways and listen carefully before you cross, to make quite sure that no train is approaching.

• Do not drive nose to tail over a crossing. Start to cross only when you can see that the road on the other side is clear.

• Do not stop on a level crossing for any reason. If you are already on the crossing when the lights start to flash or the alarms sound, carry on over.

Emergencies on the road

Stuck in snow

If you are forced to stop in snow or on ice, it is often difficult to start off again because the tyres cannot grip the surface. It is particularly easy to get stuck if you stop while driving up a hill.

The techniques described here for getting out of snow also apply to getting out of mud or sand.

If you get stuck on hard snow or ice

• Do not accelerate hard in an attempt to pull away. The spinning of the wheels will compact the snow and make gripping even more difficult; snow may also become packed into the tyre treads, lowering their gripping ability.

• Ensure that the wheels are straight so that the treads are in the best position for gripping the surface.

• Find something to pack under the driving wheels to improve their grip, such as sand, grit, sacking or twigs.

• To lessen the risk of wheel spin, start in

GETTING UNSTUCK
Give a stuck car's driving wheels something to grip by packing sacking, say, in front of them.

DRIVING ON SNOW AND ICE

• Make sure that tyres are inflated to the recommended pressures. Underinflated tyres do not give as good a grip. Radial-ply tyres, which have wide grooves, may grip snow better if they are inflated to a slightly higher pressure than normal.

• Keep your speed low because it takes much longer to pull up than on a normal surface. On ice, the braking distance can be ten times longer than normal.

• Drive in as high a gear as possible for the low speed. High gear reduces the amount of torque on the wheels, and so reduces the chance of wheel spin.

• Stay well behind the vehicle in front to give yourself plenty of room for braking.

• Use the brakes and accelerator very gently.

• Do not brake and steer at the same time.

• Brake with a pumping motion to avoid wheel lock. The brake lights flashing on and off also give a good warning to a car behind.

• Do not use the gears to slow the car. This could result in the wheels locking and causing a skid.

• Try to avoid stopping or changing gear on a hill. If necessary wait at the bottom until you can climb without interruption.

• Descend a steep hill very slowly in low gear, and use the brakes very gently and cautiously.

• In a country area, if snow is widespread use snow chains or snow traction clamps to improve tyre grip.

GETTING A GRIP ON ICE OR SNOW
Snow chains fitted around a car's tyres help to improve the tyres' grip on icy or snowbound roads.

second gear so that there is less torque (turning effort) applied to the wheels.

• Press the accelerator gently, just enough to move the car forward slowly, and slip the clutch as necessary to keep the engine revving.

• If there are any passengers in the car, they may be able to help by pushing the car forwards as you drive off. Tell them to stand at the sides – so that the car does not roll or slide into them – but well away from the driving wheels or they will be sprayed with dirt, snow and packing material.

• Once the car gets moving, do not stop to pick up passengers or gear until you have reached a firmer, level surface.

Getting out of deep snow

• It is sometimes possible to drive out of snow about 12in (300mm) or so deep by moving the car backwards and forwards to build up a track – a technique known as rocking.

• Try to move forward a few inches by engaging first gear and then revving gently, slipping the clutch as necessary to avoid stalling.

• While the car is as far forward as it will go, quickly engage reverse and move slowly backwards for a few inches.

• Repeat the backwards and forwards movements until you can mount the piled up snow and drive out of the trough.

• If this method fails, the alternative is to dig the snow away from in front of all four wheels, and use the techniques recommended above for moving off on hard snow or ice.

If you are trapped in a snowbound car

Driving is usually impossible in a blizzard, or if snow becomes deeper than about 12in (300mm). In a snowbound car, the main things to concentrate on are keeping warm and keeping awake.

• Stay in the car; it will give you shelter. Do not try to walk for help – you risk falling into a snowdrift or getting lost in a blizzard, and could die of exposure only a few yards from a building.

• Before the snow gets too deep, try to clear the area round the exhaust tailpipe. Otherwise poisonous fumes are likely to enter the car when you run the engine to use the heater.

• If you have a separate boot, take anything you need from it into the seating area. Look for an implement that you can use to make an air channel should the car become completely buried – a wheelbrace, for example.

• Keep warm by wrapping yourself up in clothing, rugs, blankets, sacking or carpet. Wrap your head up as well.

• Newspaper wrapped round limbs or stuffed into clothing helps to conserve body heat; it can also be used to improvise a hat.

• Run the engine and heater to help you to warm up for only about ten minutes every hour. Do not run them constantly; not only will the warmth make you drowsy, but you need to conserve fuel in case you are trapped for a long

time. There is also a higher risk of exhaust fumes entering the car.

• Keep awake. If you doze off, you are more likely to succumb to frostbite or hypothermia (excessive loss of body heat). Or you could suffocate if the car became buried by snow.

• Open a window to let in air occasionally. Use a window on the side away from drifting snow.

• Avoid drinking alcohol in the hope that it will warm you up. It dilates the blood vessels and so encourages the loss of body heat. It may also make you sleepy.

• Exercising gently from time to time will help you to keep awake and keep your blood circulating. For example, stretch or wriggle your toes, fingers, knees, shoulders and neck.

• Do not attempt violent exercise, as this will increase your need for oxygen, use up your body heat and make you tired.

• Do not keep the radio or car lights on constantly, or you may drain the battery.

• If the car gets completely buried by snow, open a window and poke an air channel through the snow. Use an implement such as an umbrella or wheelbrace if necessary. Keep the channel clear.

• If a number of cars are snowbound together, join forces with the other occupants. Sitting together in one vehicle generates warmth, boosts morale and helps you to keep awake.

SURVIVAL PACK

When motoring in snowy weather – especially in Scotland, northern England or the West Country – make sure the car is well equipped to keep you moving on a slippery surface and to keep you warm and occupied if you break down or become snowbound in cold, icy conditions. This is a list of useful equipment to keep in the car.

• Shovel.
• Sacking or bag of grit.
• Snow chains or traction clamps.
• Wellington boots.
• Extra clothing, rugs and blankets.
• Torch and spare batteries.

If you are going on a long journey – especially at night – in conditions where you anticipate you might be held up, consider taking some additional items:

• A hot drink in a flask.
• Emergency high-energy rations such as chocolate, biscuits or boiled sweets.
• Something to pass the time – for example, a novel, a battery-powered tape player or radio, a quiz book, a book of crosswords or pencil and paper.

Escaping from a car underwater

IF IT SINKS BEFORE YOU CAN GET OUT

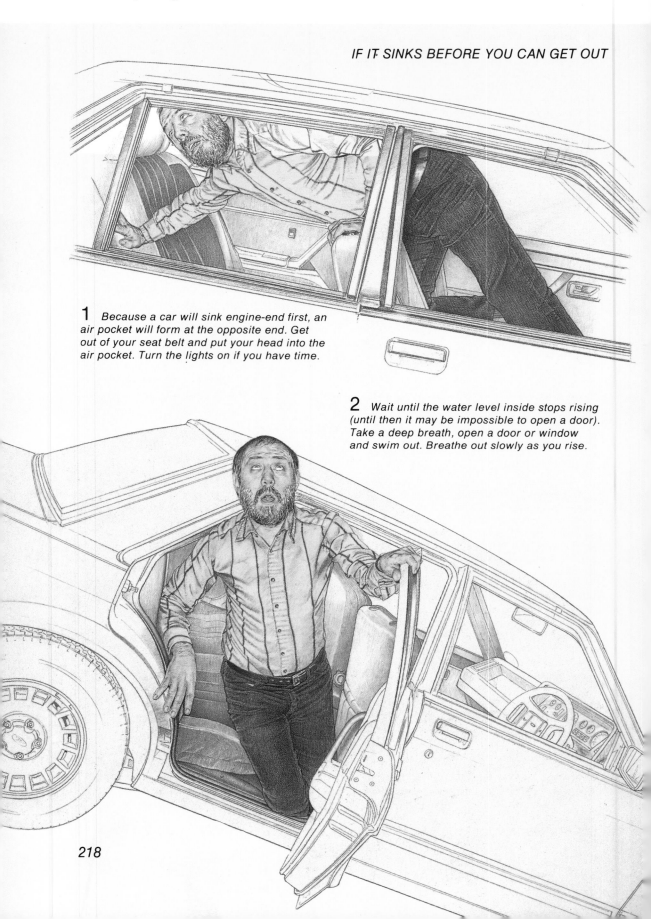

1 Because a car will sink engine-end first, an air pocket will form at the opposite end. Get out of your seat belt and put your head into the air pocket. Turn the lights on if you have time.

2 Wait until the water level inside stops rising (until then it may be impossible to open a door). Take a deep breath, open a door or window and swim out. Breathe out slowly as you rise.

If your car plunges into deep water, you may be able to escape through a door or window before it sinks – usually within a minute or so. But even if the car sinks with you inside, you can still escape because it may take 30 minutes or more to fill up with water. Precisely how long it takes depends on whether the windows are open, how well sealed the car is and how deep the water is. The deeper the car sinks, the higher is the pressure of the surrounding water and the faster it will force its way in.

How to get out of a sunken car
• A car will sink engine-end first, and a pocket of air will form inside at the opposite end near the roof. Use this pocket of air to escape.
• Release your seat belt.
• If there is time, turn the headlights and interior lights on. They will enable you to see better and will help rescuers to find the vehicle.
• Place yourself so that you can put your head into the air pocket and breathe. In a front-engined car, climb into the back seat.
• Close any open windows and ventilation ducts, if there is time, to retain air in the car.
• As the car settles, water will find its way in through cracks and holes until the pressure

inside and outside the car equalises. Keep calm and wait until the pressures equalise – when the water level inside stops rising. Until then it will be extremely difficult to open a door – and failure to do so might lead to panic, which could be fatal.
• When the level stops rising, take a deep breath, open a window or door and swim out.
• As you swim to the surface, allow air to bubble slowly out of your mouth. Because the air pocket in the car was under pressure, the air in your lungs will be as well – and will expand as you rise. If the excess is not allowed to escape, it could damage your lungs.

LIFE-SAVING BUBBLE
When Kenneth Hope's car plunged into the river at Mark in Somerset in November 1982, it turned over, trapping him inside. He crawled into the boot of the car where there was a large enough air pocket to keep him alive until he was rescued by emergency services several hours later.

He was suffering from exposure because of the chilly water, but was otherwise unharmed.

Emergencies on the road

IF THERE ARE SEVERAL PEOPLE IN THE CAR

If you are not alone in the car, form a human chain to make sure that nobody is left behind when you escape. Keep holding hands at least until everyone is out – and, if necessary, until you reach the shore and safety.

Driving through floodwater

Flooding is likely on many low-lying roads after heavy rain, and some roads have fords that are quite deep in wet weather.

• If you see a sheet of water ahead, slow down.

• If the water is obviously not very deep – other traffic may be going through, for example – there is no need to stop and check the depth. Wait until the car in front is clear of the water, then drive through slowly.

• Stop if you are uncertain of the depth. It is not advisable to drive on if the water level is higher than the bottom edge of the cooling-fan blades, because they will send a fine spray of water over the engine and could short-circuit the spark-plug leads or crack the hot engine block. In most cars, the blades are 10-12in (250-300mm) above the ground – about as high as the centre of the road wheels.

• Enter the water on the crown of a cambered road so that you keep to the shallowest part.

• Drive slowly in first or second gear – on an automatic in L (low lock) or 1 (first gear) – so that as little water as possible is splashed on the engine. But do not let the engine stall.

• To keep the engine revs high at low speed with a manual gearbox, apply steady pressure on the accelerator (keep it about half depressed) and at the same time slip the clutch by pushing the clutch pedal a little way down.

• Avoid changing gear. If you alter the engine speed there is a risk of water being sucked back through the exhaust.

• As soon as you drive out of the water, test the brakes. They are likely to be soaked and useless. To dry them out, drive slowly with your left foot pressing lightly on the brake pedal. Do not pick up speed until you have tested the brakes several times and are sure they are pulling evenly on all wheels.

HOW FLOODWATER CAN DAMAGE YOUR CAR

If you drive through even quite shallow water at speed, the car will throw up a considerable wave. The wave can be heavy enough to obscure your vision, and the water may wrench the front wheels to one side so that you lose steering control.

The surge of water may also swamp the engine compartment, damaging the electrics and causing the engine to stall. If this happens, you will either have to push the car out or wait for a tow.

If the engine stalls, water may be sucked back through the exhaust into the cylinders. This could damage the pistons, connecting-rods and crankshaft, and although the damage might not become apparent for another 100 miles (160km) or so, the repairs would be expensive.

Where the risk is greatest

Flooding is most likely: on roads beside rivers and lakes; in dips on undulating roads; on roads liable to subsidence (this is sometimes signposted); under bridges, where the road often dips; and where roadside fences and buildings ahead seem unnaturally low.

After heavy rain, keep an eye out for flood warning signs. Look out, too, for depth marker posts which are usually set up at fords and other places where flooding happens regularly.

HOW TO KEEP THE ENGINE GOING
Drive slowly but keep the engine revs high.
The flow of exhaust gases will then stop water
entering the tailpipe and stalling the engine.

Emergency repairs

When a car breaks down miles from help, there may be little or nothing you can do about it unless you happen to be carrying the necessary spare parts.

But some common causes of breakdown can be repaired temporarily on the spot with little more than ingenuity, and others can be dealt with merely by know-how.

All the methods described here have been used successfully by motorists in an emergency to get them home or to a garage.

If the fan belt breaks

If the ignition light comes on while you are driving, indicating that the generator is not charging the battery, the reason may be a broken drive belt or fan belt.

• This should not happen if the belt is regularly checked during the car's normal servicing. Check it at least once a year, and replace it as a matter of course every five years – even if it is showing no signs of wear. And carry a spare fan belt in the car.

• Do not be tempted, if the fan belt breaks, to improvise one from string, nylon tights or cord. These substitutes are often recommended, but they do not work properly.

• Modern fan belts work under much greater tension than the belts on older cars. This means that the substitutes are likely to break within a minute or two. And the broken pieces can cause expensive damage – by getting tangled up in the timing mechanism, for instance.

• If you do not have a proper replacement fan belt – or if you do not have the tools necessary to fit it – get to a telephone and call a motoring organisation or a garage for help.

• If getting to a telephone is impossible, you can, in an emergency, drive on without the belt.

• If you decide to do this, wait first of all for the engine to cool off – a process which usually takes about half an hour. Remove any loose pieces of belt from the engine compartment while you are waiting.

• After that period, drive on – keeping the engine speed as low as possible by getting into a high gear quickly – for no more than 3 miles (5km). If you drive any farther than this, you risk overheating the engine and causing expensive damage.

• Then stop and let the engine cool off again for half an hour. Repeat the process until you reach a garage.

• One good way to extend the driving range of the engine between stops is by turning the car heater to maximum. The heater will draw more heat from the engine, preventing the engine from overheating so quickly even if you get uncomfortably warm, and allowing you to drive a few extra miles before stopping.

• During the journey, the battery will not be getting topped up. So keep all the car's electrical systems turned off as much as possible. Otherwise you will in time drain the battery, and

without electrical power for the spark the engine will not work.

• In many modern cars, the fan that cools the engine is driven by an electric motor, not a fan belt. If your car is one of these, the ignition light coming on and staying on as a steady bright red probably means that the belt which drives the alternator (the modern equivalent of a generator) is broken. If this is the case, the engine will not overheat if you drive on without the belt. But you will, in time, drain the battery.

• Stop and remove any loose pieces of belt from the engine. Turn off all unnecessary electrical systems – including the heater fan and any radio – so as to preserve the battery's charge for as long as possible.

• Drive on to the nearest telephone or garage and get the belt replaced.

• At night, a fully charged battery will usually keep the engine going, with the headlights on, for at least an hour – although the lights will become progressively dimmer. During the day, if no lights or other electrical systems are being used, a fully charged battery will keep the engine going for several hours.

• If the ignition light comes on only intermittently or dimly, the reason is not a broken fan belt. Usually, it means that the engine is turning over too slowly. Rev up the engine a little and the light should go out.

If the petrol gets low

If the petrol gauge reads very low, you may, by careful driving, be able to conserve fuel long enough to reach a filling station.

• Drive smoothly, but not fast, in top gear – normally about 25-30mph (40-50km/h). Do not, however, use an overdrive or a fifth gear.

• Avoid stopping and starting if you can. Anticipate conditions ahead so that you can slow down as much as possible simply by taking your foot off the accelerator. The more the accelerator is pressed, the more petrol is consumed.

• Try to approach traffic lights at such a speed that you can cruise through without stopping. If you have to stop and start again, get into top gear smoothly and as early as practicable.

• When approaching a hill, gently build up speed beforehand. Do not stay in top gear too long as you go up the slope so that you lose speed and have to increase acceleration. Instead, change down so that you can keep going in a lower gear without having to press hard on the accelerator.

• Coasting down hills in neutral with the engine switched off is not recommended, both because it limits your control of the car and because, in the absence of the help provided by the engine vacuum, you may need to press twice as hard on the brake pedal to achieve the same braking effect. On automatic cars, it can lead to the gearbox overheating. On cars with power brakes and power steering, the effort required to operate the brakes and steering will be alarmingly increased. On a car with a steering lock, you could lock the steering as well.

• Try to avoid driving until the petrol runs out completely, because dirt and moisture from the tank bottom will be dredged through the fuel system and probably cause a blockage.

• If the petrol does run out, the engine is likely to splutter and falter a little before it finally stops. Pull off the road if this happens.

• If you are stranded on a motorway, pull onto the hard shoulder and use the nearest emergency telephone to call for assistance.

• On other roads, call out a garage or motoring organisation for help, but you may find somewhere to buy a can of petrol as quickly as you can find a telephone.

• It may be difficult to pour petrol into your tank from the can. If necessary, improvise a funnel from a rolled-up newspaper or magazine.

If the windscreen wipers fail

If the windscreen wipers break down in rain and you cannot put the fault right, you may be able – on older cars – to improvise a way of operating them manually.

• The fault may be that the drive cable from the wiper motor has broken. If it has not, disconnect the cable anyway – it is usually under the dashboard or bonnet near the base of the wipers. Otherwise the arms will be too stiff to pull.

• Tie a piece of string or flex to the wiper arm on the driver's side and stretch it through the open driver's window. An alternative could be a scarf or belt.

• Tie another string from the driver's wiper to the passenger-side arm and run it through the passenger window into the car.

• Ask the front passenger to pull the wipers back and forth across the windscreen by hand as needed to clear it. A driver alone should not attempt this, because it would limit his control of the steering.

• Alternatively, improvise a return spring such as linked elastic bands or a pair of braces from one of the wiper arms. Retain it against the jamb of the closed door on the same side. This may make the arms easier to operate manually by a driver alone, because he only has to pull one string. Again, though, it is safer for a passenger to operate the arms so that the driver has both hands free for steering.

• On a modern car, it may be difficult, if not impossible, to disconnect the wiper arms from the motor without an array of tools and considerable time. In these circumstances, abandon any idea of operating the arms manually.

• Either wait for the rain to stop; or, if you have to continue your journey for some overriding reason, drive on very slowly without the wipers, stopping as often as necessary to clear the windscreen by hand. Get the wipers mended as soon as possible. Driving a car with faulty wipers is against the law.

If you lose the wheel nuts

• If you lose the nuts on a wheel, perhaps while changing a wheel at night, remove one nut from each of the other three wheels, and use them

HOW TO WORK BROKEN WIPERS BY HAND
On older cars, disconnect the cable that drives the wipers, and tie something elastic such as a pair of braces to the driver's wiper. Clamp the other end in the door. Tie string between
the arms and run it through the passenger's window. If the wipers are stiff, though, as they often are on newer cars, do not force them. Wait until the rain stops, or do without.

SHARING OUT WHEEL NUTS
If you lose some wheel nuts while changing a
wheel, share out the remaining nuts so that
there are at least three on each wheel. Put any
extra nuts on the front wheels, not the back.

as replacements, so that you have three nuts
on each wheel.
• Drive on smoothly – braking gradually and
using only gentle acceleration – at no more than
30mph (50km/h), to lessen the strain on the
remaining nuts.
• Get a full set of nuts on each wheel as soon
as possible.
• If the wheel has only three nuts (or bolts) to
start with – as on a Renault, for example – it is
still possible to borrow from the other wheels.
But it is not advisable unless you have no alternative, because the strain on the remaining two
nuts is greater than with three on a four-nut
wheel, or four on a five-nut wheel.
• If you lose only some of the wheel nuts so
that you have a total of, say, 14 nuts between
the four wheels, put the extra nuts on the front
wheels rather than the back, because the front
wheels have to take the additional strain of the
steering. Also, in many modern cars, the drive
is through the front wheels.

If the engine is flooded with petrol
If you use too much choke or pump the throttle
when trying to start the car, the points of the
spark plugs can become soaked with petrol, and
the engine will not fire.
   Similarly, if the car stalls when you stop at a
road junction shortly after setting off, and will not
start again, overuse of the choke has probably
fouled the spark plugs.
• If the engine has a manual choke, push it right
in to increase the flow of air to the cylinders.
• Slowly press the accelerator to the floor and
hold it there. This also increases the airflow.
• With the accelerator held down, turn the
starter for a few seconds. This should blast the

plug ends dry and clear over-rich mixture from
the combustion cylinders. The engine should
then fire.
• If it does not fire, wait for about ten minutes
and then repeat the operation.

If the engine fades out because of vapour lock
Petrol sometimes vaporises in a car's fuel line
if it gets very hot – and the restricted fuel supply
will cause the engine to misfire or cut out
altogether.
   Such a vapour lock might occur on an older
car after a long drive at high speed, or in a
lengthy traffic jam, or in unusually hot weather.
It may also happen if you are driving at high
altitudes – across the Alps, say – where the
lower atmospheric pressure reduces the boiling
point of liquids, including water and petrol.
• Park safely in the shade and wait for the
engine to cool and the fuel to condense. This
will probably take at least half an hour. Then
start up again.
• There is no need to cool the inlet manifold
and carburettor by wrapping a wet cloth round
them. Waiting will do the job almost as quickly,
and with much less effort.
• If the trouble recurs, get the car checked.

If the accelerator jams
If the accelerator stays down when you ease off
it while driving, the return spring near the pedal
or the carburettor may be broken. This means
the engine will continue at high revs – it will not
slow down automatically.
• Try to hook your toe under the accelerator
pedal and raise it. This will slow down the revs
and stop the engine racing.
• Signal left and check in the mirror whether it
is safe to pull over and stop the car.

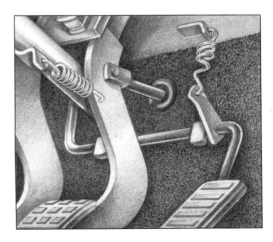

WHEN A THROTTLE SPRING BREAKS
Shape the larger part of the broken spring by
hand to form a new spring, if possible. If you
cannot improvise a spring, slip your foot
under the pedal and lift it to slow the engine.

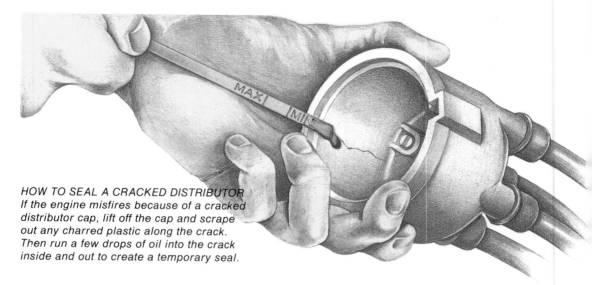

HOW TO SEAL A CRACKED DISTRIBUTOR
If the engine misfires because of a cracked
distributor cap, lift off the cap and scrape
out any charred plastic along the crack.
Then run a few drops of oil into the crack
inside and out to create a temporary seal.

• If it is, switch off the ignition and brake to a stop. Be careful not to turn the key so far that it engages any steering lock on the car.
• If you cannot pull over and switch off immediately – if you are on the outside lane of a motorway, for example – keep going until you can, braking if necessary.
• Remember, though, that the car's braking power will be below normal because of the counter-effect of the high engine power.
• Once you have stopped, you may be able to repair the return spring temporarily by unwinding part of the spring, forming the end into a new hook shape, and refixing it.
• If not, improvise a temporary spring using strong rubber bands, for example, or a piece of elastic.
• Fix the ends of the improvised spring in position with something that will not melt, such as wire, because the fixed point of the spring is often close to the exhaust pipe.
• Drive smoothly and slowly – no faster than 30mph (50km/h) – to a garage to get a new spring fitted. Do not jab the accelerator, or you will put too much strain on the temporary spring and probably break it.

If the distributor cap is cracked

A hairline crack may develop in the distributor cap because of damage or old age. This gives the high-tension current to the spark plugs an easy alternative path, so the engine becomes difficult to start or misfires.
• Lift off the cap and look inside for a telltale blackened track burnt into the plastic along the line of the crack by the escaping current.
• Scrape away as much of the burnt plastic as possible with something sharp, such as a small screwdriver or a nail file.
• Seal the crack with nail varnish, if you have any to hand, or run a small amount of oil from the end of the dipstick into it.

• If it is a bad crack, put the sealant on both sides – inside and outside the cap.
• Have a new distributor cap fitted as soon as possible.

If a fuse blows and you have no spare

If one part of the car's electrical system fails but others do not – if, for example, the lights go out but the brake lights and indicators work – the reason is most likely a blown fuse.
• Open the fuse box. The car handbook will tell you where it is – usually under the bonnet near the bulkhead or inside the car under the dashboard. Sometimes there is a spare fuse supplied in the box.
• The blown fuse will probably be obvious because it will show signs of burning. If not, take out each fuse and inspect it to see which has its wire strip burnt out.
• If possible, transfer a fuse of the same rating from a circuit you can temporarily manage without to the position of the blown one – for example, the fuse covering the rear window heater. In most fuse boxes there is an indication of which fuse covers which circuit.
• If the fuse you have transferred blows as well, there is a short circuit in the system – perhaps a chafed wire or a faulty switch. Try to find it and rectify it.
• If you cannot discover the fault, either drive on if possible – without using the faulty circuit – or call out a garage or motoring organisation. Do not try to drive on by replacing the blown fuse with a temporary fuse that is too strong for the circuit. It will not blow, but cables will overheat and you risk starting a fire.
• If you can discover and cure the fault, it is possible, in an emergency, to make a temporary substitute fuse by wrapping fuse wire round the core of the blown one. If the fuse is a rectangular type, push the wire between the connectors.
• Use 13 amp household fuse wire if you have

any in the car. If you have no fuse wire, abandon the idea of making a substitute. Never bridge a fuse with ordinary wire, or with some other piece of metal such as a paper clip.

• In addition, engineers do not recommend using a layer of silver foil from a cigarette or chocolate packet wrapped round the fuse holder – a method sometimes suggested as a last resort. This is because you run a high risk of damaging a major component or setting the car on fire.

Thawing a frozen door lock

If you cannot get the door key in the lock on a frosty or snowy morning – or if it will not turn when inserted – the lock is probably frozen. To free it, use one of the following methods:

• Heat the end of the key with a match or lighter, then put the key in the lock. Repeat the process several times until the lock turns freely. Do not force it.

• If the weather is not too cold, hold your bare hand over the lock for a few seconds – body heat is often enough to melt the ice in the lock. Alternatively, warm the end of the key in your mouth for a few seconds.

• Squirt a few drops of lighter fuel or antifreeze into the lock, but take care not to get it on the paintwork. Using a de-icer spray is not recommended because you cannot avoid spraying it on the surrounding paintwork, and it may damage the surface.

• To prevent the lock freezing in future, put one or two drops of light oil on the end of the key and work it round the lock so that it coats the interior. This will help to stop the lock interior getting wet. Repeat the procedure regularly, particularly during the winter.

Emergencies on the road

SPARE PARTS FOR EVERYDAY MOTORING

Carrying a few spares of the parts most likely to fail, as well as some tools and a few repair aids, can save any motorist hours of trouble.

• Generator drive belt (or fan belt) – a replacement of the type used for your make of car. Emergency fan belts are also available, but are not recommended. They do not last long and may be awkward to fit.

• Fuses – one or two of each type of fuse used in your make of car.

• Light bulbs – packaged sets are available for different makes.

• Spark plug – one of the type suitable for your car. You do not need to carry a complete set, because it is rare for all to fail at once.

• High-tension lead – a length of heavily insulated lead of the type used between the coil, distributor cap and spark plugs. Carry a length equal to the longest HT lead in your car, and any tools necessary to fit it.

• Duplicate ignition key – keep it in a magnetic box, which can be fixed to the outside of the car in a concealed spot.

• Emergency windscreen – a clear plastic screen packed in a cardboard holder.

• Can of fuel – useful if you are journeying in a remote area. The can should be of metal and clearly marked with the word 'Petrol'. Storage cans can be bought with built-in pouring spouts. Replace the petrol every three months or so. Petrol deteriorates in time, so that after a few months 4-star petrol will degrade to 2-star quality.

• Tools – a straight-bladed and a cross-headed screwdriver; a circuit tester; spanners of the sizes most common on your car; and a spanner for removing spark plugs.

Useful extras

• Torch.

• Radiator sealant.

• Water-repellent lubricant.

• Exhaust bandage and sealing cement.

• PTFE plumbers' tape – useful for packing out worn screw threads.

• Strong adhesive tape.

• PVC insulating tape.

• Tyre inflators – proprietary get-you-home tyre seals that contain compressed air and sealant. They are suitable for a flat tyre caused by a puncture and handy if you have difficulty in changing a wheel. But if there is any damage to the tyre structure, they may make the tyre difficult to repair later, and garages may be reluctant to handle them.

• Magnet – for retrieving small metal parts dropped into inaccessible areas.

• A coil of baling wire – soft, galvanised iron wire suitable for innumerable small repairs such as fashioning a temporary exhaust hanger.

• Jump leads – useful for obtaining a start from another car if your battery is flat. They are not safe to use, though, if your car has fully electronic ignition and fuel-injection equipment; check in your handbook to see if your car is of this type. When using jump leads, always connect the two batteries positive terminal to positive terminal (+ to +) and negative to negative (− to −). Connect the negative lead (usually coloured black) first, and disconnect it last.

• Tow rope.

• A length of cord.

• A packet of strong elastic bands.

Menaced by a hitchhiker

More often than not, someone thumbing a lift is quite harmless and intent only on being helped on his way. But there is always a risk that he is planning to rob you, and even if not, there have been cases of hitchhikers slashing the back seat or doing other damage. Police crime prevention experts advise motorists never to give a lift to a stranger.

• If a hitchhiker you have picked up threatens you with a weapon, do as you are told and drive on. Do not attempt to struggle with him.

• Look for the first opportunity to get out of the situation. The police suggest that, if possible, you stop the car at a place where there are a lot of people about – a bus station, say – and attract attention by yelling and screaming.

• Another way is to stall the car deliberately at busy traffic lights and pretend it will not re-start. With the build-up of other traffic and irate drivers, the attacker may run off, or you may manage to get away from the car.

• If you cannot shake off the attacker, hand over money, car keys or other possessions if ordered to do so.

• As soon as the hitchhiker leaves or you escape, write down all you can remember about the incident – where and when it happened, what the hitchhiker looked like, and what was said. Sign and date what you have written, and take it to the police; it will be powerful evidence if the hitchhiker is later caught and prosecuted.

If a girl tries to blackmail you

• If, as a male driver, you give a lift to a girl who threatens to rip her blouse and scream 'rape' if you do not give her money, remain calm. Make no attempt to touch her or argue with her.

• Drive straight to the nearest police station, flag down a passing police car or stop where there is a large crowd.

• Tell someone what is happening and ask him or her to call the police.

If you are flagged down at night

There is a possibility that what appears to be an accident or someone in need of help is a ruse to stop a car driver and rob him. This is most likely to happen to a motorist who is known to be carrying money and who regularly uses a particular route.

• As you approach the person flagging you down, lock all doors from the inside.

• Slow down and change to a low gear so that you can accelerate away if necessary.

• Turn your headlights to full beam to light up the scene so that you can assess the situation.

• If you slow to a stop, do not turn off the engine or get out of the car until you are satisfied that the situation is genuine. Be ready to drive off quickly.

• If you are not sure whether the situation is genuine, drive on and call the police from the nearest telephone.

Safety on two wheels

More than 70,000 motorcyclists are injured on British roads every year. Motorcyclists make up about one in five of all road accident casualties and they are about eight times more likely to be involved in a crash than a car driver. The commonest motorcycle accident is a collision with a motorist turning onto a major road, and it happens because the car driver simply fails to see the machine in time – even in daylight on an urban road.

The same circumstances account for most bicycle accidents as well. Four out of five of the 20,000 serious cycling accidents in Britain each year happen within a few yards of a junction.

For this reason the most important safety rule for motorcyclists and cyclists is: be visible.

On a motorcycle

• Make sure you can be seen. Wear brightly coloured clothing, or a fluorescent sash or waistcoat.

• Keep the headlight on constantly while riding, even during the day. But do not assume that the headlight alone will make you conspicuous. On smaller machines, particularly – 250cc and under – the light is not powerful enough to be very bright.

• Before overtaking, flash your headlight to make sure the driver has seen you. If you have been riding behind the offside edge of the car, his view of you may have been masked.

• Do not overtake on the inside. The car driver may not see you and could pull over towards the kerb or turn left in front of you.

• If the car in front of you turns left, beware of another vehicle pulling out across your path from the same side road. The driver may not have seen you behind the turning car.

• When motorcyclists ride in a group, the one in front should take up the best position on the road. Those behind should be staggered to right and left so that they have as much vision and braking space as possible.

• For a safe braking distance in dry weather, road safety experts recommend keeping as far behind the vehicle in front as you can travel in two seconds, which means allowing about 1yd for each 1mph (2m for every 3km/h). You can measure the distance using a roadside marker such as a postbox. You should be able to say: 'Only a fool forgets the two-second rule' (which takes about two seconds to repeat) in the time between the vehicle in front passing the marker, and passing it yourself.

• In wet weather, braking distances may be doubled, so you need a four-second gap between your machine and a vehicle ahead.

• If you want to brake when riding upright on a firm, dry surface, the safest and most effective way is to pull more firmly on the front brake than on the rear brake.

• On a firm but wet surface, put even pressure on both front and rear brakes.

• When riding with the machine leaning to one

side, when turning, or when riding on a poor surface such as loose chippings, avoid using the front brake at all.

On a bicycle

• Wear brightly coloured clothing, and a fluorescent sash and arm or leg bands.
• At night, make sure your lights are on. You must, by law, have working front and back lights and a rear reflector.
• Slow down when you approach a turning and look out for vehicles coming unexpectedly across your path. Be ready to brake suddenly.
• Keep at least 1yd (1m) from the kerb – to give yourself space to swerve into if a passing car comes too close. Give parked cars a wide berth; a driver getting out might not see you.
• Remember that a bicycle is a road vehicle like any other. It is just as illegal for a cyclist to cross against a red light or to go the wrong way up a one-way street as it would be for a driver.

PROTECTIVE CLOTHING: WHAT TO WEAR ON A MOTORCYCLE

• Your safety helmet, which is required by law, should conform to the British Standards Institution specification 5361 (1976) or 2495HP (1977).
• Wear goggles or a visor, whether part of the helmet or not. The law does not require you to wear them, but if you do, it requires them to conform to BS4110.
• A well-fitting, two-piece windproof suit (jacket and leggings) is convenient for normal use on a motorcycle. Leather gives the best protection from abrasions if you fall from the machine and slide on the road, but it will not keep out the cold and wet for long. For riding long distances or in very wet or cold weather, wear a one-piece waxed cotton stormsuit over your normal riding gear.
• Protect your hands with gloves whatever the weather. In summer wear thin, unlined leather. In cold weather, wear leather lined with silk or lambswool. Alternatively, you can buy heated gloves that have a small wire heating element along each thumb and finger. The elements are powered from the motorcycle battery and are quickly detachable.
• Wear strong, waterproof boots. When you buy them, make sure there is room for extra socks in cold weather. Zip-up boots are easy to fit, but in cold weather they may lose more heat than lace-up or strap-up types; a rear zip may also let in the rain.

If police stop you

The police can stop any motorist and question him – whether or not they suspect him of an offence. But they are not entitled to delay him for longer than he reasonably consents to stay, unless they make an arrest or have some other authority, such as a search warrant.
• You are not obliged to stop if you are flagged down by a civilian, even if he is a plain-clothes police officer, because you have no way of knowing whether he is a policeman or a thief.
• If a uniformed policeman stops you, give your name and address when asked. If you are genuinely in a hurry – rushing to see someone seriously ill in hospital, say – explain your haste and ask to give the details later.
• If the policeman does not agree to this, though, he can insist on taking your name and address on the spot anyway.
• You are not obliged to carry any motoring documents such as a driving licence with you. But if you have them, show them if asked. It will save you time. If you do not show them, or if you do not have them on you, the police can insist in any case that you produce them at a police station within five days.
• You must obey a policeman if he asks you to move your vehicle. Otherwise you can be prosecuted for obstructing the police – regardless of whether or not you were blocking the road and regardless of whether or not you were legally parked.
• If the police are looking for a stolen car, they may ask questions about your car, such as the registration number or the make of the tyres. Answer the questions as best you can – you will be helping to confirm that the car is yours.
• Be polite and cooperative, but do not answer any questions that you think might incriminate you. You are under no legal obligation to do so.
• If the police say they are going to arrest you, they must give you the reason for the arrest. Do not resist, even if you are innocent, otherwise you could be charged with resisting arrest or obstructing the police. And you could be convicted of that even if the courts find you not guilty of the charge for which you were arrested.
• Make a note of the reason you are given for the arrest – it could help your defence later – and when you reach the police station, ask to contact a solicitor.

If you are asked to take a breath test

• Only an officer in uniform can ask you to take a breath test.
• If you are asked to take the test, you are allowed a minute or two to consider it. But if you refuse to take the test, you can be arrested and are liable to be fined, jailed or to lose your licence – regardless of whether or not you were over the limit.
• If the breath test proves positive, you will be taken to a police station for further tests, but you will not be officially arrested unless you are uncooperative.

Emergencies in the water

If you fall into a river, lake or canal

Shock and cold are the biggest hazards in British waters. Inland waters are often very cold, and cold quickly saps the strength of even a good swimmer. Concentrate your efforts on getting out as fast as possible.

Deep, steady breathing will help to calm you. Keep your strokes slow and steady as you swim or tread water. Apart from these unavoidable movements, move as little as possible to slow up heat loss.

• As you fall, try to hold your breath, pinch your nose and avoid swallowing water. Once in the water, try to stand up; many canals and rivers are not very deep.

• If the water is too deep for standing and you cannot reach the bank at once, keep afloat by treading water. See if there is any floating debris at hand to cling to. If there is, use it.

TREADING WATER
One way to stay afloat is to tread water. Pedal with your legs as if you were cycling, and scull your hands back and forth in the water. Leave your clothes on; they help to keep you warm.

• Do not remove any clothing; you need it to keep warm. Air trapped between clothing layers may also aid buoyancy. But do discard heavy shoes and anything heavy in your pockets.

• Remove wellington boots if you are wearing them – they will fill with water and weigh you down. But do not discard them. If you cannot swim, you may be able to use the boots as air cushions to help to keep you afloat; turn them upside down, empty them of water and hold them under your arms.

• If you can swim, make for the nearest suitable bank. If there is a current, do not waste strength fighting it. Go with the flow and swim diagonally across it to work your way to a bank. If the river curves, head for the inside of the curve where the water is likely to be shallower and the current less powerful.

• If you cannot swim, call for help but avoid tiring yourself by screaming frantically. Stay calm and cooperate with anyone who is trying to rescue you. If he has swum to your aid, relax and leave him to take charge. Do not cling to a rescuer, or you may both drown.

• If the side is steep and you find it difficult to get out, look for a handhold while you choose the most likely escape point. Work towards it by edging from one handhold to another. If necessary, remain clinging to a good handhold and breathe deeply in between calls for help.

How to tread water

To keep your head above water without swimming, kick your legs as if you were cycling and continually paddle with your arms to add support and balance.

Alternative methods of kicking are with both legs brought up, knees outwards, and pushed down together (like breast stroke when swimming); or keep your legs straight and use a fast, beating movement of each leg alternately below the knee, as in the crawl stroke.

AVOIDING AN ACCIDENT

About three out of four of the people who drown in Britain each year die in inland waters, not in the sea. Many of the casualties are people who did not intend going into the water – they fell in while fishing, walking, playing, boating or cycling.

• Be cautious when alongside water. Banks are often wet and slippery, or may crumble underfoot.

• Never disregard danger notices. Do not be over-confident because you can swim. Swimming in cold water is very different from swimming in a pool.

• Do not go fishing on your own.

Rescuing someone from a river, lake or canal

Water-safety experts use a four-word rhyme to summarise the safest ways of getting to someone who has fallen in the water. It is: reach, throw, wade, row.

Never get into the water yourself unless there is no alternative and you are a strong swimmer. The shock of the cold water, the possibility of injury from submerged obstacles, and the risk of being pulled under by a panicking victim could put you in danger as well.

Reach

• If the person is not far from reach, give him encouragement while you find something to stretch out to him, such as a stout stick, a rope, or a piece of clothing.
• Lie on your front at the water's edge and anchor yourself in some way if possible. Hook your ankle round a post, or get someone to hold you. Tell the person in the water to grasp the stick or rope. Then haul him in steadily.

Throw

• If the person is out of reach, throw something, such as a life buoy or a child's rubber ring, to help him to keep afloat while you get help.

Wade

• If you decide to wade out to get nearer to the person in trouble, first test the temperature of the water and note any currents.
• Test the bottom with a stick before each step forward. There could be submerged obstacles or sudden changes of depth.

Row

• If a boat is available and you have the skill to manage it, use it to get near to the person, but take care not to get too close. Otherwise the

weight of the boat may push him under, knock him out or injure him. To lessen the risk of capsizing the boat as you haul him aboard, bring him in over the stern.
• If no other method is possible and you are a good swimmer, swim out with something buoyant such as a life buoy or tyre, preferably with

USING AN IMPROVISED ROPE
Reach from the bank using anything to hand. Tie pairs of trousers, jackets, scarves or towels together to make an improvised rope.

IT'S NEVER TOO LATE
Brian Miller's face was blue. He wasn't breathing and his heart was still. The teenager had been that way for 35 minutes. Yet his four friends went on working to revive him, blowing air into his lungs and pumping his chest to force blood round his body.

Brian had been pulled from the Nacimiento River in California after he fell into tumbling rapids and became trapped underwater against rocks. His friends – led by the youngest, 15-year-old Peter Anderson – had been trained to give artificial respiration (the kiss of life) and chest compression. They had gone to work on him at once. And that afternoon, March 29, 1983, not one forgot the teacher's insistence on never giving up.

Five minutes later – 40 minutes after Brian had been dragged seemingly lifeless from the water – his arm twitched, and he started to breathe again. After a spell in hospital, he made a complete recovery.

THROWING OUT A LIFE BUOY
Throw a life buoy underarm and aim beyond
the person in the water to be sure of reaching
him. Once he has hold of it, haul him in steadily.

a line attached to the shore (see also *How to deal with a panicking swimmer*, page 240).
• Keep your clothing on to combat the cold, but discard heavy shoes and anything heavy in your pockets before you enter the water.
• Tell the person to hold on to the life buoy, then tow it back. But let go if he attempts to climb on it or to grab hold of you directly.

If someone falls into a canal lock
• Never get into a canal lock to rescue someone while the lock is filling or emptying. The turbulence caused by the open sluices or valves can make it impossible for even the strongest of swimmers to stay afloat.
• If someone falls in in these circumstances, shut the sluices before you go into the water.
• If there is a boat in the lock, ask the skipper to stop his engine.
• Whatever the situation, make sure, before you go in, that there is a ladder for you to get out by; and throw in at least one life buoy with a line made fast to the lock's side.

Getting the victim ashore
• In a river, if there is a strong current, it may be difficult to haul the person straight to the bank. Instead, move downstream and haul him diagonally across the current. If there is a bend, aim for the inside bank where the water will be shallower and the current less powerful.
• If the side is steep, as in a canal lock or some gravel pits, try to tow the person to something he can grasp – a chain, say.

• Lifting a person out where the side is steep is very difficult on your own. Keep him from submerging by tying a line round him under the armpits. Tell him firmly and clearly why you are doing this; the cold and shock may have made him confused.
• Climb out of the water, holding the other end of the line; then tow him to a better landing point, or secure him while you get help.

KEEPING CHILDREN SAFE

• Keep a watchful eye on children playing near water, especially children under five – they can drown within a few minutes even in quite shallow water.
• Rivers, canals and gravel pits are not the only dangers for children. Other dangers include water butts, water tanks and garden pools. Make sure that butts and tanks are covered; where there are toddlers, cover garden ponds with a grid which is strong enough to support a child.
• Be prepared for accidents by getting expert instruction on artificial respiration and life-saving techniques.
• When near waterways, make sure you know where to find life-saving equipment and the nearest telephone.

Cut off by the tide

If you visit a bay, cove or islet and are unable to return because the water has risen and cut you off, it may be more than 12 hours before the tide retreats far enough for you to walk back by the same route. This is the average time between one low water and the next.

• Do not climb any higher than necessary to get out of the reach of the tide, and do not attempt to scale cliffs. If you get stuck, or fall and injure yourself, you will make rescue more difficult.

• When out of the reach of the water, wait for help. Keep a lookout, and wave a shirt or something similar if you see anyone who can help or can call the rescue services.

• If you are marooned on a sandbank, shout and wave for help. If you are some way from the beach, it is usually better to stay where you are and await rescue than to attempt to wade ashore, because there may be currents or deep channels between you and the beach.

WARNING FLAGS AT THE BEACH

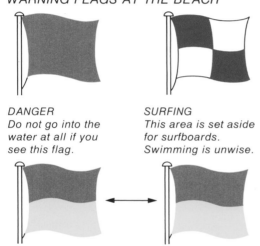

DANGER
Do not go into the water at all if you see this flag.

SURFING
This area is set aside for surfboards. Swimming is unwise.

PATROLLED BEACH
The stretch of beach between two red and yellow flags like this is supervised by lifeguards.

SIX HOURS ON A SEASIDE CLIFF

Seven schoolboys and their three instructors huddled together in the dark on two small cliff ledges above the Bristol Channel. All were shivering. Two were wet as well after falling into the water earlier.

The schoolboys – all 11 or 12 years old – were on an adventure course on the North Devon coast and they had set out with their instructors on the morning of March 28, 1983, to explore caves in Combe Martin Bay near Ilfracombe. Rounding a headland near the bay that afternoon, an instructor and one of the boys had fallen into a deep rock pool. By the time the pair had been rescued by the rest of the party, a spring tide had risen, blocking their way out. Trapped, they scrambled up the cliff to the ledges beyond the reach of the waves.

At dusk, the course organisers raised the alarm and at about 10pm the group were spotted by the Ilfracombe lifeboat. They were rescued – cold but unhurt – after six hours on the cliff. A course organiser said later: 'The party just got a bit behind schedule.'

But rescue experts point out that even such a small detail can matter. Coupled with the afternoon rock pool accident, the delay was enough to put ten lives at risk.

KEEPING ABOVE THE WAVES

An average of about one person a day in Britain has to be rescued by coastguards after being cut off by the tide. Each year, another 250 or so people have to be rescued from cliffs, where many take refuge after being cut off. The highest tides in Britain occur in estuaries. On the River Severn around Avonmouth and Cardiff, for example, the water can rise 40-50ft (13-15m). For most of Britain, the average distance between high and low water is about 13-16ft (3-4m).

Most resorts have two tides a day, with each high water about 12 hours 25 minutes after the one before. Southampton and the Solent, however, have four tides a day – a peculiarity caused by the sheltering effect of the Isle of Wight. Generally, high tide occurs 50 minutes later each day. The highest tides are spring tides, which occur every two weeks at about the time of a new moon or full moon. The lowest tides (neap tides) occur when the moon is half full – a week either side of a full moon.

• To avoid the risk of getting cut off, check the times of high tide before setting out. The time is often displayed on the beach; if not, look in a local newspaper or check with a tourist office.

• Use the tide table to estimate when the rising water will reach any part of your route off the beach. Allow a generous safety margin on top of your estimate. Weather conditions, currents and land configuration can all affect the predicted time.

If you get into difficulties while swimming

Cramp, exhaustion and strong currents are the commonest problems facing swimmers. Cramp and exhaustion can both be caused by cold.

If you get cramp

• Stop swimming. Turn on your back and float.
• Stretch the cramped muscle. If the cramp is at the front of your leg, point your toes and straighten the leg. If the cramp is in your calf or the back of your thigh, turn your toes upwards and straighten the leg. Use your hands if necessary to pull your foot upwards.
• When the cramp goes, swim to shore using a different stroke. If you must use the same stroke, keep alert in case the cramp returns.

If you become exhausted

• Swim ashore as soon as you begin to feel cold or tired. If you are too far out, or are too exhausted to reach the shore at once, turn on your back and float to conserve your strength.
• Raise one arm, keep it straight, and move it from side to side as a distress signal.
• When someone comes to help you, relax and let him take control. Do not try to cling to him.
• If nobody comes, float until you feel better, then make for the shore.

Caught in a current

• Do not try to swim against a current.
• If you are swimming in a river, swim diagonally across it to land farther downstream. If the river bends, aim for the bank on the inside

edge. The current will be at its weakest there.
• On the coast, waves piling into the beach can trap water behind offshore sandbanks. The sandbanks may be completely submerged at some or all stages of the tide. Gaps in the sandbanks then become outlets for the water, generating rip tides which may be invisible from the beach. Rip tides can flow out to sea at 4-5mph (6-8km/h) – impossible to swim against. But they usually dissipate within a short distance of the gap.
• If you are caught in a rip tide, let the current take you, then strike vigorously across it parallel to the beach. Once you are free of the current, turn back towards the beach.

If you get caught in waterweeds

• Unless you are carrying a knife with which to hack away weeds, try to kick yourself free.
• If kicking fails, try to roll the weeds from your limbs as if rolling down a sock. Duck your head under the water when you do this so that you can see what you are doing.
• Once free of the weeds, swim with a shallow kick until you are clear of them.

How cold water affects a swimmer

When you plunge into cold water, the first few seconds are taken up by huge, involuntary gasps (doctors call this hyperventilation), followed by anything up to several minutes of increased blood pressure and faster heartbeats as your body responds to the shock. At this time,

---

DO'S AND DON'TS OF SAFE SWIMMING

The highest proportion of drownings in Britain – more than one-third – occurs among men aged between 15 and 35, who are often the strongest swimmers. They die usually because they have ignored the safety rules recommended by experts.
• Never swim on an empty stomach or just after a heavy meal. Doing either can cause painful and disabling cramp. Allow at least an hour for your meal to digest.
• Test the water temperature before you get in. Do not swim if it is too cold.
• Always swim in a group, not by yourself.
• Look out for red flags or markers. They indicate areas unsafe for swimming. Flags or markers in other colours denote patrolled areas, surfing areas and so on (see *Warning flags at the beach*, page 233).
• Do not swim in water-filled gravel or sand pits, or in flooded quarries. They are cold and often deep with steeply shelving sides that may be impossible to climb out of. There may also be submerged obstacles.

• Never dive into water unless you are sure that the water is deep enough – at least 10ft (3m) – and free from underwater hazards such as weeds, rocks or other obstacles. Climb down or wade in if you can, but if you have to jump, do so feet first.
• Swim parallel to the shore and keep within easy reach of standing depth. Unless you are a strong swimmer, do not go out of your depth at sea at all. Wade out, then swim back.
• Watch for underwater hazards. Their presence is sometimes, but not always, indicated by visible breaks in the usual pattern of waves or currents.
• Keep an eye on a shore mark so that you can see if you are being carried out to sea or along the beach. Do not swim out with a current. You may not be able to swim back.
• Do not swim in the sea using inflatable swimming aids. You may be carried out of your depth without realising it – and be unable to get back.

there is a high risk of breathing water into your lungs and drowning. Hyperventilation also reduces the amount of carbon dioxide in the blood, and this can lead to cramp.

Loss of body heat is very fast in water. Even with a water temperature of around 20°C (68°F) it can exceed the body's capacity to produce heat. The body reacts to cold-water immersion by forming a cold outer shell to insulate the inner core, and the consequent cooling of muscles and nerves in the arms, legs and outer trunk weakens movement and reduces coordination. Even a good swimmer may drown quickly under these circumstances, and in water below 10°C (50°F), swimming ability commonly fails in less than 15 minutes.

The length of time you can hold your breath underwater is also severely affected by the tem-perature. In cold water it is likely to be only one-third as long as in a heated swimming pool; in water below 15°C (60°F) the average time is about 15-25 seconds.

In an indoor swimming pool the water tem-perature is generally between 26 and 29°C (80 and 84°F), but the sea around Britain's coasts averages only 7-10°C (45-50°F) in the south, with short-lived summer temperatures of 15°C (60°F). In the north-east it is generally about 3°C (5°F) lower. Inland waters such as rivers, lakes and streams are even colder.

If you have to swim in cold water, it is best to get in gradually, keeping your head well above water until the initial shock is over, and to try to control your breathing consciously. Wear a wetsuit as well, if possible. It will lessen the effects of the cold on your body.

HOW TO GET RID OF CRAMP
If you get cramp in a leg, float on your back and stretch the affected muscle – with your hands if necessary – until the pain goes. Then head for shore using a different stroke.

HOW TO SIGNAL THAT YOU ARE IN DISTRESS
To signal for help, wave one arm from side to side stiffly and deliberately. Tread water hard to counteract the extra weight out of the water.

Getting out of trouble in surf

The continuous pounding of heavy breakers soon saps the energy of an inexperienced swimmer, and can be hazardous even for a strong and proficient swimmer. Do not be tempted to swim in heavy surf if your swimming ability and experience do not go beyond swimming in a pool or in sheltered water.

How to swim ashore through surf

• Use the waves to get ashore. Between waves rest and wait, then swim vigorously shorewards as each wave crest approaches and keep kicking to get the maximum ride forward.
• To increase the forward motion, use a technique known as bodysurfing. Just as the wave catches you, stiffen your body. Hold your head up with chin thrust forward. Either hold your arms straight in front of your head, or back beneath your body, to make your body into a living surfboard.
• When the wave has gone past, tread water, and watch over your shoulder for the next wave.
• Once you are able to stand up, brace yourself against the strong pull of the water as it flows backwards between the waves. If necessary, crouch and hold onto the bottom.

How to get out onto rocks

• Time your landing so that you go ashore just behind the crest of a wave, to avoid being hurled against the rocks.
• Quickly get a good handhold on a rock so that you are not pulled back into the water as the wave falls back.

BODYSURFING TO GET ASHORE

1 *To bodysurf on a wave, swim hard towards the shore as the wave crest approaches. Watch it over your shoulder as you go.*

2 *As the wave catches you, straighten your body. Thrust your arms out, with your hands tilted up to help to keep you on the surface.*

- Hold on while the wave recedes.
- Scramble up the rocks as quickly as you can before the next wave reaches you.

How to cope with turbulent breakers

Waves become turbulent and thus difficult to swim through only after they get close to the shore and break. Before then, the easiest way to swim seawards past a wave – or to hold your position while the wave passes you – is to jump, float or swim over its crest.

Once the wave has broken, however, the water forms a turbulent tube, rolling over and over as it foams towards the beach.

Any swimmer caught in this turbulence can be tumbled helplessly, losing his sense of up and down, being unable to breathe, and risking – in shallow water – being hurled against the bottom and stunned.

A wave's turbulence usually affects only the upper layers of the water. So a swimmer who wants to get past the wave without being caught in the turbulence needs to get below it.

- As the wave approaches, dive well below the surface. The heavier the surf, the deeper you will need to dive.
- If necessary, dive right to the seabed and hold on by digging your hands into the sand while the wave passes overhead. It is often possible to feel the turbulent water skim your back as it passes.
- When the wave has gone by, gather your legs beneath you and push back to the surface. Watch for the next wave as soon as you emerge.

SWIMMING OUT THROUGH LARGE WAVES

1 *Avoid the turbulence of a large broken crest by facing the wave and diving towards and beneath it just before the foam reaches you.*

2 *Stay low, by crouching on the bottom if necessary and holding on, while the wave rolls over you. Then surface and watch for the next.*

Snorkelling: what to do if things go wrong

With a face mask, a breathing tube (snorkel) and a pair of flippers, a swimmer can breathe with his face below the surface and so watch the underwater world without interruption. But difficulties can arise, particularly in open water. All need prompt, calm action.

If water fills the tube

An unexpected wave or a careless dip of the head can send water down the breathing tube without warning.

• If this happens, do not breathe in. Make sure that the end of the tube is above water.

HOW TO CLEAR THE MASK UNDERWATER
Tilt your head back, hold the top of the mask and breathe out slowly through your nose. The air will force the water out of the bottom.

• Tilt your head up so that water can flow more easily from the tube.
• Blow out forcefully to expel the water.

If water leaks into the mask

• On the surface, one easy way to clear water from a mask is to lift your head above the water and pull the mask away from your face with your hands to drain it. Tread water with your legs while you do this.
• To clear the mask while you are still below the surface – during a dive, say – tilt your head well back until you are looking upwards towards the surface.
• Press the top of the mask firmly against your forehead.
• Breathe out slowly through your nose. This will fill the mask with air and force water out of the bottom. Stop breathing out as soon as the mask is clear, to retain the maximum amount of air in your lungs.

How good a swimmer you need to be

Because of the extra swimming ability needed to go snorkelling in safety, the British Sub-Aqua Club recommends that no one should take up the sport until he or she can:
• Swim 200m (220yds) freestyle (except back-stroke) without a stop.
• Swim 100m (110yds) backstroke.
• Swim 50m (55yds) freestyle wearing a 10lb (4.5kg) weight belt.
• Float on his back for five minutes, using hands and legs if desired.
• Tread water with his hands above water and using legs alone for one minute.
• Recover six objects in succession from the deep end of a swimming pool with only one dive for each object.

CHOOSING THE RIGHT EQUIPMENT

• Ask if the snorkel you buy meets the safety requirements of British Standard BS4532. Equipment made by a reputable manufacturer normally does, although it may not be so marked. Cheap equipment often does not.
• The best tube is a simple J shape, 12-14in (300-350mm) long with an internal diameter of 0.6-0.8in (15-20mm). Longer or narrower tubes are harder to breathe through. Do not buy a tube with air valves – these often look like table-tennis balls. If a valve jams it can cut off the air supply.
• The mask should be fitted with toughened safety glass – not Perspex, which is less strong and mists up more easily.
• The mask should cover nose and eyes only and should have a 'compensator' – a shaped nose-piece. It allows you to hold your nose through the mask, if necessary, and thus to clear your ears during a dive.
• Test that the mask fits by holding it against your face without putting on the straps. Breathe in through your nose. A well-fitting mask will stick to your face.
• The breathing tube should be separate from the mask. A built-in tube is dangerous because it can let water into the mask. It is also more difficult to clear.
• If you plan to snorkel in places where there could be weeds underwater, buy a diver's knife with a serrated edge (see *If you get into difficulties while swimming,* page 234).
• Buy buoyant flippers. They are less easily lost in the water.

Menaced by a shark

Each year there are about 50 shark attacks on humans around the world. Most of the attacks take place in tropical waters. But three out of five of the victims survive.

Two of the largest species of shark – the basking shark, which grows as long as 45ft (14m), and the gigantic whale shark, reputed to reach up to 60ft (18m) – are harmless plankton-feeders. All other shark species, however – and there are some 250 of them around the world – should be treated as dangerous.

If you see a shark near someone else
• Call a warning to anyone in the water if you spot a shark nearby.
• Make a noise – it may frighten the shark away. If you are in a boat, start the engine or bang on the hull.
• Help those in the water to get ashore or aboard a boat as quickly as possible.

If you are in the water
• Do not try to swim away fast if a shark approaches you. You cannot outswim a shark, and the frantic movement may simply add to the danger by attracting its attention.
• If you are spear-fishing, release at once any fish you have speared. Blood in the water tends to attract sharks.
• Make a noise in an attempt to frighten the shark away. Shout into the water, for example, or beat on diving tanks if you have them.
• Swim slowly back to the boat or to the shore. Swim backwards if necessary. Keep facing the shark all the time as you go, preferably underwater, to reduce the chances of being attacked from beneath or behind.
• A shark attack is often preceded by a nudge. If this happens, strike the shark as hard as you can with your fists, feet or any object to hand in order to startle it and drive it off.

LESSENING THE CHANCES OF AN ATTACK

Along Britain's coasts there is little danger of swimmers or skin divers being attacked by sharks, although the blue shark – which is dangerous to man – migrates from the Atlantic to Britain's south-west coast in summer. Usually, however, it keeps to deep water, far from beaches.

Most Continental waters are also reasonably safe from sharks, but swimmers and divers in the Adriatic or Aegean seas – off the coast of Italy and off Yugoslavia and Greece – should keep a watch for them.

Most attacks occur in or near the tropics, in water warmer than 21°C (70°F). The most dangerous places include New Zealand, eastern Australia, South Africa, the West Indies, Mexico, and the coasts of California and Florida in the USA.

Wreck survivors in warm waters on the open ocean are also at risk.

Sharks are unpredictable, and there is no reliable way of telling when they will, or will not, attack. Nevertheless, shark experts do recommend some ways of reducing the risk of an attack.
• In areas where there may be sharks, keep away from dark and murky water; sharks seem particularly adept at detecting prey in these conditions.
• Do not swim too far from shore or near deep channels. Sharks rarely swim into water that is shallow enough for a man to wade in.
• Do not swim at dusk or at night, when sharks are more likely to be looking for food.
• Do not swim or skin dive alone. Having another person close by helps you to keep an all-round lookout, and may deter a shark.
• Do not go into the water if you have a cut or scratch. Blood may attract a shark.
• Do not carry captured fish if you are spear-fishing. Put them in a boat.
• Where there are known to be sharks, make and carry what the French oceanographer Jacques-Yves Cousteau calls a shark billy – a stout stick about as thick as a broom handle and 3ft (1m) long, with a loop for the wrist at one end and a circle of small nails, points outward, at the other end.
• Jab the billy firmly into the snout of any shark that comes within reach. The nail points prevent the stick sliding off the shark's skin and help to keep him away from your body without wounding or angering him. A shark billy rarely drives a shark off completely, however; it only keeps it at bay.
• If you see sharks in the area where you are swimming or skin diving and you are close to shore or a boat, leave the water as quickly as possible.
• But remember that you are in most danger as you leave the water. For this reason, try to time your exit so that any shark is well out of striking range when you climb out.
• Clothing or a diver's wetsuit appears to give some protection from sharks. A naked person seems to be more liable to attack than a clothed one.
• Be careful if you have a partial suntan, with white areas exposed while swimming. Areas of light and shade also seem to attract sharks and make an attack more likely.

Emergencies in the water

How to deal with a panicking swimmer

A person in difficulties in the water is often panic-stricken and will cling with the strength of desperation to anything that offers a safe hold – including someone trying to help him. Never swim to the aid of a swimmer in distress if there is any other way of reaching him – from the shore, say, or from a boat (see *Rescuing someone from a river, lake or canal*, page 231).

Even trained life savers are taught to go into the water only as a last resort. An untrained rescuer runs a still greater risk of losing his own life in the attempt to save another's.

• If you decide that you have to swim to the rescue, try to stay out of the swimmer's reach. If, however, you need to get close to him – because he does not respond to your instructions, say – and he suddenly tries to grab you,

avoid his grasp by reversing immediately into backstroke and swimming vigorously out of his reach.

• Once at a safe distance, offer him one end of a piece of clothing, a towel or one side of a lifebuoy and tell him to hold on to that. Tow him to the shore by holding the other end.

• If he tries to pull himself towards you, let go of your end and swim out of his reach.

• If you have no choice but to make contact with the swimmer, approach him from behind.

• Grasp him firmly and support him in the water. Calm him down by talking, and tow him to shore using one of the techniques shown on the pages overleaf.

• Keep an eye on him as you swim and keep talking, if you can, to calm him.

AVOIDING THE SWIMMER'S GRASP
If the drowning person tries to grab you as you approach her, turn quickly onto your back and swim out of reach. If she grabs your leg, fend her off by pushing her away with your free foot.

IF YOU ARE GRABBED FROM THE FRONT
If the drowning person grabs you from the front, tuck your chin into your shoulder and take hold of her arms. Push them up and over your head and get well away.

Breaking a hold

• If a panicking swimmer grabs you, break free at once. If he grasps your leg, push it down into the water and thrust against his shoulder with your free foot.

• If he clutches you from the front round your head and shoulders, tuck your chin down into your shoulder, grasp him under the arms and push him up and away.

• If he grasps you from behind round your head and shoulders, lower your chin to protect your throat. Then grasp him by the wrist of his upper-most arm and pull down, at the same time pushing up his elbow with your other hand. In this way you both break his clutch and keep hold of him.

• As a last resort, take a deep breath and allow yourself to be pushed underwater. The aim of most panicking swimmers is to stay on the surface. Swim downwards until he lets go, then return to the surface out of his reach and grab him from behind.

Helping an unconscious or panicky person

• Tow an unconscious person by the chin from behind. Use a side stroke and keep your towing arm straight so that your legs are clear of the victim and you can look forwards regularly to see where you are going. Make sure you keep his face out of the water.

• If he is conscious but panic-stricken and needs firm control, grasp him under the chin, draw him close (ear to ear) and clamp his shoulder firmly with your elbow. If necessary,

IF YOU ARE GRABBED FROM BEHIND

1 *If the drowning person puts her arms around your neck from behind, tuck your chin down to guard your throat. Grasp the elbow and wrist of her uppermost arm.*

2 *Push her elbow up, at the same time holding her wrist down. Slip your head out through the arch that is formed. Then either get out of her reach or move round behind her.*

restrain him with your other arm as well. Tell him to stop struggling. Keep talking to him to try to keep him calm while you swim.

• In rough water, it is better to tow the person by holding him across the chest. This enables you to swim on your side, breathe more easily, and see where you are going.

Helping a swimmer with cramp

• Support him in the water while he tries to relieve the cramp by stretching the muscles.
• If the cramp does not go, tell him to lie on his back and tow him ashore using one of the life-saving techniques shown here.
• Once ashore, wrap him in a coat, towel or blanket. Stretch the affected muscle gently and massage it to relieve the cramp.

SAFETY FIRST

The central rules for a rescuer – recommended by the Royal Life Saving Society – are to stay out of the water if you can, and to avoid making direct physical contact with the victim if you can.

Specialised training in all the techniques shown here, and others, is available through swimming clubs or from the Royal Life Saving Society at Mountbatten House, Studley, Warwickshire B80 7NN; telephone Studley (052 785) 3943.

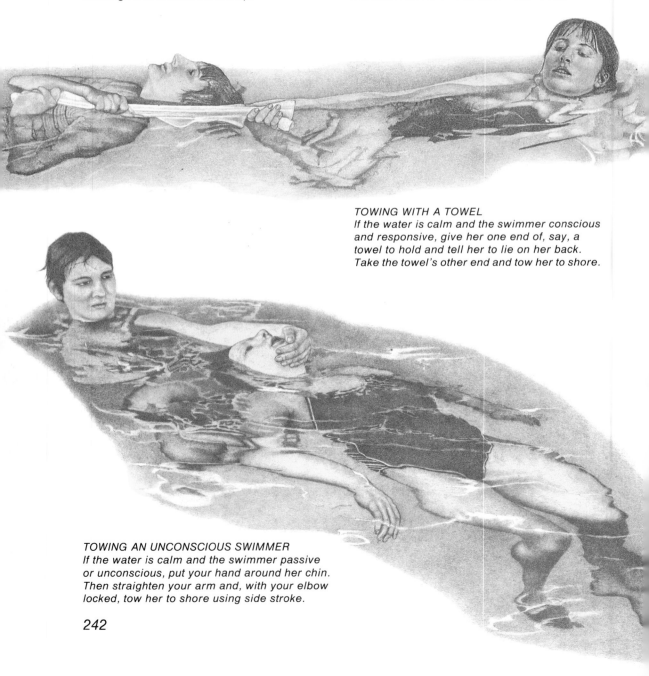

TOWING WITH A TOWEL
If the water is calm and the swimmer conscious and responsive, give her one end of, say, a towel to hold and tell her to lie on her back. Take the towel's other end and tow her to shore.

TOWING AN UNCONSCIOUS SWIMMER
If the water is calm and the swimmer passive or unconscious, put your hand around her chin. Then straighten your arm and, with your elbow locked, tow her to shore using side stroke.

TOWING A FRIGHTENED SWIMMER
*If the swimmer is nervous and you need firm
control, take her by the chin and pull her, face
upwards, until her head is by yours. Grip her
shoulder with your elbow and make for shore.*

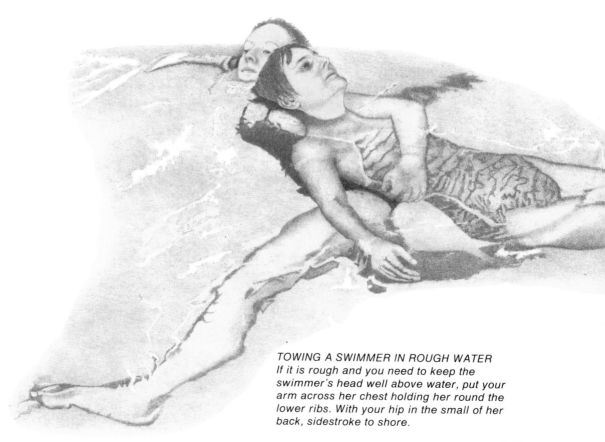

TOWING A SWIMMER IN ROUGH WATER
*If it is rough and you need to keep the
swimmer's head well above water, put your
arm across her chest holding her round the
lower ribs. With your hip in the small of her
back, sidestroke to shore.*

243

If you fall through thin ice

Inland waters in Britain do sometimes freeze solidly enough to be used safely as skating rinks. The country's changeable island climate, however, means that it is not possible to predict with any certainty when any particular patch of water will freeze up to this degree, nor how long it will stay solid.

The biggest danger for anyone who goes onto a frozen patch of water is not an inability to swim; clothes contain enough air, initially at least, to help to keep afloat anyone who falls in. The biggest peril is the shock of the cold water, which can paralyse the muscles and render even the strongest of swimmers helpless in a matter of a few minutes.

- Do not wait to be rescued. Get yourself out if you can. Cold will quickly sap your strength.
- Keep afloat by treading water – kick your legs as if you were cycling and continually paddle with your arms. Breathe deeply and slowly. It helps to prevent panic.
- Break the ice around you – moving generally towards the bank – until you find some that seems strong enough to hold you.
- Extend your arms forward onto the stronger ice and kick your legs behind you to bring your body up so that it is almost level.
- Keep kicking to drive your body forward, and pull at the same time until you are out of the water. If the ice cracks under you, keep flat and keep edging forward.
- When you reach ice that is firm enough to take your weight, roll away from the broken area towards the bank.
- Once safely on firm ground make for shelter and warmth. Keep moving to stay warm. If dry clothes are available, put them on. Otherwise, keep your wet clothes on until you reach somewhere warm.

TREADING WATER TO KEEP AFLOAT
If you cannot get out at once, tread water to keep your head and neck out of the water, and to stop yourself getting trapped under the ice.

BREAKING THE ICE
Use your fists to smash the ice around you, looking for areas that are strong enough to hold you. Move generally towards the shore, where the ice is likely to be thicker.

EDGING YOUR WAY TO SAFETY

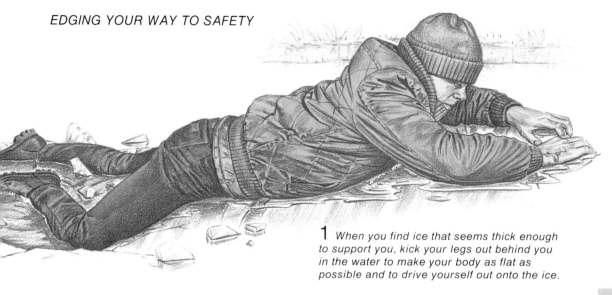

1 *When you find ice that seems thick enough to support you, kick your legs out behind you in the water to make your body as flat as possible and to drive yourself out onto the ice.*

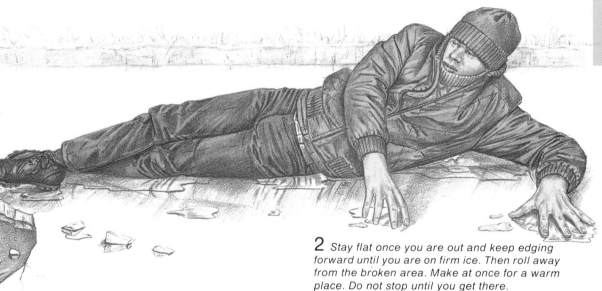

2 *Stay flat once you are out and keep edging forward until you are on firm ice. Then roll away from the broken area. Make at once for a warm place. Do not stop until you get there.*

DANGER – THIN ICE

• Never venture onto ice without first testing its strength. Find a firm handhold on the bank while you stamp with one foot at the edge in several places. Throw the largest stone you can find into the middle of the water area.

• Ice over shallow water is usually the safest. Ice over flowing water or underwater vegetation is weaker because the water is relatively warmer.

• Ice is not uniformly thick over a whole stretch of water. It gets thinner towards the centre. Ice also weakens as the sun's warmth builds up during the morning and early afternoon, and if the weather gets warmer.

• Never allow children onto ice without the supervision of a responsible adult. Do not allow a child onto any ice if the water below is deeper than the height of the child's waist.

• Make sure that rescue equipment is available – a light ladder, say, a strong rope, or a pole with a looped line attached. Take it with you if necessary.

If someone falls through the ice

A person who falls through ice into a pond or river – even someone who is ordinarily a competent swimmer – can drown within minutes. Even if the person can keep a head above water, the shock affects breathing and the cold can paralyse the limbs (see *Drowning – the perils of the cold*, page 251). For rescuers, therefore, the priority is speed.

Helping a conscious victim

• Stay off the ice yourself unless there is no other way of reaching the victim and there is someone else to pull you back if you fall in.

• Slide a stick, with a rope attached, across the ice towards the victim. If necessary, make a rope from sweaters or scarves.

• If you cannot reach the victim from the shore, lie flat on the ice so that your weight is widely distributed.

• Slide forward cautiously, pushing the stick in front of you, until it is within the victim's reach. Do not go any farther than absolutely necessary. Ice generally gets thinner towards the centre of a river or pond.

• Tell the victim to stretch her arms forward on top of the ice and kick back to keep her body as level in the water as possible. This will lessen the chance of her being pulled under the ice by any current, and make it easier for her to get out onto the ice.

• Tell her to grasp the stick or rope with one hand and break the ice in front with the other until the ice is strong enough to support her. Pull on the other end to help her haul herself out of the water.

• Tell her to kick her legs as if she were swimming and to slide forward onto the ice. Do not hold her directly or let her hold you, unless you are well anchored. Otherwise she could pull you into the water.

• Once she is on the ice, tell her to lie flat. Pull her in.

• Another way to help a conscious victim is to stretch a rope from bank to bank – of a pond, say – across the spot where he or she has fallen in. Tell her to grab hold of the rope and haul herself in, hand over hand.

Forming a human chain

• If there are several people to help and there is no other way to reach the victim, form a human chain.

• The first person should lie flat on the ice and slide towards the victim. The next should lie flat

REACHING A VICTIM FROM THE SHORE
Try to reach the victim without going on the ice yourself. Use a long stick, say, to push a rope within reach of her hands. Get someone to anchor you before you pull her in.

and hold the ankles of the person in front, and so on until the chain is long enough to reach from a safe position on shore to the victim.

Using a ladder on ice

• The easiest way to rescue somebody who has fallen through ice is by using a light ladder.
• Lie on the ice with the ladder flat in front of you and push it towards the victim.
• Tell the victim to pull herself onto the ladder and lie flat. Pull the ladder back.

If the victim is too weak to hold on to a rope

• To help a weakening victim, attach a looped rope to the end of a pole or light ladder.
• Slide the pole across the ice until the loop is within reach of the person in the water. Tell her to put the loop over her head and shoulders and under her arms. Then pull her in.
• If you cannot pull her in, tie the other end of the rope to a tree or post on the bank to support her in the water while you get help.
• If you have no rope or pole, slide over the ice at full length, grab the victim's arms or clothing and try to pull her out onto the ice.
• If this is impossible, hold her so that she does not slip beneath the water. Shout for help.

Once back on shore

• As soon as the victim is out of danger, check that she is breathing. If not, begin artificial respiration at once (see page 50).
• If the victim is breathing, wrap dry clothes or blankets over her own wet clothes and move her to a warm sheltered place. If she is unconscious, put her in the recovery position (see page 136) and move her on a stretcher.
• Once in shelter, take off her wet clothes and wrap her in any dry clothes, blankets or a sleeping bag (see *Hypothermia*, page 108).

HAULING ON A ROPE OVERHEAD
On a narrow stretch of ice, hang a rope from bank to bank. Tell the victim to haul herself hand over hand to the bank, if necessary breaking the ice with her feet as she goes.

Emergencies in the water

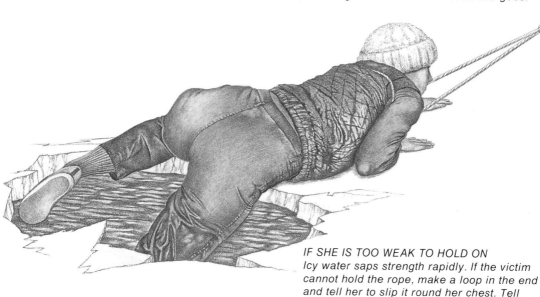

IF SHE IS TOO WEAK TO HOLD ON
Icy water saps strength rapidly. If the victim cannot hold the rope, make a loop in the end and tell her to slip it round her chest. Tell her to lie as flat as she can while you pull.

If you fall overboard

Falling into water unexpectedly can cause shock (see page 120). Cold water also saps the strength quickly, leading to loss of coordination, confusion and exhaustion.

- Call out to alert other crew members as soon as you feel yourself start to fall.
- Once in the water, inflate your life jacket (unless it is a permanently buoyant type). It will automatically bring you back to the surface.
- If you are wearing a life jacket, keep warm by adopting a foetal position with your knees drawn up to your chest (see picture, page 276).
- Raise one arm so that you can be seen from the boat more easily. Even though you may well lose sight of the boat before it turns – particularly in rough water or at sea – other crew members will be able to pinpoint your position more easily by your arm.
- If you are not wearing a life jacket, remove heavy boots or shoes and any heavy objects from your pockets, but do not remove clothing, especially in cold water. Even soaked through, it will help to conserve vital body heat.
- Tread water if necessary to stay afloat, but otherwise conserve heat by moving as little as possible. Float on your back if you can.
- Do not try to swim after the boat whether or not you are wearing a life jacket. You will make little progress wearing clothes, and the effort will quickly exhaust you.

Ways of keeping afloat without a life jacket
- In cold water, continue to float on your back if you can, or tread water while you are waiting for the boat to return. Breathe slowly and move

as little as possible; both will help to conserve energy and body heat.
- In warm water, use the drownproofing technique (see box, opposite).
- Alternatively, in warm water use a piece of clothing to construct a makeshift float. Remove trousers or slacks and knot each ankle. Hold the waistband open behind your head, the legs pointing away from you, then whip the trousers over your head into the water in front of you. Air will be trapped in the trouser legs.
- Pull the waistband down against your chest, and float in the crotch, with the legs under your arms like a child's water wings.
- A polo-neck sweater can be used in much the same way. Remove it by bunching it up under your arms, then pulling it over your head in one movement.
- Knot the neck and both wrists, and flick it over your head to fill it with air. Hold the sweater open waist-down underwater with the sleeves under your arms and the knotted neck against your chest.

Getting into a life buoy
- If someone on board throws you a ring life buoy, do not duck dive and try to come up inside it. Putting your head underwater will only make you colder and tire you more quickly. Instead, stay on the surface.
- Grasp the life buoy, bend your head and lift its near edge over your head and one arm.
- Work your other arm through the life buoy so that it supports you under both armpits and across your chest.

FLOATING TO CONSERVE ENERGY
If you have no life jacket, try to float on your back, sculling with your hands if necessary. It is less tiring than treading water.

HOW TO IMPROVISE A FLOAT

1 *Clothing can be used to make an improvised float. To make one out of a pair of trousers, take them off and tie a knot in each ankle.*

2 *Hold the trousers behind your head with the waistband open, then whip them forwards and down so that you trap air in the trouser legs.*

3 *Tuck the legs under your arms and float in the crotch of the trousers. Air will probably leak out slowly through the fabric, so repeat the process as necessary. Use this technique only in warm water. In cold water, keep your clothes on to help to conserve your body heat.*

DROWNPROOFING – A TECHNIQUE FOR SURVIVAL

In warm water, one of the easiest ways to stay afloat for an extended period without a life jacket is to use a technique known as drownproofing.

• Take a deep breath, relax, and hang in the water with your face under the surface and arms forward – as if lying over a barrel.

• To breathe again, breathe out underwater, pull down with your arms and lift your head until your mouth is just clear of the water.

• Take a deep breath, and continue alternately relaxing and breathing.

In warm water, this technique allows a swimmer to stay afloat with very little effort for hours, or even days. It works because the totally submerged human body with a lungful of air is slightly lighter than the same volume of water – and so will float naturally. Keeping part of the body constantly above the surface requires more effort and is more tiring.

Drownproofing should not be used in cold water – such as open water in and around Britain – because immersing the head speeds up the rate at which the body loses heat. It is better in cold water to float on your back, using the hands if necessary, or to tread water slowly, so that your face and most of your head stays out of the water.

Man overboard

When someone falls overboard from a motor boat or sailing dinghy, the priorities for action can be summed up in eight words: turn; shout; throw; watch; and approach to leeward.

• Start turning the boat as soon as you notice the accident.

• If there are other crew aboard, shout: 'Man overboard.'

• Throw a life buoy, or anything else that will float, to the person in the water. Make allowance for the wind when you throw.

• Keep watching the person in the water, or get someone else aboard to do so. If you lose sight of him, especially in rough water or at sea, it may be difficult to find him again.

• Steer the boat so that you approach from downwind of him. That way, there will be no danger of the boat being blown over him.

• Slacken any wire or rope guard rails around the deck so that they do not make it more difficult to get the person back on board.

• On a sailing dinghy, turn the boat into the wind as you come alongside and let the sails flap so that the boat stops. On a motor boat, stop the engine.

• Help the person in. In calm water, lift him over the stern (stop any propeller first). In rough water, though, bring him in over the side. Otherwise the drag of his body on the stern may swing the boat broadside to the wind and waves, and could cause a capsize.

• If the person's weight or exhaustion make pulling him aboard by hand impossible, tie a bowline in a piece of rope and put the loop over his head and under his arms.

• Get another member of the crew to hold the person while you tie the knot, both to keep his head above water and to stop him floating away from the boat.

• Hoist him aboard. If necessary, attach the rope to a halyard (the tackle used for hoisting the sails) to give yourself extra leverage.

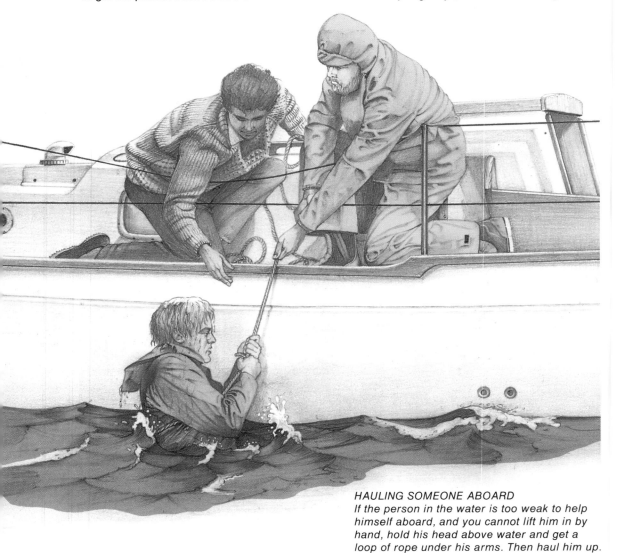

HAULING SOMEONE ABOARD
If the person in the water is too weak to help himself aboard, and you cannot lift him in by hand, hold his head above water and get a loop of rope under his arms. Then haul him up.

HOW TO MAKE A BOWLINE KNOT

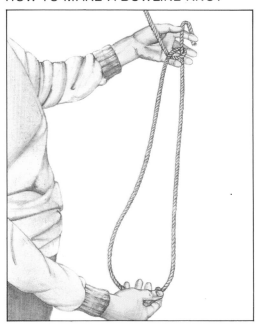

1 To make a rope loop which will not slip, twist a small ring in the rope about 4ft (1.2m) from one end, and pass the end through it.

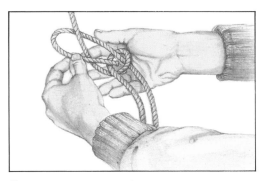

2 Take the end round behind the rope and slip it back through the same ring.

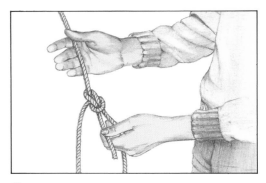

3 Pull the rope tight to form the completed bowline knot.

DROWNING – THE PERILS OF THE COLD

Nearly 1000 people drown in Britain each year, and many of them die not because they cannot swim, but because of the cold.

In 1984, doctors at the Institute of Naval Medicine in Gosport, Hampshire, tested the strength-sapping effects of cold water on ten volunteers, all capable of swimming fully clothed in warm water for at least ten minutes.

The swimmers went fully clothed into water at a temperature which is typical of British inland waters in winter: 5°C (41°F). Seven of the ten foundered after between two and seven minutes, and had to be helped out. Even the three who stayed afloat were exhausted by the experience.

The test's most striking result was that those who breathed slowly and deeply lasted longest. Those who breathed fastest failed. The doctors recommend that if you fall into cold water and decide to swim to safety, you should not start swimming at once. Instead, wait – moving as little as possible – until your breathing is under control. Provided you do not panic, your breathing will slow down naturally after four to five minutes.

If you are wearing a life jacket, hug your knees in a posture known as HELP while you wait (see picture, page 276).

When cold water can be a life-saver
At ordinary swimming pool temperatures, a swimmer will die after seven minutes underwater. He will become unconscious long before that, but he can be revived with the kiss of life. At very low temperatures, however, he can survive much longer, even if he appears to be dead.

Early in 1984, a four-year-old boy named Jimmy Tontlewicz was under ice and water for 20 minutes in Lake Michigan, USA, before he was pulled out by divers. The rescuers thought he was dead, but doctors at a nearby hospital were able to revive him.

The boy lived because the icy water had lowered his body temperature to less than 30°C (86°F) – 7°C (12.6°F) lower than normal – slowing his metabolism and reducing his brain's need for oxygen.

The message for rescuers is clear, doctors believe. Keep trying to resuscitate a victim of drowning until medical help arrives. Even when all apparent signs of life have ended, the effort could save the victim's life.

Emergencies in the water

Safety for windsurfers

The fast-growing sport of windsurfing has its dangers as well as its thrills. But following a few commonsense rules should keep you or get you out of trouble.

• Wear a life jacket or buoyancy aid and, on all but the hottest days, a wetsuit or drysuit.

• Do not windsurf at dusk, at night, or when visibility is poor. Never put out to sea in an offshore wind (one blowing away from the beach). The land and any buildings act as a windbreak, and by the time you feel the wind's true strength, it may be too late to get back to shore safely.

• Do not windsurf in places where there are no other people about. But do keep clear of others using the water.

• Carry a towline, in case you need to be pulled back to shore. Tie the sail rig to the board, so that you will not lose it if the foot of the mast jumps out of its housing.

• Always swim towards the board if you fall off, and stay with it if you get into trouble. If you start feeling tired, or the weather is too much for you, head for shore *before* you get exhausted and while you still have some energy.

What to do if you get into trouble

There are two recognised ways for a windsurfer in trouble to signal for help. Whichever you use, the first step is to lower the mast and sail into the water.

• Kneel on the board and raise both arms above your head as if in surrender.

• Alternatively, stand on the board. Hold on with one hand to the uphaul line (used to pull the mast up) for stability. Wave the other arm stiffly and vigorously from down by your side to above your head, and back. Some windsurfers carry a small red flag, or a red cloth, strapped to the ankle, to make the SOS message plain. Distress flares can be carried, too.

• If you are out of sight of possible rescuers and unable to sail back to shore, lower the mast and sail into the water and sit astride the board.

• Remove the foot of the mast from its housing. Hold the outer end of the wishbone – the end of the boom away from the mast – and lay the mast alongside the board in the water. Untie the sail from the wishbone and swing the wishbone up to the top of the mast.

• Roll the sail tightly towards the mast, removing the battens as you come to them and folding them into the sail.

• Lash the rolled-up sail and wishbone to the mast with the uphaul line and lay them lengthways on the board. Tie them to the board, too.

• Lie face down on the board, with your shoulders across a narrow section near the front, and paddle back to shore.

• If the wind, tide or current is against you, aim diagonally across it, not directly into it.

• If the sail rig gets seriously in your way as you paddle, roll it overboard and abandon it; it is not worth risking your life for.

Righting a capsized dinghy

A squall, a freak wave or a mistake in manoeuvring can tip a small dinghy over with little warning, throwing the crew into the water. Whatever the cause, the action to take is the same. The techniques described here are not difficult, but they do need some practice. Try them out several times by capsizing a boat deliberately in calm water close to the shore.

• Get clear of any entangling ropes or sails, and make sure that any other crew members are clear too.

• If the hull turns completely upside down, trapping you underneath, take a deep breath in the air space that will be left under the hull, then swim out underwater.

• Do not leave the boat, even if you cannot get it back upright. It will stay afloat indefinitely, and rescuers will be able to spot the hull more easily than they will see a swimmer.

• If the boat is completely upside down, a partial vacuum will be formed under the hull, sucking the boat against the water surface and making it difficult to turn onto its side. Pull down or climb onto one corner of the stern to break the vacuum, then roll the boat onto its side.

• Free the sheets – the ropes used to set the angle of the sails – so that the sails can swing

GETTING BACK ON BOARD
A practised sailor can step straight back in over the side of the boat as his weight on the centreboard pulls the hull upright. For an inexperienced sailor – especially in strong winds – it is usually safer to drop back into the water without letting go as the boat comes up, then to climb aboard over the stern.

freely. Otherwise the wind will fill them as the boat comes upright, and may tip it over again.
• Check that the rudder and tiller are secure and not tangled in the ropes.
• Make sure that the centreboard is fully down, then climb onto it, keeping your feet close to the hull to avoid breaking the centreboard off.
• If it is difficult to get onto the board, ask a crew member to throw one of the jib (front sail) sheets over the hull, and use the rope to pull yourself up.
• Once on the board, hold the side of the boat – the gunwale – or the jib sheet, and lean back, pressing with your feet against the centreboard. Your weight should pull the boat back upright.
• An agile sailor can climb in over the side directly from the centreboard as the boat rolls upright, but there is a risk that he could pull the boat over again on top of him, unless there is someone else in the boat to balance it. If you have not practised this technique, pull yourself round to the stern instead, and climb in there.
• If the weight of water on the sails prevents the boat from coming upright, lower the sails and try again.
• If there is more than one person in the boat, ask one of them to swim into the cockpit while the boat is on its side and to lie along the inside of the hull. He or she will be scooped up into the boat when you pull it upright, and can help to stabilise it while you climb in. The crew may also need to bail out the boat partially to improve its buoyancy before you get back in.

HOW TO AVOID A CAPSIZE

If the force of the wind threatens to tip your dinghy over – in any sailing situation – let go of the sheets (the ropes from the sails) so that the sails flap freely.

At the same time, steer into the wind (if you are sitting on the windward side of the boat, this means pushing the tiller away from you) and move quickly into the centre of the boat to balance it.

Whatever the situation, steering into the wind and letting the sails flap freely will end the sideways pressure on the boat and allow it to come upright again.

Avoiding collisions at sea

There are a number of internationally recognised 'rules of the road' on the water to stop boats colliding with each other. The rules are contained in detail in the International Regulations for Preventing Collisions at Sea (1972), available from Her Majesty's Stationery Office at 49 High Holborn, London WC1. These are the main rules:

• When two sailing boats are on a collision course, the one with the wind to port (coming from the left-hand side of the boat, looking forwards) must keep out of the way. If two sailing boats have the wind on the same side, the boat upwind must give way.

• Power boats must give way to sailing craft if they can, but a large power boat following a narrow channel may not be able to do so. In this case, the sailing boat should keep clear. All boats should give way to fishing boats, which have right of way while fishing.

• If a sailing boat is using its engine it is treated as a power craft, and must give way to boats under sail.

• Power boats approaching each other end on (or nearly end on) should both turn to starboard (to the right). If power boats are crossing each other's course, the one that sees the other on its starboard (right-hand) side must keep out of the way.

When there is a risk of collision, boats can also signal their intentions to other nearby boats by means of a whistle or siren. One short blast means: I am altering course to starboard. Two short blasts mean: I am altering course to port. Three short blasts mean: My engines are going astern.

If a sailing boat crosses your path
If you are in a sailing boat with the wind coming from the left-hand (port) side of your boat, you must give way to a sailing boat which is crossing your path on the opposite (starboard) tack. Steer your boat behind the other's stern to be sure of missing it.

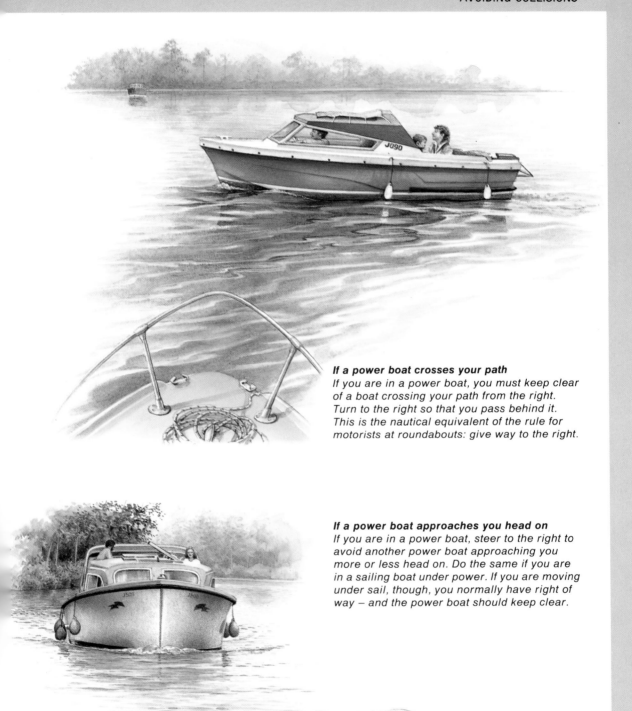

If a power boat crosses your path

If you are in a power boat, you must keep clear of a boat crossing your path from the right. Turn to the right so that you pass behind it. This is the nautical equivalent of the rule for motorists at roundabouts: give way to the right.

If a power boat approaches you head on

If you are in a power boat, steer to the right to avoid another power boat approaching you more or less head on. Do the same if you are in a sailing boat under power. If you are moving under sail, though, you normally have right of way – and the power boat should keep clear.

Running aground

A grounded boat must be freed quickly – provided that its hull has not been holed or damaged below the waterline. What to do depends to some extent on the wind direction, the type of keel and – in coastal waters – the state of the tide. If the tide is rising, the boat must be prevented from being driven farther aground. If it is falling, the boat must be moved off fast or it will be left high and dry. The easiest route off is usually the same as the route on.

• On a lee shore (with the wind blowing shorewards) or in a rising tide, drop all sails at once or turn the boat into the wind and let go an anchor to prevent the boat being driven farther aground. On a weather shore (with the wind blowing away from the shore) set the sails so that the wind helps to swing the bow towards deeper water.

• At the same time that you trim the sails, start the engine, applying moderate power in reverse. Your own wake rolling under the stern may free the boat.

Using a kedge anchor

• If these actions do not free the boat, try to haul it into deeper water by means of a kedge anchor – a light anchor with a chain and rope attached.

• Secure the end of the rope to a winch or run it through a pulley on the boat.

• Coil the rest of the rope and the chain in a dinghy or rowing boat and suspend the anchor over its stern. This saves you having to lift it over the side.

• Row away from the stuck boat into deeper water, paying out the rope as you go, then drop

HAULING A BOAT BACK TO DEEPER WATER
If you cannot get a grounded boat afloat on its own, try hauling it off with a light kedge anchor which has been weighted – with a chain, say. Tie one end of the anchor's rope to the stuck boat. Take the anchor out to deeper water in a dinghy. Drop the anchor. Return to the boat and haul in the rope to pull the boat free.

the anchor. Once the kedge anchor is firmly gripped on the bottom, return to the boat and pull in the rope to haul the boat free.

• If necessary, shift heavy weights onto the dinghy to lighten the load on the stuck boat.

Using the weight of the crew

• Another method of freeing a boat is to get the crew to rock it from side to side. This may break the suction of mud on the keel.

• If the rocking does not work and the boat does not have twin keels (known as bilge keels), it may be possible to free it by using the weight of the crew to heel, or tilt, it to one side; somebody can sit on the end of the boom if necessary. This will help to loosen the keel from mud or sand and may lift it sufficiently to free it.

• In a boat with a full single keel, which is

TILTING THE BOAT FREE
You can sometimes free a stuck boat by getting one or more people to sit on the end of the boom and then swinging the boom out. This will tilt the boat and loosen the keel, and it may lift the keel enough to set the boat free. The boat can then be hauled off with a kedge anchor (see opposite).

TABITHA

Emergencies in the water

normally deeper towards the stern, try moving all the crew well forward. This may weigh down the bows sufficiently to free the keel.

Leaving the boat high and dry
• If getting off proves impossible, prepare the boat for being left aground until you can get more help or until the next high tide. Normally, a boat will refloat as long after low water as the period before low water that it ran aground.

If a boat runs aground at the height of a spring tide (a high tide occurring near the time of a new or full moon) it could be about two weeks before the water reaches the same level again.
• Leave the kedge anchor in position and put out the main anchor as well.
• A boat with a single keel will heel onto one side as the tide recedes. Make sure it lies with

the keel towards deep water by weighting the deck – with an anchor chain, say – on the side towards the shallows. This will protect the superstructure from waves when the tide returns.
• As the water level drops, wedge sailbags, fenders and other padding under the leaning hull to prevent it being damaged as the returning waves pound it against the ground.
• Secure all loose gear on board. Shut off fuel and water supplies to prevent spillage. Close all seacocks and plug tank ventilator pipes. If possible, offload batteries onto a dinghy to avoid the risk of acid spilling from them.
• Pump out the bilge so that there is no waste water to weigh the boat down or to affect its balance while it is righting. Batten and seal all hatches to prevent seawater entering.
• If you can stay on board till the tide returns,

WAITING FOR THE NEXT TIDE
If you cannot get a boat afloat, leave it until the next tide. First, though, put out the anchors. If the boat has a single keel, weight it – with a chain, say – towards the shallows, so that it comes to rest with the keel towards deep water. Put fenders and other padding under the leaning hull to protect it. Secure loose gear. Shut off all pipes and pump out the bilge.

fill bags, pillow cases and buckets with sand. Store them on the boat until it begins to float, then empty them overboard. This will minimise the pounding the boat gets as the water rises.

• Alternatively, a deep-keeled boat can be kept upright by rigging beaching legs (props that fit under the hull on each side). If you have no ready-made props, improvise with a boom or spinnaker pole lashed to the boat's rigging.

• As a last resort, if there is heavy surf and a hard bottom, scuttling the boat will prevent it being pounded to pieces as the tide rises. To do this, leave the anchors in position, move out as much gear as possible, and open the seacocks so that the boat settles on the bottom.

• Later, as the water deepens again, close the seacocks and pump the boat out so that it rises with the tide and floats free.

TIPS FOR STAYING AFLOAT

• Bear in mind the state of the tide and the time of low water. Study charts of the area. Never sail too close to a lee shore.

• Be aware of any change of motion in the boat — such as a shorter rise and fall — that might indicate shallow water. If you are in any doubt, sound the depth with a lead and line.

• Bear in mind, too, the depth and shape of your keel. You may not be able to sail as close to the shore as other boats of apparently similar size.

PROPPING UP THE BOAT
If you have no beaching legs, use a boom as a prop. Tilt the boat with weights towards the shallows. Remove the boom and rest one end on the seabed on the shallow side. On mud or sand, put a plank underneath to stop it sinking in. Then lash the boom to the shrouds both at its top and at deck level. Stop the boom slipping by tying the top to a strong deck fitting.

Emergencies in the water

Dealing with a hole or leak

Colliding with a rock, a floating log or another boat can all put a hole in the hull of a small boat. But a hole need not mean that the boat will sink at once, or even at all.

Plugging a large hole
• On a sailing boat, if there is a hole on or near the waterline, sail the boat on a suitable tack to heel it over slightly and raise the hole from the water. On a sailing boat or motor boat, re-arrange movable equipment and the crew's position for the same purpose.
• If the hole is below the waterline, use the bilge pump or bail out by hand to control the water level while you make emergency repairs inside and outside the hull.
• Plug the hole first from the inside with any suitable material, such as sailbags, cushions or mattresses. Wedge the plugging in place with something solid, such as a table or seating boards. Alternatively, use a damage-control device (see box, this page).
• Then, if you have no purpose-built device, make what sailors call a collision mat. The idea is to spread the mat – which could be a tarpaulin or a spare sail – across the hole on the outside of the hull so that water pressure helps to hold it in place.
• If the hull is so shaped that canvas will not lie flat against it, wrap the tarpaulin or sail round a foam mattress or cushion, which is more likely to shape itself to the hull. Then use the bundle as a mat.

• To move the mat into position, tie chains or ropes to each corner. Then tie two or three corners of the mat to fittings on the damaged side of the boat.
• Loop the remaining rope or ropes over the front of the boat and work them along under the hull until the mat is pulled tight over the hole. Tie the ropes to fittings on the undamaged side of the boat. Then make for shore at once.

Repairing a small leak
• If a boat starts shipping water slowly, it may be difficult to find the source of the leak. So make a systematic check of the likely places where water could get into the boat.
• Check all seacocks – the valves that prevent a back-flow of water in any pipe that goes through the hull. Seacocks are usually built into the galley, toilet, engine intake and exhaust, bilge pump and cockpit drains.
• Check any fittings which pass through the hull, such as the rudder shaft.
• Check the stuffing box – the greased stuffing compressed round the propeller shaft where it goes through the hull.
• Check the water tank or tanks.
• Check seams in the hull.
• Once you find the leak, plug it firmly with caulking cotton (cotton fibre and sealant), greased rags, underwater resin, towels or any other similar material.
• Make permanent repairs as soon as possible when you get back to shore.

HOW TO USE A DAMAGE-CONTROL DEVICE

Specialist boating shops usually sell purpose-built damage-control devices. The devices, which resemble umbrellas, are designed to be used at sea to plug a hole in a hull until more permanent repairs can be made when the boat gets back to port.

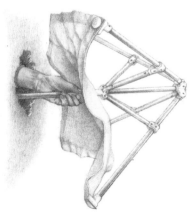

1 Close the device and push it out through the hole. Then open it like an umbrella.

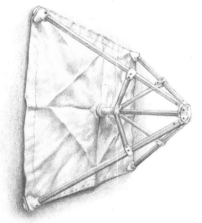

2 Pull it back against the hull to seal the hole. Tie the handle to a fitting inside.

TWO WAYS TO PLUG A HOLE IN A BOAT

1 *Tie three corners of a tarpaulin to the holed side. Loop the remaining rope under the bow and tie it to the other side. Adjust the ropes' lengths to position the tarpaulin over the hole.*

2 *Loop two ropes under the hull. Loosely tie them to fittings. Slide a mattress into place under the rope straps, then pull them tight.*

Fire on board

Because the fittings in most family-size sailing boats and power boats are largely made out of wood, and because the boats often contain fuel tanks and gas cylinders in a fairly small space, a fire, once started, can spread at alarming speed. If you are away from land at the time, there may be no easy escape route, either.

For these reasons, fast decisive action is imperative if a fire breaks out on board.
• Shout 'Fire' to raise the alarm.
• If the engine is running, turn it off.
• Throw burning equipment such as mattresses overboard. Do not, however, try to move a burning chip pan (see *Fighting a fire*, page 150).
• Never throw water on burning petrol or gas. It spreads the blaze, sometimes explosively. Instead, use a fire extinguisher containing dry powder or foam.
• In a sailing boat, if the wind is light, drop the sails; if the wind is strong, minimise its ability to fan the flames by sailing downwind.
• If the fire is below decks, make sure everyone is out, then stop air reaching it by closing doors, hatches and ventilators. Fight the blaze from above or from somewhere where you can retreat easily if necessary.
• If you cannot extinguish the fire quickly, evacuate the area or abandon ship if necessary.
• After the fire is out, damp down the area thoroughly with water.

GUARDING AGAINST A BLAZE

Most fires in boats are caused by sparks or naked flames igniting petrol or gas leaks or accumulations of petrol vapour (likely to collect where there are drip trays, spills, or loose caps on an engine or fuel tank).

You can cut the risk of fire on board, however, by following a few commonsense rules.
• Make sure that bilges (the space between hull and floor in a boat) and engine spaces have ventilation hoses that reach right to the bottom. Petrol vapour and bottled gases are all heavier than air, and so will accumulate at the lowest levels. Each fuel tank should have a vent pipe to disperse petrol vapour; the pipe should go out through the hull and be covered with wire gauze. You can also buy equipment for the automatic detection of petrol vapour or gas in bilges or cabins. Ask at a chandler's for information.
• Before starting a petrol engine, open all doors and vents and allow air to circulate for at least five minutes.
• Fit carburettors with drip trays (covered with wire gauze to prevent anything being

FIGHTING A FIRE BELOW DECKS
Get everyone on deck and shut any ventilators. Fight the fire from above so that you can escape if necessary. Aim the extinguisher at the base of the flames, sweeping it from side to side.

dropped in), and clean the trays before starting the engine. That way you will minimise the chances of leaking fuel collecting in the bottom of the boat.

• Fit flame traps in the air intakes.

• Check wiring and plugs regularly and replace faulty parts. Make sure that connectors have the correct fuse; a fuse with too large a capacity will allow cables to overheat.

• Ensure that generators and all switches are as far as possible above the bilges to minimise the chance of water causing short circuits.

• Do not strike matches, smoke, or use a kerosene or any other open-flame lamp inside the engine space. Anywhere on board, use only safety matches. Other types of matches, and also cigarette lighters, can spark if they are rubbed accidentally or dropped.

• Cover batteries so that tools cannot fall on the terminals and cause a spark.

• Avoid overfilling petrol tanks – leave some space for the fuel to expand. Check for leakages regularly. The top of the filler pipe should reach to the open deck so that any spillages will run overboard and not down to the bilges. Do not use petrol for cleaning. Instead, use clean cotton rags – and dispose of them, and all other rubbish, regularly.

Fire-fighting equipment

• Carry one fire extinguisher of at least 3lb (1.5kg) capacity, containing dry powder, carbon dioxide or foam. Extinguishers containing a chemical known as halon or BCF (bromochlorodofluoromethane) are less appropriate for a boat because they give off poisonous fumes which are dangerous in a confined space. Carry two extinguishers if there is a galley on board. Keep them in a place accessible from the open deck so that a fire can be fought from a safe position (see *Protecting your home against fire*, page 152; *Using bottled gas*, page 154).

• Carry a fire blanket and keep it near the galley. Never leave a cooking stove unattended while it is in use.

• Keep two bailer buckets with lanyards on deck for hauling up seawater.

DEALING WITH A FIRE IN THE GALLEY
If a cooking stove or a chip pan flares up, do not use water. Turn off the gas, then smother the flames with a fire blanket, holding it up as you approach to guard your face.

Deciding what to do in heavy weather at sea

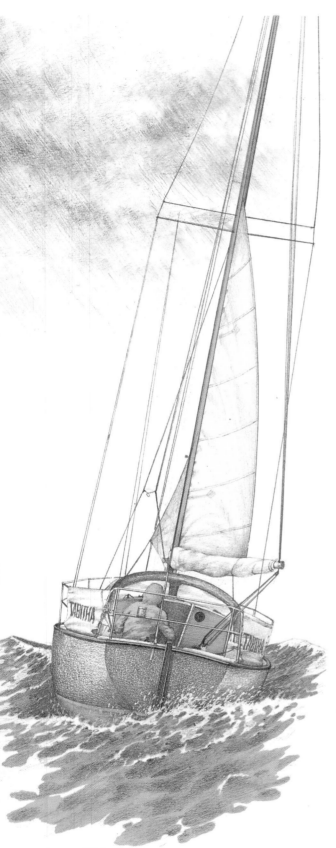

If the sea gets very rough while you are out in a sailing boat or motor boat, you have to decide whether to continue on course (under reduced power or sail so that you can keep control of the craft), head for port as fast as possible, heave to (stop moving), or run before the storm.

If in doubt, it is usually safer to stay at sea rather than to head for harbour and risk being swept and battered against the shore.

Whatever your decision, the boat needs to be rigged for stormy conditions (see *Caught in a storm*, page 270).

Rough seas are no place for the novice, though. Before you contemplate taking any boat into the open sea yourself, learn about the problems and risks at first hand by crewing for experienced sailors and boat-owners. Local yacht and boat clubs can often put you in touch with knowledgeable skippers. The clubs may also run training courses.

Continuing on course
Carrying on under reduced sail or power is a viable option if the wind is blowing in a direction suitable for the course you want to follow. If the wind is unfavourable, take other action.

Heading for port
Running for shelter is worth considering if the wind is right and the weather is worsening slowly enough for you to be able to beat it to a port or other refuge (such as the sheltered side of a headland). Remember, however, that heavy seas will slow you down.
• A motor boat or a sailing boat with an engine is likely to be able to head for port faster than a boat travelling under sail alone. But first check how much fuel is in the tank – refuelling from a petrol can may be impossible in rough water.

Heaving to
• Stopping at sea without anchoring – what sailors call heaving to – is safe only if you are well away from a lee shore: one the wind is blowing towards. But even a boat which is hove to still drifts slightly with wind and current. It could drift at 2 knots (just over 2mph) or more, and a storm could last up to 30 hours.
• The advantage of heaving to is that the boat's motion in the water is more comfortable for those on board. Also, little effort is required from the crew once the boat has been prepared.
• The disadvantages are that the boat will move gradually across the wind and downwind, which

HOW TO HEAVE TO
To hold a boat more or less in position at sea, pull the front sail to the upwind side of the boat and keep steering into the wind. The boat will then sail a roughly crescent-shaped course: forwards until it is almost nose-on to the wind, then back and sideways again as the wind pushes more on the front sail.

could carry it into more dangerous waters, and there is constant strain on the sails and rigging.

• There is also a risk of the boat being swung broadside to the waves and capsizing. This is more likely with a shallow, unballasted hull such as a flat-bottomed centre-board vessel.

• If you decide to heave to, the aim in effect is to sail the boat into the wind at the same speed that the wind is blowing it downwind.

• Back the front sail (the jib) – that is, set it so that the wind is pushing it backwards. It then counterbalances the forward thrust of the mainsail.

• Reduce the area of the mainsail so that little sail is exposed to the wind.

• Lash or hold the tiller or wheel to keep the boat pointing towards the wind.

Running before the storm

• Sailing downwind in a storm is a viable option only if you have plenty of sea room – that is, if you are far enough from land not to be blown onto rocks or the shore. You can reduce sails to a jib only if necessary, or run with bare poles.

• The advantages are that the boat remains under control and manoeuvrable, and the strain and wear on sails and rigging is kept to a minimum.

• The disadvantages are that the crew must be on the alert, with someone constantly at the helm to keep the boat pointing downwind; and the cockpit is exposed to the seas.

• There is also a risk that the following waves will break over the stern. This can be offset by trailing ropes behind the boat, looping the very long ones, so that the waves break on the ropes, and their force is diminished. The drag of the ropes also helps to slow down the boat, making it easier to control. In addition, it helps to keep the stern into the wind, lessening the chance that the boat will swing sideways to the waves and capsize.

• As a last resort, if you are well clear of land and shipping lanes, lower all sails, stow everything securely, shut all hatches and retreat below decks until the weather eases.

USING ROPES TO CALM THE WAVES
If you are sailing with the wind behind you in a storm, there is a danger of following waves breaking over the stern and perhaps swamping the boat. Cut the risk by trailing several long ropes so that the waves break on them instead. Loop the longer ropes and tie spare sail bags to them to slow the boat and increase the effect of the improvised breakwater. Trail the ropes and bags about one wave length behind the boat.

Emergencies in the water

Wind and weather

Around Britain's coasts, bad weather never arrives suddenly or unexpectedly. There are always warnings, such as changes in wind and clouds and falling barometric pressure – and the more abrupt the drop in a barometer's reading, the more severe the bad weather is likely to be. All the same, the weather at sea may be quite different from weather on land. So listen to shipping forecasts before planning to put to sea.

Weather forecasts for small-boat users are broadcast on BBC Radio 3 medium wave (247m/1215kHz) at 6.55am (7.55am on Saturdays and Sundays), and local forecasts are often posted outside a harbourmaster's office. Gale warnings are broadcast on BBC Radio 4 (1500m/200kHz) and also by coastal radio stations on frequencies listed in the British Telecom publication *Notice to Ship Wireless Stations*. If there are storm or gale warnings, stay in port. A small boat is unsafe at sea in winds of Force 4 and upwards, when waves are likely to be at least 3ft (1m) high.

Bad-weather signs

The pictures opposite show the visible clues a sailor or a hiker should watch for. All of them indicate that bad weather is on the way.

Other bad-weather clues can only be felt, not seen, or become apparent only over a period of time. These are the main ones:

TEN WEEKS IN A LIFE RAFT
Playful dorado fish kept yacht designer Steven Callahan alive when he was shipwrecked in mid-Atlantic in 1982. Swimming around his tiny life raft and following it as it drifted across the ocean, the dorados became his only food. The 29-year-old American speared them from the raft and ate them raw.

Solar stills – part of his survival kit on the raft – provided him with 3 pints of water a day (a little over 1.5 litres), just enough to live on.

The dorados also helped in his rescue. As he drifted near the Caribbean Leeward Islands, the fish attracted flocks of birds – which were spotted by a fishing boat. When the boat picked up Callahan on April 21, 1982, he was 3 stone (20kg) lighter than normal but remarkably fit after 76 days adrift.

Four years earlier, in 1978, two middle-aged Americans were washed out to sea during a fishing trip after the motor on their boat broke down. They survived the blistering heat of the Gulf of California by making their own still to turn seawater into fresh.

The two men improvised a stove by burning a mixture of petrol and oil from their broken-down outboard motor in two open tins. After their matches ran out, they lit the stove by sparking wires from the motor's battery against a petrol-soaked piece of cardboard.

They used the stove to boil seawater in a jerry-can. The steam condensed as it passed through a hose stuffed in the neck of the can, and trickled into a plastic bottle. The two men were found by a US Coastguard plane after a week and a half in their open boat – hungry but otherwise unhurt.

• The wind changes suddenly after several days of constant direction.
• The wind increases in the afternoon or evening.

Some weather signs indicate the approach of severe weather: a storm or gale. Mares'-tail clouds, and a copper-coloured sunset or sunrise are both danger signals. So are a number of other clues:
• A rapidly falling or unsteady barometer.
• Increasing humidity.
• A heavy but inexplicable swell at sea.

HOW TO READ A BAROMETER

The barometer most commonly used by sailors is the aneroid type shown below. Aneroid means 'without air'.

The pointer moves as air pressure squeezes a vacuum-filled metal bellows inside. The words on the dial – 'Fair', 'Stormy', 'Rain' and so on – are more traditional than useful. What matters more is a *change* in the reading. Generally, a drop in pressure indicates a storm is on the way. Steady or rising pressure usually means fair weather ahead.

MESSAGE IN THE SKY *Large, anvil-shaped and often fuzzy-edged expanses of cloud, such as that in the centre of this picture, mark the* approach of more blustery weather. The change will probably bring showers, and may build into a thunderstorm.

ICE HALO *A halo round the moon, formed when light is refracted by ice crystals, signals rain, or perhaps a storm, within 36 hours.*

OUTRIDERS OF A GALE *Mares'-tail clouds – high wispy streaks across the sky – are often a warning of high winds on the way.*

COPPER SUN *A copper-coloured sunset or sunrise is a warning of a gale or storm. A yellowish sunset indicates rain and wind.*

RED SKY AT MORNING *If the sunrise is red, or clear but with a red tinge, the weather is likely to take a turn for the worse soon.*

The wind and the sea

The Beaufort wind scale, devised in 1805 by the British admiral Sir Francis Beaufort (1774-1857), is still widely used in shipping forecasts and by sailors. It enables sailors to estimate the strength of the wind simply by observing its effects and without the need for precise measuring instruments. The scale begins at Force 0, when the wind is less than 1mph and the sea is flat calm, and rises to Force 12, a hurricane. The chart below shows how to judge the wind on land and sea, and gives the probable maximum wave height for each wind force. Average wave heights are lower.

FORCE THREE *A touch of foam on some crests and a few white horses mark a Force 3 wind – what sailors call a gentle breeze..*

FORCE FIVE *A wind of Force 5 or above can be hazardous even for experienced sailors.*

FORCE SIX *In a strong breeze, the waves can be anything from 8 to 13ft (2.5-4m) high.*

THE BEAUFORT SCALE ON LAND AND AT SEA

FORCE ONE: LIGHT AIR

Land: Smoke drifts slightly – but the wind is not enough to move a wind vane.
Sea: Tiny ripples shaped like fish scales form on the sea's surface. No foam crests.

Maximum wind speed: 3mph (5km/h).
Probable maximum wave height: Nil.

FORCE TWO: LIGHT BREEZE

Land: Breeze felt on the face. Wind vanes move and leaves rustle.
Sea: Small wavelets form. Crests are pronounced and have a glassy appearance, but they do not break into foam.
Maximum wind speed: 7mph (11km/h).
Probable maximum wave height: 1ft (0.3m).

FORCE THREE: GENTLE BREEZE

Land: Leaves and small twigs in constant motion. The breeze extends a light flag.
Sea: Large wavelets form. Crests begin to break into foam and there are occasional white horses.

Maximum wind speed: 12mph (19km/h).
Probable maximum wave height: 3ft (1m).

FORCE FOUR: MODERATE BREEZE

Land: The wind raises dust and loose paper and moves small branches on trees.
Sea: Small waves form and some begin to join together to make longer lines of waves. There are frequent white horses.
Maximum wind speed: 18mph (29km/h).
Probable maximum wave height: 5ft (1.5m).

FORCE FIVE: FRESH BREEZE

Land: Small trees sway, if they are in leaf. Crested wavelets form on inland waters.
Sea: Moderate-sized waves form into long lines. There are many white horses and some spray.

Maximum wind speed: 24mph (39km/h).
Probable maximum wave height: 8ft (2.5m).

FORCE SIX: STRONG BREEZE

Land: Large branches move. Telegraph wires whistle. Umbrellas used only with difficulty.
Sea: Some large waves, extensive white foam crests and some spray.

Maximum wind speed: 31mph (50km/h).
Probable maximum wave height: 13ft (4m).

FORCE NINE *The hull of a 60ft (18m) fishing boat is almost concealed by waves and driving* *spray as it plunges through a strong gale off the Outer Hebrides in Scotland.*

FORCE SEVEN: NEAR GALE

Land: Whole trees in motion. Inconvenience felt when walking against the wind.
Sea: Sea heaped up. White foam from breaking waves blows out in streaks with the wind.

Maximum wind speed: 38mph (61km/h).
Probable maximum wave height: 20ft (6m).

FORCE EIGHT: GALE

Land: The wind generally impedes progress. Twigs break off trees.
Sea: Waves are long and moderately high. Spray, or spindrift, blows from their crests. Foam blown in clearly defined streaks.
Maximum wind speed: 46mph (74km/h).
Probable maximum wave height: 25ft (7.5m).

FORCE NINE: STRONG GALE

Land: Slight structural damage – chimney pots and slates are blown off.
Sea: Waves are high, their crests toppling, tumbling and rolling over. There are dense white streaks of foam and spray reduces visibility.
Maximum wind speed: 54mph (87km/h).
Probable maximum wave height: 33ft (9.75m).

FORCE TEN: STORM

Land: Rare in inland Britain. Considerable structural damage and trees uprooted.
Sea: High waves, with long overhanging crests, tumble heavily, shock-like. Sea surface appears white. Visibility poor.
Maximum wind speed: 63mph (101km/h).
Probable maximum wave height: 42ft (12.5m).

FORCE ELEVEN: VIOLENT STORM

Land: Widespread damage caused.

Sea: Exceptionally high waves, sometimes concealing small and medium-sized ships. Crests blown into froth. Foam everywhere. Visibility poor.
Maximum wind speed: 72mph (116km/h).
Probable maximum wave height: 53ft (16m).

FORCE TWELVE: HURRICANE

Land: Mostly confined to the tropics. Widespread damage caused.
Sea: The whole of the sea's surface is white with driving spray. Foam and spray fill the air and visibility is bad.
Maximum wind speed: Over 72mph (116km/h).
Probable maximum wave height: Unlimited.

Caught in a storm

The safest strategy for a small boat caught in a storm is to reduce power in order to steady the vessel and make it easier to control, and to secure everything movable.

In a sailing boat
- Reduce the sail area. Lash down deck gear.
- In stormy weather, it is usually safest to sail as nearly into the wind as possible – provided that this course does not take you into dangerous waters (see *Deciding what to do in heavy weather at sea*, page 264).

- Check the security of lifelines and jackstays (lines to which safety harnesses are clipped). Put on a life jacket if you are not already wearing one. Strap on a safety harness, too.
- Pump the bilge dry and check that the cockpit drains are clear. Close all other hatches, seacocks, ventilators and exhausts.
- Start the engine (if there is one) to check that it is working. Then shut it down to conserve fuel in case you need it later.

In a motor boat
- Head for the nearest shelter.
- Get passengers to squat as low as possible to improve the boat's stability.
- Head into the waves if possible, keeping speed low (to cut down spray and water from the waves). But keep up sufficient speed to maintain full steering power.
- If the engine fails, ride at anchor or put out a sea anchor – a cone-shaped canvas bag that

HOW TO USE A SEA ANCHOR
A sea anchor acts as a drag on a boat, keeping whichever end it is tied to pointing into the wind. It is usually trailed from the front.

IMPROVISED SEA ANCHORS

If you have no proper sea anchor, an old tyre or fender, weighted with chain, can be used as a makeshift but effective sea anchor.

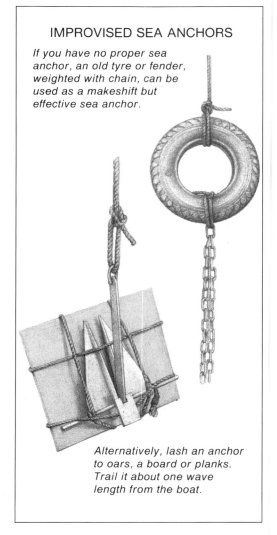

Alternatively, lash an anchor to oars, a board or planks. Trail it about one wave length from the boat.

will help to keep the front pointing into the wind.
• Avoid letting the boat swing sideways on to the waves. They could swamp or overturn it.

SAVED BY A CHILD'S CHATTER
On May 3, 1981, the Jeffery family – Les, a 37-year-old airport firefighter, his wife Virginia, son Darren, his 12-year-old daughter Tracy-Leigh and a family friend, Stewart Greenough – set out on a cruise off the east coast of Australia in their 47ft (14m) yacht Jedda.

Seven days later, in the early hours of the morning, battered by storm-force winds, they were forced to abandon ship. Roped together, the five tried to transfer from the Jedda *to a rescuing oil tanker. But as the ships rolled, they were tossed into the water and pulled right under the tanker by the undertow.*

The rope broke and Darren and Stewart were swept away. Their bodies were found later.

When Tracy-Leigh surfaced she found herself still tied to her mother and father. Her father was injured and her mother was floating face down – dead. In the darkness the tanker lost sight of the bobbing figures.

Tracy-Leigh knew that once her father lost consciousness he would drown in the huge waves. His only chance was to stay awake, so she talked to him – chattering about anything and everything. As she talked, she clung to her mother's life jacket because her own had been torn away against the tanker's hull.

Her talking worked. By the time a helicopter found them at dawn six hours later, she was exhausted – but her father was still alive.

Plotting a storm path
Storms are spirals of strong wind whirling around a low-pressure centre. In the Northern Hemisphere, the wind always blows in an anti-

WAYS OF SIGNALLING FOR HELP

The internationally recognised distress signal Mayday (which comes from the French phrase *M'aidez*, meaning 'Help me') should be used only when you are in grave and imminent danger and require immediate assistance. If you urgently need help but are not in imminent danger, use the signal Pan Pan (from the French *panne*, meaning 'breakdown'). Pan Pan is also the correct signal for man overboard.

Under the International Convention for the Safety of Life at Sea, there are a number of other recognised ways of calling for help. A ship's captain who sees any of these distress signals is legally obliged to respond to them.
• Gun or other explosive signal fired at intervals of about a minute.
• Continuous sounding of a fog signal, such as a foghorn.
• Rockets or shells throwing red stars fired one at a time at short intervals.
• Morse Code SOS (three dots, three dashes, three dots) transmitted by any means available.
• International Code flags NC (flag N above flag C), or a square flag with above or below it anything resembling a ball.
• Flames on a vessel (for example, burning tar, oily rags).
• Red parachute flare or red hand flare.
• Orange-coloured smoke.
• Slowly raising and lowering outstretched arms.

An additional sign – a piece of orange canvas with a black square and circle – can be used to attract the attention of aircraft. The British Merchant Navy's Red Ensign flown upside down has been used as a distress signal, but it is not internationally recognised under the convention.

Making a Mayday call
To call for help by radio, tune your transmitter to the international distress frequency: Channel 16 VHF or 2182kHz MF.
• Repeat the word 'Mayday' three times.
• Give the name of the craft three times.
• Repeat 'Mayday' once more.
• Repeat the name of the vessel once and then give its position, a brief description of the emergency and the help needed. Say 'over' at the end of the message.
• Listen for an acknowledgment before putting out the distress call again.

The phonetic alphabet
Phonetic alphabets use specific words to identify individual letters, in order to help to clarify a radio message. This is a widely used and internationally recognised list.

Alpha	Juliet	Sierra
Bravo	Kilo	Tango
Charlie	Lima	Uniform
Delta	Mike	Victor
Echo	November	Whisky
Foxtrot	Oscar	X-ray
Golf	Papa	Yankee
Hotel	Quebec	Zulu
India	Romeo	

clockwise direction around the storm centre. In addition the storm as a whole moves like a wandering top across the planet's surface at up to 25mph (40km/h).

If you are facing into the wind, the centre of a Northern Hemisphere storm is to your right. With your back to the centre of an approaching storm, the storm's fiercest weather is always to your right.

As the storm passes over, the direction of the wind changes. Sailors use the term 'veering' for a wind that shifts in a clockwise direction round the compass (N-E-S-W). A wind is said to be 'backing' if it shifts anti-clockwise around the compass (N-W-S-E).

You can roughly plot your position in relation to the storm centre and thus predict the likely weather by noting these changes in wind direction and keeping an eye on a barometer (see *How to read a barometer*, page 266). The barometric pressure falls as you get closer to a storm centre, and rises as you get towards the fringes. The faster the changes, the stronger the storm or the closer you are to the path of the storm centre.

The pictures on the right show how barometric pressure and wind direction change as a storm passes over three boats, all of which are sailing parallel to the storm path.

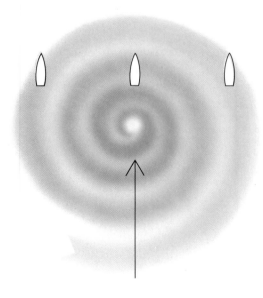

ANATOMY OF A STORM
In a full-blown storm, winds of more than 54mph (87km/h) whirl anti-clockwise around a relatively calm eye. In addition, the eye moves across the surface at anything up to 25mph (40km/h). The boats on this diagram are not to scale; a large storm can be 100 miles (160km) across, and gales can sweep out 50 miles (80km) beyond its fringes.

LEFT OF THE STORM CENTRE

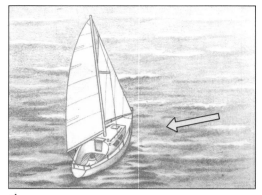

1 *A wind 'backing' anti-clockwise round the compass and a falling barometer mean you are left of the centre. Worse weather is coming.*

IN THE PATH OF THE STORM CENTRE

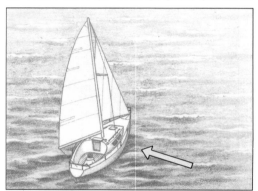

1 *As a storm overtakes a boat in front of the central 'eye', the barometer drops, but wind direction is steady. Weather worsens rapidly.*

RIGHT OF THE STORM CENTRE

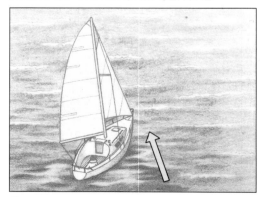

1 *A wind 'veering' clockwise round the compass and a falling barometer mean that you are in front of and to the right of the centre.*

2 *Abreast and left of the storm centre, the barometer is steady and low, and the wind continues to back. The weather is at its worst.*

3 *A rising barometer means that the storm is moving away. The wind will go on backing, but the weather will gradually improve.*

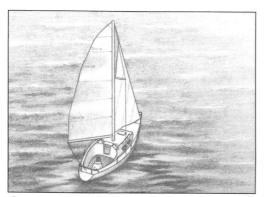

2 *In the eye, the barometer is low and steady, and the wind drops away. But high winds will return soon – from the opposite direction.*

3 *A rising barometer means better weather is on the way. The wind, having reversed its direction, remains steady, but will ease soon.*

2 *Abreast and right of the centre, the barometer is low and steady, but the wind continues to veer. The weather is at its fiercest.*

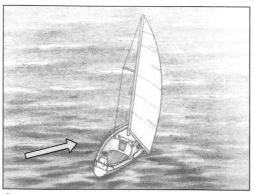

3 *As the storm moves away, the wind goes on veering and the barometer starts to rise. Better weather is on the way.*

Emergencies in the water

Abandoning ship

A small boat – even one that is badly holed – may take at least five minutes to sink. This gives you time to dress warmly, send out a distress signal and prepare to take to a life raft or the water. Do not abandon ship unless there is obviously no other course open to you. The greatest hazard you have to combat is the cold.
• Put on as many layers of warm, woolly clothing as possible, including a hat – and wear a final layer of waterproof clothing.
• Wear socks and light shoes as well to help to keep your feet warm.
• Put on a life jacket over the top of your clothes.

• Take with you personal and ship's papers and money, in a waterproof bag if possible.
• Send out a distress signal by radio, giving your position; or fire a distress flare or rocket (see *Ways of signalling for help*, page 271).
• Leave the boat from well forward or well aft of the mast to avoid being struck by spars or rigging if the boat heels over.

Taking to a life raft
• If you decide to take to a life raft, make sure that it has a line tied securely to the boat before you throw it overboard.

CHOOSING A LIFE JACKET

Not even a good swimmer can keep afloat in cold, rough seas for long without a life jacket. A life jacket for leisure use of a type approved by the British Standards Institution should carry the institution's kite mark and be marked with the number BS3595. A life jacket of this standard has 35lb (16kg) of buoyancy when inflated and will turn even an unconscious person to float face upwards within five seconds of entering the water.

There are three main types of life jackets: those that have to be blown up, either by mouth or by gas (a cylinder with a quick-release cord); those that are partly inflatable and partly made of permanently buoyant material; and those made wholly of permanently buoyant material.

Anti-splash hoods that can be fitted to most

types of life jacket are now available. They protect the head from being swamped by splash and spray, which can drown anyone in a life jacket in even mildly choppy seas. The clear plastic hood is in a package that hooks to the jacket ties. It can be unrolled in the water and pulled over the head.

Inflatable life jackets are suitable for adults who swim well. Adults who cannot swim well should have partly inflatable types which provide at least some buoyancy while they inflate; and children (who are less buoyant than adults) should wear permanent-buoyancy types. A child should get used to putting on his own life jacket and to floating in it.

Waistcoat-type buoyancy aids are handier for good swimmers boating in sheltered or inland waters.

BUOYANCY AID *The waistcoat-style aid is less bulky than a life jacket but not so buoyant.*

LIFE JACKET *A good life jacket will keep even an unconscious person floating face upwards.*

• If the life raft is an inflatable type, it will usually be fitted with an operating line to open the gas cylinder which inflates it. The line also acts as a mooring rope.

• Secure the operating line to the boat, throw the raft container overboard, then pull the line to inflate the raft.

• Board the raft as quickly as possible. The first aboard should be a strong, fit man to help in children or injured or weaker people.

• When everyone is aboard the raft, cut the line. On most inflatable rafts there is a covered-in area, and near its entrance is a safety knife. The knife is specially designed so that it can be used to cut the line without running the risk of causing accidental damage to the raft.

• Do not take off wet clothing. It will give some protection against heat loss.

• Unless you are within easy reach of shore, put out a sea anchor – a cone-shaped canvas bag that acts as a drag in the water. A sea anchor is often part of a life raft's equipment. It helps to keep the raft stable in heavy seas and helps to stop it drifting (see *Caught in a storm*, page 270).

• Try to stay as near to the wreck or its last position as possible. Rescuers will concentrate their search around the boat's last known position, and so you will have a better chance of being spotted and rescued quickly.

• Bail out any water in the raft bottom.

• Arrange a rota of lookouts to watch for rescuers. But keep the raft entrance closed as much as possible to keep warmth in.

• If the floor of the raft is inflatable, keep it topped up with air to provide insulation against the cold water below. Take anti-seasickness tablets as soon as possible on the raft. Seasickness is common in survival craft and hastens the onset of cold and exhaustion.

If you have to jump into the water

• If there is no time to climb into a life raft and you have to jump straight into the water, go to the windward side – the side facing into the wind – so that the boat will not drift into you once you are in the water.

• Hold your life jacket down and away from your chin by crossing your arms over your chest. Cover your nose and mouth with one hand to keep the water out.

• Look straight ahead and jump feet first with your legs straight and together. Do not look down or you may fall forwards and land flat in the water, which is painful and could wind you.

• Your life jacket will bring you up to float at the surface within seconds. If you have an anti-splash hood on the jacket, unroll it and fasten it over your head (see box, opposite).

• Get well clear of the side of the vessel, especially if it is a large one. If you do not, you run the risk of being sucked under as it sinks.

Survival in the water

• Do not try to swim for the shore unless land is very near, because you will quickly become exhausted. The shore is often farther away than it looks, and rescuers are more likely to see the wreckage than to spot a lone swimmer.

• If you can, cling to floating wreckage with as much of your body out of the water as possible to cut down heat loss. The greatest loss of body

PROVISIONS FOR A LIFE RAFT

What you need on a life raft depends to some extent on the circumstances. If you are not far from shore, for example, you do not need to take food.

Most life rafts come supplied with survival packs on board. But before you go out to sea, make sure that the pack on your life raft has everything you are likely to need if you get into trouble. This is a list of the most important pieces of equipment:

Knife
Waterproof torch
Distress signals (flare pack)
Bailer bucket
First aid kit
Anti-seasickness tablets
Oars/paddles
Sea anchor and rope
Water and drinking cup
Length of buoyant rope – about 100ft (30m) –

with life buoy or rescue-quoit attached, for throwing to survivors in the water.

Coastguard Yacht and Boat Safety Scheme

When a small sailing boat or power boat is lost or in distress at sea, help may be delayed because no one knows anything about the boat. The Coastguard Yacht and Boat Safety Scheme aims to provide rescue services with the necessary information about small boats in their area.

All the sailor has to do is fill in and return to the coastguards a special postcard giving details of where he normally sails and in what sort of boat. The postcards are available from Coastguard Stations and most harbour offices and yacht clubs. Then, if the boat is overdue and a friend or relative ashore notifies the coastguards, they will have an idea where to look and what to look for.

heat is from the head, the neck, the armpits and the sides of the chest, and the groin.

• Stay in a group if there are several of you, to improve your chances of being spotted.

• If you are in a group of three or more in the water (all wearing life jackets), huddle close together for warmth with arms around each other's shoulders.

• Keep body movements to a minimum to preserve heat. If there is a child, sandwich him in the middle of the group, because children lose body heat faster than adults.

• If you are not in a group (and are wearing a life jacket), conserve body heat by sitting in the water, bringing your knees up and hugging them firmly to your chest. You do not need to paddle; the life jacket will keep you afloat. This is known as the Heat Escape Lessening Position (HELP), because it exposes as little of the body as possible to the water. In water of 10°C (50°F) – a typical sea temperature in British coastal waters – the average survival time before death from hypothermia is two and a half to three hours. Using the HELP position can enable you to survive for an hour or so longer, giving yourself more time to be found by rescuers.

THE 'HELP' POSITION
The Heat Escape Lessening Position enables you to survive longer in cold water. Bring your knees up and hug them to your chest. Trust the life jacket to keep you afloat.

ADRIFT IN A SMALL BOAT

Anyone adrift in a small boat – a canopied life raft or an open boat – for any length of time has three crucial needs: protection from the weather; a supply of water; and some means of attracting attention.

Food is less important. Exposure to extreme heat or cold can kill much more quickly than starvation. A person can live for four weeks or so without food – but only days without fresh water.

• Try to limit your boat's movement through the water to make it easier for rescuers to find it.

• To help to keep your boat 'parked' in the water, turn the front into the wind and trail a sea anchor about one wave length away on the side from which the wind is blowing (see *Caught in a storm*, page 270).

• To conserve supplies, do not drink any water for the first 24 hours. Your supply of body fluid will still be adequate.

• After that, unless there is plenty of water from heavy rain, ration water to about 1¾ pints (1 litre) a day for each person aboard (more if possible in high temperatures). Drink it in small quantities throughout the course of the day.

• Send out distress signals at regular intervals. When using rockets or flares, fire them in groups of two, firing the second in the pair a few seconds after the first goes out. The first may be ignored, but the second will confirm the signal and may help to give rescuers a bearing. But use the flares sparingly, so that you keep a supply for use when help is in sight.

• In hot weather, keep as cool as possible. Shade your body, if you can. Avoid unnecessary movement. And soak your clothing in seawater during the day; this minimises the loss of body fluid through perspiration. Allow clothing to dry before nightfall, when it is likely to be much cooler.

• In cold weather, keep warm by huddling together and by regularly moving limbs, especially fingers and toes, to maintain blood circulation. Wrap up in as much clothing and blankets as possible.

• Collect rainwater or water that condenses on any cold surfaces on the craft – morning dew, for instance.

• Do not drink seawater, or use it to ease parched lips. Its salt content is three times greater than the amount the body can cope with, and it can cause death.

• If necessary, alleviate thirst by sucking a small object such as a button.

• Do not eat unless you have some water to drink with the food. Digestive processes use up precious body fluid.

When a canoe capsizes

A kayak (a covered-in canoe which is propelled with a double-bladed paddle) may have a small or large cockpit for the canoeist to sit in. In types with a small cockpit, canoeists often wear a soft, elasticated spray cover – or spray deck – which fits over the lip of the cockpit and keeps it watertight. There is a strap on the front of the spray cover which releases the cover from the cockpit lip when the strap is pulled.

• If you are thrown out when a large-cockpit canoe overturns, immediately grasp the boat and work your way along to one end, where it is easier to hold on.

• If you are trapped in your seat by a spray cover and you cannot right the canoe at once with your paddle, lean forward underwater and pull the spray-cover strap. Get out with a forward roll. If necessary, help yourself out by pushing against the boat just behind your hips.

• Once you are out, work your way along to the end of the hull. Hold onto it.

• Hang onto your paddle as well if you can.

• Do not try to right the canoe, but swim with it downstream across any current to the shore.

• If the land is too far, or you do not think you can reach it, stay with the canoe and wait for rescue. The boat will support you in the water.

Canoeing through surf

Canoeing off a beach calls for strength and a skill that can be learnt only by practice, starting in easy conditions. If you are caught in surf by accident, the golden rule is never to let the canoe get broadside to the waves.

Never launch a canoe into surf near rocks, swimmers, or a rip tide where there is a strong current moving out from the shore.

• If you are canoeing seawards, paddle firmly to maintain enough speed to be able to steer, and travel as far forward as possible between

waves to get beyond the breakers. Meet each wave head on. At the same time lean back away from the crest and press your knees up against the deck to lift the bow over the wave.

• If you are heading for the shore and you do not have experience of riding waves, face into them – turning round between waves if necessary. Keep the bow pointing into the waves and paddle towards them as they break to keep the canoe straight.

• Between breakers, paddle shorewards or let the canoe drift backwards.

CANOEING IN SAFETY

• Do not use a canoe unless you can swim at least 55yds (50m) wearing light clothing. Before setting out, pack extra buoyancy – in the form of special canoe air bags or empty plastic containers – into the ends.

• Always wear a life jacket or buoyancy aid – a buoyant waistcoat designed to allow maximum freedom of movement.

• Learn how to canoe safely at a club or on a course. Many canoe clubs in Britain organise proficiency tests designed by the British Canoe Union. The tests include dealing with a capsize.

• The union – whose head office is at 45 High Street, Addlestone, Weybridge, Surrey KT15 1JV; telephone Weybridge (0932) 41341 – has details of local canoe clubs and training courses. It also prepares specialist canoeing maps.

STAY WITH THE CANOE
Work your way to the end of a capsized canoe – it will be easier to hold on there – and use it as a float. Swim with it to shore if you can, or wait with it for rescue, but do not leave it.

Canoeing: if you are caught in rapids

The noise of falling water and possibly a narrowing of the river are signs that you are approaching rapids. A white line of foam or spray may also be visible, or the water may appear to end unnaturally short of the horizon.

• Beach the canoe well before the start of the rapids, then walk along the bank and try to work out a safe route through them. If there is no safe route through, carry the boat round.

• If you are accidentally caught in the rapids, paddle firmly either forwards or backwards so that your speed is faster or slower than the water. This will help you to retain control of your course. If you let the water take you at its own speed, you will have no control.

• Areas of white, disturbed water and spray indicate rocks, fallen trees or other obstacles, which may or may not be visible. Avoid them.

• Aim for areas of darker, smoother water between disturbed, white-water patches. The channel will be deeper and safer there.

• If the canoe is swung right round by the current, do not try to turn it back again or you may be carried sideways and hit an obstacle. Continue through the rapids backwards, watching over your shoulder.

• Take bends on the outside if possible. The water is deepest there and flows faster, but be careful not to get swept against trees or banks.

• If the canoe slews round and is caught sideways against a rock, do not let it tilt upstream, or water will flood the cockpit.

• Throw your weight against the rock or obstruction to tilt the boat towards it. Hold the rock and use it to lever yourself and the canoe into a position where you can go forwards. (Take care not to let go of your paddle.)

• If this does not work, get out of the canoe quickly. Hang onto the rock and wait for rescue.

If you are swept over a weir

Weirs are perilous in the extreme, even for canoeists wearing full life jackets. Beginners should avoid them. Even if you are experienced, avoid a weir unless you are with others who have shot it before and who know what to do in an emergency. Never approach a weir where there are warning signs such as notices, cones or a boom. Stop well upstream and carry the canoe round it.

The reason for the danger is that water falling over a weir rolls back on itself after it hits the bottom, creating an endlessly circulating current – a spinning cylinder of water trapped by foaming breakers known as stopper waves. A swimmer or a boat caught in this deadly turbulence is tumbled over and over, and is constantly thrown back against the weir.

• If you are in a boat which gets trapped or capsized at the foot of a weir, abandon it.

• Dive down and away from the weir, *beneath* the turbulence.

• Swim underwater until you are well clear of the turbulence (you will be able to feel the swirling currents ease as you swim), then surface and make for the bank.

PLANNING YOUR ROUTE

Never canoe down a river or any other waterway until you have studied it on a map and noted any steep descents (where rapids are likely) and any weirs.

On specialist canoeing maps, such as those prepared by the British Canoe Union (see *Useful addresses*, page 385), rivers are graded according to an international coding system for rough water. The grades appear as the letters RW (Rough Water) or WW (Wild or White Water), followed by a number in Roman numerals. Grades I, II and III are easy, medium and difficult respectively. Grades IV-VI are taxing even for experts.

Always canoe in a group. Go through moderate rapids in single file, far enough apart to avoid collisions and for each canoeist to pick his own route. Severe rapids should be left to experienced canoeists, and then shot by one group member at a time, with the most experienced going first.

HOW TO GET PAST AN OBSTACLE
If the current sweeps you against a rock, lean downstream to keep water out of the cockpit and push the boat round it with your hands.

HOW TO COPE WITH ROUGH WATER
*In turbulent water, lean away from waves,
using your paddle for balance, to stop water
swamping the canoe. Wear a helmet in case
you fall in and get thrown against rocks.*

Emergencies
in the water

279

Emergencies on holiday and in the country

Travelling abroad

Air travel and holiday companies have brought some of the most exotic parts of the world within reach of millions of British holidaymakers.

But long-distance travel – particularly to tropical or Third World countries – carries special risks and problems as well.

You may, for instance, need to arrange visas or special immunisation against tropical diseases. You may need to take with you medicines that are freely available in Britain but almost unobtainable in the country you plan to visit.

It is worth thinking, too, about how you should take your spending money – as cash or travellers' cheques, for example – about which currency you should take, and about whether it makes sense to take notes and cheques in small denominations rather than large ones.

Once you arrive you may also, depending on where you are, have to take precautions against heat or altitude sickness, and to take care about what you eat and drink.

All these risks and difficulties are most likely to arise in tropical or Third World countries, not in the West. But some travel problems, such as the collapse of a holiday firm or travel agent, can affect holidaymakers anywhere (see *If your holiday firm goes out of business*, page 286).

Visas

• Check with the airline or travel agent at the time you book your flight whether you need a visa for the country you plan to visit.
• If you do need a visa, contact the country's embassy or consulate in Britain to find out how to get it. Alternatively, ask a travel agent to make the application for you. Many countries charge a fee for the visa and you may have to supply one or more passport-type photographs with your application.
• Allow extra time if you need more than one visa. Your passport will have to go to each embassy or consulate in turn to be stamped with the visa, and some countries can take several weeks to process the application.
• If you plan to visit countries which are politically hostile to each other – Israel and some of the Arab states, for instance – you may save yourself unpleasantness at the frontier by making sure that visas or entry stamps for the opposing countries do not appear in the same passport.
• In circumstances like these, it is sometimes possible to arrange for one or both of the visas to be stamped on separate sheets of paper which can be clipped to your passport and removed after the visit. Ask the consulates or embassies concerned whether they will agree to do this.
• Alternatively, contact the Passport Office in London and ask for a second passport valid only for one or other of the opposing countries. You can then take both passports with you and show one at each border.
• If the offending visa or stamp is the result of

an earlier trip, it is also possible simply to surrender your old passport – regardless of how long it has to run – and buy a new one.

Immunisation

• Find out from the airline or travel agent what the immunisation rules are in the country you are visiting. Airlines have an interest in keeping you up to date about the rules because they have to fly you home at their expense if you do not have all the right jabs.
• Consult a doctor about immunisation as well. Whatever the formal regulations, it may be medically advisable to get other jabs too, because people who live in a temperate climate such as Britain's have no natural immunity to diseases prevalent in the tropics and subtropics.
• Check up on immunisation at least three weeks before you travel. For immunisation against some diseases you will have to be given two injections at least a week apart and, if you need protection from several diseases, it may not be possible or medically desirable to have all the jabs at once.
• It is usually simplest to get immunised at an official immunisation centre. Your doctor can help you to find the nearest one. The advantage is that the centre can issue you with an officially stamped and internationally accepted certificate on the spot. If your doctor gives you the jab, the certificate has to be taken to the Health Department of the local town hall for stamping.
• Immunisation may be advisable against any or all of a number of diseases. The main ones are: cholera; hepatitis; poliomyelitis; typhoid; and yellow fever. Smallpox vaccination is no longer necessary for any foreign travel because the World Health Organisation has declared the whole world to be free of the disease.

CHOLERA The vaccine gives limited protection. The course is two injections 7-14 days apart.

HEPATITIS (jaundice) Injections of gamma globulin give limited protection against the disease, which is common in many tropical countries.

POLIOMYELITIS (infantile paralysis) The disease is still common in many parts of the Middle East and North Africa. The vaccine is usually dripped onto a sugar lump which is eaten.

TYPHOID Immunisation is advisable for all travellers going to the Mediterranean coastlands, Asia or the tropics, and is effective for a year. It takes the form of a single injection if time is short, or two injections at least 14 days apart.

YELLOW FEVER The disease, which is confined to the equatorial regions of Africa and the northern, tropical parts of South America, is spread by mosquitoes. Immunisation against the disease consists of a single injection which is effective for ten years.

Malaria

Travellers in tropical areas are particularly at risk from malaria, which is spread by mosquitoes. There is no system of immunisation, but

preventive medicines provide some protection.
• Contact a hospital for tropical diseases, an immunisation centre or an airline medical department and ask them for advice on which medicine to use. You usually have to start taking the medicine some days before entering a malarial area, and to keep taking it for some time after you have left it.
• Also get medical advice on a suitable insect repellent to reduce the risk of being bitten.
• Apply insect repellent in the evening, and put on a long-sleeved shirt and long trousers after dark, because malarial mosquitoes fly at night.
• If possible, stay only in air-conditioned hotels. Mosquitoes dislike cool places. If this is not possible, sleep under a mosquito net, and spray your room with insecticide before going to bed.
• If there is an electric fan in your bedroom, leave it on all night – mosquitoes also dislike draughts.

Medicines

• If you need to take medicines regularly, take a sufficient supply with you to last the entire holiday. Many drugs are unobtainable – or enormously expensive – in other countries.
• Consider taking pain-killing medicines, such as aspirin, and antidiarrhoeal medicines with you for the same reason.

Money

• If you become ill while you are out of Britain, you may have to pay on the spot for medical treatment, even if you have medical insurance and even in European countries which have social security arrangements with Britain. Take extra money to cover this possibility (see *Seeing a doctor overseas*, page 288).
• Carry minimum amounts of cash on you. Women should carry nothing of value in a handbag. It can easily be snatched.
• Instead, keep passports, air tickets and travel documents, travellers' cheques and other money in a hotel safe.
• If you have to carry valuables on you, use a money belt. Keep a note of your passport number, and its date and place of issue. It will speed up the process of getting a new passport from the nearest British consulate if the passport is lost or stolen abroad.
• Credit cards are now widely accepted in many countries. But keep a separate note of each number so that you can tell the company at once – by phone or telegram – if you lose it (see *Lost credit card, cheque book or cheque card*, page 383).
• If you take money in the form of travellers' cheques, get them from a company which has offices in the country you are visiting and which will guarantee to replace them quickly – within a day or so – if they are lost or stolen.
• Buy insurance against the risk of your cash being lost or stolen; but remember that British insurance companies will usually refund the lost money only after you get home. You will not be able to replace it during the holiday.
• Get advice from a travel agent or airline about which currency is most easily negotiated. In some countries, cash and travellers' cheques in US dollars, German marks or Japanese yen are more readily accepted than sterling.
• During the holiday, shop around for the best

Emergencies on holiday and in the country

DIARRHOEA AND DYSENTERY

Despite taking precautions you may come down with traveller's diarrhoea – also called Montezuma's Revenge, Rangoon Runs, Aztec Two-Step, Delhi Belly and other names, depending on where you catch it. It generally lasts only two or three days and is often accompanied by vomiting, abdominal cramps and sweating. You can usually treat it successfully yourself.
• Drink bottled water in sufficient quantities to replace lost body fluid. Add a teaspoon of salt to each pint of water. Do not take any food or milk drinks.
• Take antidiarrhoeal medicines.
• When the vomiting and diarrhoea have settled for a few hours, start to eat bland food such as dry biscuits, jelly, blancmange and clear soup. Avoid tea, coffee and acid drinks such as fruit juice because they will further irritate the stomach lining.

Dysentery
Traveller's diarrhoea usually causes only a few days' discomfort and inconvenience. Dysentery is a much more serious cause of diarrhoea. There are two forms, one caused by bacteria and one caused by an amoeba. The amoebic form is more serious and very rare in Britain, but the symptoms of both kinds of dysentery are the same: severe diarrhoea and vomiting; stools often streaked with blood, pus or mucus; and gripping pains, tenderness and swelling in the abdomen. The symptoms usually appear 6–48 hours after eating infected food.
• See a doctor if: the symptoms are severe, persistent or getting rapidly worse; the disease was contracted in a country where amoebic dysentery is known to occur; or blood or mucus occur in the stools. Otherwise, treat as for traveller's diarrhoea.

rate of exchange. Hotels often give poor rates compared to banks, for instance. Some gift shops will also accept payment in foreign currency at better-than-usual rates.

• Aim to buy any international travel tickets you need – particularly air tickets – before you leave Britain. Immigration authorities in many Third World countries insist on travellers having a ticket to take them out of the country. If, on arrival, you do not have a return or onward ticket, you may have to pay a hefty deposit – which is sometimes difficult to reclaim later – or you may have to buy a ticket on the spot. In some countries, foreigners have to pay for such tickets in foreign currency at exchange rates which are much worse than usual.

• If you are visiting a country with a high rate of inflation, such as Israel or some South American countries, take your money in small-denomination banknotes and travellers' cheques. Exchange rates in these countries can change on a daily basis, so converting only small amounts into the local currency each day can make your money go significantly further.

• Many Third World nations have strict regulations governing how much of their local currency can be taken into or out of their country. Check with the country's embassy or consulate in Britain.

• Towards the end of your holiday, run down the amount of local cash you are carrying. It may not be possible or permissible to change local currency back into sterling before you leave, and the currency may have little value once you get back to Britain.

Clothing

• In hot and humid climates, clothes should absorb sweat, be loose-fitting, and reflect the heat. They should, therefore, be lightweight and light in colour.

• Cotton is the best material for hot-weather clothing. It is capable of absorbing 50 per cent of its weight in water. Avoid drip-dry clothes and those made of man-made fibres, particularly next to the skin. They have little ability to absorb sweat. As a result, sweat stays on the skin, encouraging prickly heat (see page 107).

• Take a lightweight hat and sunglasses for protection against hot sunshine and glare. In areas where snakes are likely, wear boots, not open sandals.

How to treat travel sickness

Seasickness, car sickness, air sickness – all are the same affliction, and about nine out of ten people suffer from it at some time or other. The symptoms include nausea, vomiting, sweating, faintness, pallor and diarrhoea.

Travel sickness occurs when the movement of a vehicle disturbs the relationship between what the eye sees and what the balance mechanism in the ear feels. The eye adjusts to the motion but the ear does not.

• If you feel sick, put your head back and hold it still. Lie flat, if you can, without a pillow.
• Take travel sickness pills.
• Get some fresh air – go up on deck if you are on a boat, or keep the car window open and make regular stops.
• Take small amounts of fluid regularly to avoid dehydration. Try also to eat small amounts of food regularly, even if you are vomiting.
• Stay away from smokers – particularly if you are a non-smoker. The smell may otherwise make you feel more queasy.

Food and drink

Numerous tropical and subtropical diseases are transmitted by food and drink which have been infected by bacteria, or contaminated by flies

---

PREVENTING TRAVEL SICKNESS

The most effective way to avoid feeling sick on a journey is to use travel sickness pills. The first one usually needs to be taken about 30 minutes before setting out. The pills may cause drowsiness, impair driving performance and enhance the effects of alcohol. Do not drive or operate machinery until the effects have worn off. This may take from four to six hours.

Travel sickness pills usually contain either hyoscine or an antihistamine. Hyoscine is the more effective but it can cause a dry mouth and constipation.

Antihistamines (such as cinnarizine, cyclizine and phenergan) are not quite as effective but have milder side-effects. The name of the active ingredient in the pills is given on the packet. If you have any health problems – particularly urinary or eye disorders – or are taking medicines, consult your doctor before taking travel sickness pills.

Several other techniques can also help to alleviate or avoid the miseries of travel sickness – whether or not you have taken a travel sickness pill.

• Do not have a large meal or alcohol before setting out.
• Eat small, easily digested meals before and during the journey.
• Keep occupied. This will keep your mind off feeling sick. But do not attempt to read or write during a car journey.
• Look out of the front of the car. Watching to the side at objects flashing past windows can make nausea worse.
• Look at the horizon, not at objects close by. This helps to keep the head still and lessens feelings of queasiness.

or unhygienic handling. The diseases include cholera, hepatitis and dysentery.

If you have any doubt at all about the cleanliness of the food and drink you buy or are offered, you can minimise the risks of infection by following a few guidelines.

• Avoid milk and tap water, unless they have been thoroughly boiled. Black tea or coffee, for instance, is likely to be safe to drink.

• Avoid unbottled cold drinks, ice cream and ice for the same reason. Freezing does not kill bacterial contamination – it merely suspends it until the ice melts. Bottled cold drinks are, however, usually safe.

• Avoid uncooked foods such as salads, locally prepared mayonnaise, raw vegetables and peeled fruit. All may have been washed in contaminated water, or made with contaminated milk, or contaminated by handling. Fruit you peel yourself, however, is safe to eat.

• Avoid eating in fly-blown restaurants. If flies are hovering thickly about the tables, the kitchen is likely to be much worse.

Altitude sickness – how to treat it
Climbing too high or too quickly in the mountains, or travelling in an unpressurised aircraft, can cause altitude sickness because of the reduced level of oxygen in the air.

The signs of a mild attack are breathlessness, palpitations, headache, loss of appetite and insomnia.

The symptoms of severe altitude sickness – which can cause serious lung damage if left untreated – are dizziness, nausea, vomiting, convulsions, severe thirst, weakness, drowsiness, blurred vision and hearing difficulties.

People usually begin to be affected on mountains over 10,000ft (3000m), but the symptoms can occur at as low as 6500ft (2000m).

• If you get a mild attack of altitude sickness, avoid all strenuous exercise until you become acclimatised. Go to bed and rest. The symptoms usually disappear on their own in 24-48 hours.

• If the symptoms do not ease in that time, or if they are severe, get medical help.

• Take a few breaths from an oxygen canister, if one is available. It will give immediate relief in a mild attack, and will be of some help even in a severe attack.

• If no medical help is available and severe symptoms persist, the only solution is to descend to a lower altitude at once. The symptoms will ease automatically as you lose height.

• Spend several days at a lower altitude before attempting to climb once more. Ascend in easy stages, getting acclimatised at each level before going higher.

When the sun is an enemy
Too much direct exposure to the sun can cause painful burns, especially to fair-skinned or freckled people. Darker skins respond more readily to sunlight than fair skins, by producing

HOW TO AVOID SUNBURN
• Avoid the sun as much as possible if your skin is very fair or freckled.
• Keep small children well covered.
• Use sun-tan cream or lotion applied frequently. Remember, though, that artificial tan preparations which simply colour the skin may not protect you. Consult the chemist when buying.
• Limit your time in the sun to no more than half an hour on the first day, an hour on the second, adding 30 minutes on succeeding days.
• Take care when sailing, swimming or skiing – you can still get burnt even when you are feeling cool.
• Protect your skin in cloudy weather – most of the ultraviolet rays in sunlight can penetrate clouds.
• Men should not use aftershave.
• The main defences against heat exhaustion and heat stroke are to wear a hat that shades the back of the neck, and to drink plenty of water. In extreme conditions, take salt tablets as well.

a brown pigment (melanin) which screens out harmful rays. Freckled skins are particularly prone to solar burns because their melanin does not spread evenly.

Too much heat – in or out of direct sunlight – can induce heat exhaustion or heat cramp, and a more dangerous condition, heat stroke, which can kill (see *Heat exhaustion and heat stroke*, page 106).

Particular care is needed when visiting countries hotter than Britain, and in mountains, where thin air offers less protection against the sun's rays than the more absorbent atmosphere at lower levels.

In minor cases of sunburn, the skin reddens for three or four days with little discomfort, then tans. In more severe cases, the reddened skin becomes painful and tender, the tissues swelling up after a few hours.

Within 48 hours, when the condition is at its worst, the skin may blister and perhaps crust. Finally, a few days later, it peels.

This sequence of discomforts results from the body's complex reaction to the ultraviolet rays in sunlight, as the skin releases potent chemicals that include histamine, prostaglandins, kinins and serotonin.

A sun-tan preparation offers some protection – but keep applying it. Severe cases need treatment (see page 135). Complete recovery – even from severe sunburn – is normal within 30 to 60 days.

If your holiday firm goes out of business

Holidaymakers travelling on package tours from Britain are very unlikely to be stranded abroad for more than a day or so if the holiday firm they book with goes out of business during the holiday. Rescue schemes, financed by holiday firms and administered by the Association of British Travel Agents (ABTA) or the Civil Aviation Authority (CAA), protect most holidaymakers against this risk.

The ABTA scheme covers all holiday firms which are members of the association – whether they carry passengers by air, sea or land. The CAA scheme covers holiday firms to which the authority has issued an Air Travel Organiser's Licence (ATOL), but which are not ABTA members.

By law, any holiday firm offering air tickets on a charter basis must have an ATOL. Each ATOL has a number, and the holiday firm should quote its ATOL number in its publicity material. You can check whether your holiday firm has an ATOL by telephoning the CAA at its head office in London on 01-379 7311.

ABTA members should also display the association's symbol in their publicity material. You can check whether the firm is a member by telephoning the association's head office in London on 01-637 2444.

There is, in addition, a third rescue scheme, run by a group of the larger British tour operators – the Tour Operators' Study Group (TOSG). All members of the group are also members of ABTA, though, so it makes no practical difference to the holidaymaker if help comes from ABTA or the group. Both the ABTA and the TOSG schemes try to ensure that people already on holiday can continue their holidays with little or no interruption. The CAA scheme usually concentrates on bringing holidaymakers back to Britain.

• If you are in any doubt whether the company you plan to use is covered by one of the rescue schemes, check with ABTA or the CAA before you part with any money – not afterwards.

• If you book a holiday which does not involve air travel, make sure that the firm you use is a member of ABTA. Otherwise you will not be protected and will need to buy insurance to guard against the risk of the firm's collapse.

• If your holiday firm collapses before you leave, contact ABTA if it is an ABTA member or the CAA if it has an ATOL. The CAA will give you a refund. ABTA will offer you a refund or, whenever possible, an alternative holiday.

• If your holiday firm is covered by one of the rescue schemes and it collapses while you are on holiday, there should be no need for you to do anything yourself. The holiday firm's local representative, or officials from the rescue scheme, will normally make the necessary arrangements and keep you informed.

• Nonetheless, take extra money on holiday with you. Even if you are protected by one of the rescue schemes or are fully insured, you may have to pay certain bills on the spot and claim the money back later. Your hotel, for example, may demand money for your room and meals – even though you have already paid the holiday firm.

• Keep receipts for all expenses you incur. If you have to organise any journey on your own, keep all booking documents and ticket stubs. You will need them to claim a refund.

• If your holiday is cut short by the collapse of a holiday firm which is covered by one of the rescue schemes, ABTA and the TOSG will offer you the choice of an alternative holiday later or a refund. The CAA will only refund you.

• If your holiday firm was not covered by a rescue scheme, you can claim compensation from the collapsed firm. But there is likely to be a long wait, and you are very unlikely to get all your money back.

• Another way to cover yourself against the costs of a broken holiday is through insurance. Some holiday firms include cover for these expenses as part of a standard insurance package which is offered to holidaymakers. The insurance policy will explain exactly what costs are covered. Alternatively, get advice from an insurance broker, your travel agent or from one or more insurance companies.

If your travel agent goes out of business

The Association of British Travel Agents (ABTA) also administers a scheme designed to protect holidaymakers if the travel agent they book through goes out of business before they travel.

If, for example, you have already paid for an airline ticket but have not received the ticket from the travel agent before it goes out of business, ABTA will make sure you get the ticket or a refund. This scheme, though, covers only agents who are ABTA members.

• Make sure that the agent you use is a member of ABTA. The scheme does not protect you if a non-member goes out of business between the time you pay him and the time the holiday firm confirms your booking. If the agent does go out of business during this period you are very unlikely to get your money back.

• Once the holiday firm's confirmation comes through, however, the collapse of the travel agent will not affect your holiday – regardless of whether the agent was a member of ABTA.

• Travel agents who are members of ABTA should have a sign in their office saying so. But you can check by telephoning ABTA on 01-637 2444. If in doubt, contact ABTA before handing over any money.

If your airline goes out of business

If you travel overseas with a holiday firm, the firm remains responsible for looking after you, should any airline it uses go out of business. It is the holiday firm's responsibility to find a replacement airline or to compensate you if it cannot. If you have bought your ticket direct

SYMBOLS OF SECURITY

Look out for these symbols at your travel agent and on holiday brochures.

You will be protected if an ABTA member goes out of business.

International Air Transport Association airlines may help IATA ticket-holders.

The Civil Aviation Authority will get you home if your firm has an ATOL licence.

be able to get on another flight depends on what type of ticket you have.

If you have paid the full normal fare, the ticket will be valid for a year and will not restrict you to a specific flight.

A charter, special excursion or cheap ticket is likely to have conditions attached to it. Restrictions such as 'Valid only for flights and dates shown' will be written on the ticket.

• Show your ticket to the person at the check-in desk and explain what has happened. Ask to be put on the next available flight.

• If you have an unrestricted ticket, the airline is obliged to put you on the first flight with seats available, possibly with another airline.

• If the next few flights are fully booked, ask for a connecting flight to another airport and get a flight to your destination from there.

• If you have bought a cheap ticket, the airline company may be willing to find you an alternative flight, but is not obliged to.

• The only reliable way to avoid the risk of missing a flight and perhaps having to buy a new ticket is to give yourself plenty of time to reach the airport.

If you make your own holiday arrangements

If you arrange a foreign holiday as an individual – booking directly with a foreign hotel, say – and the hotel goes out of business, there are no official schemes to help you to get back to Britain or to help you to get your money back.

You could sue the foreign company for compensation, but it would probably not be worth doing unless the sum involved was very large.

The only reliable way to guard against the risk is to book through a travel agent which is a member of ABTA.

If your journey is held up

If bad weather, technical faults or industrial disputes delay your journey, in Britain or overseas, the airline, ferry company or coach firm you have booked with will often provide refreshments and even overnight accommodation during the delay.

But airlines, ferry companies and coach firms are not obliged to look after passengers during a delay. So if you are held up for days because of a dock strike, you cannot claim compensation from the ferry company. You can only claim under an insurance policy – if you have one that covers such risks.

On a package holiday – where you have booked with a holiday firm rather than directly with a transport company – the same principles apply. The holiday firm will usually look after holidaymakers held up at docks or airports. But it is not obliged to unless its booking conditions contain a promise to do so.

If the booking conditions do not contain such a promise, consider buying insurance to cover the costs of delays. Many holiday firms include this cover in their standard package.

from the airline, however, you may have to find some other way of reaching your destination. You are very unlikely to get the full cost of your ticket back from the failed airline.

• Take your ticket to another airline flying the route you want to travel, and ask the airline to book you onto one of its flights. Airlines which are members of the International Air Transport Association (IATA) will usually accept tickets issued by other member airlines, and may accept tickets from non-member airlines as well. But they are not obliged to.

• If you cannot persuade another airline to accept your existing ticket, you will probably have to pay for a new ticket yourself. If you are insured against this possibility, though, you will be able to claim the cost of the new ticket back from the insurance company later.

If you miss your plane

If you arrive at the airport and discover that you have missed your plane, go immediately to the airline check-in desk for help. Whether you will

Emergencies on holiday and in the country

Seeing a doctor overseas

Medical treatment abroad can be extremely expensive – especially in the USA. The safest way to guard against the expense of an accident or illness is to buy medical insurance. In some countries, however, it is possible to get some treatment free or at reduced rates.

Major bills – for a stay in hospital, say – may be settled by the insurance company direct. Smaller bills, however, for a visit to a doctor or a dentist, or for medicine, will usually have to be paid on the spot, and the money reclaimed after you get back to Britain.

Getting free or cheap treatment

Britain has health agreements with a number of countries, under which UK citizens and residents are entitled to free or cheap medical treatment – and, sometimes, dental treatment.

The main countries are other members of the Common Market, including Spain and Portugal which joined in January 1986, and the Scandinavian countries. Other countries which in 1985 were offering free or cheap treatment under similar agreements were: Austria; Bulgaria; the Channel Islands; Czechoslovakia; Finland; East Germany; Hong Kong; Hungary; Iceland; Isle of Man; Malta; New Zealand; Poland; Romania; Russia; Yugoslavia; and a number of British Dependent Territories including Anguilla and the Falkland Islands.

The agreements do not, however, cover the cost of getting you home if you are ill, nor do they cover non-medical costs, such as repairs to your car after a crash or making alternative travel arrangements. You can guard against these expenses by buying insurance.

The details of the entitlements vary from country to country. In West Germany, for instance, medical and dental treatment are normally free, but you have to pay for treatment in hospital. In Norway, by contrast, treatment in hospital as an in-patient is normally free, but you have to pay for medical and dental treatment.

The entitlements also change from time to time depending on the policy of the government involved. Whatever the detailed rules, however, the initial steps to take are the same.

• At least a month before you travel, ask the nearest office of the Department of Health and Social Security for a copy of the leaflet SA30, *Medical Costs Abroad*. The office's address will be in your telephone directory, listed under 'Health'. The leaflet explains in detail what you are entitled to in each country, and how you can claim it. The claiming procedure varies from country to country.

• In some countries, the only evidence you need to establish your entitlement to free or cheap treatment is a passport. In other countries, however, you may need to show a driving licence, a National Health Service medical card, or a special certificate known as an E111.

• If you need an E111 – the leaflet makes clear whether you do or not in the country or countries you are visiting – fill out the application form which is inside the leaflet and send the form to the DHSS. The countries for which UK citizens needed an E111 in 1985 were: Belgium; France; West Germany; Greece; Italy; Luxembourg; and the Netherlands. But since international agreements can change at any time, it is always worth checking with the DHSS.

• Take the E111 and the leaflet with you on your holiday.

• In some countries – Denmark, for instance – you have to pay the bill and claim a refund before you return to Britain. The leaflet and the E111 explain how to claim a refund in each country. In many countries, though, you will not get all the money back. In Belgium and France, for example, the refund amounts to only about three-quarters of what you pay.

• If you do not have enough money with you to pay the bill, contact your bank in Britain by phone or telegram, or go to a local bank and make contact from there.

• If you cannot raise the money from your bank, contact the nearest British consulate.

Medical insurance

Insurance against medical emergencies abroad can be bought through travel agents and motoring organisations, or direct from insurance firms. It is often included in a package covering cancellation and lost or stolen baggage and money. The policy will make clear which risks are covered, and for how much.

Some travel insurance packages now include unlimited medical cover for little more than the standard premium. This option may be attractive to holidaymakers such as motorists and skiers, who run extra risks, or to people travelling to countries such as the United States and Canada, where medical costs are much higher than in Western Europe.

• Make a copy of the policy or certificate to leave at home, and take the original with you on holiday as evidence that you are covered (a photostat copy may not be acceptable). Show it to the hospital or doctor you see, if you want to delay paying the bill until you get home.

• How much cover to buy depends in part on your age and medical condition. For Europe, cover of about £50,000 will be adequate for most people. The premium for this amount for a fortnight is likely to be between £10 and £20.

• For North America, cover of about £100,000 (which, for two weeks, is likely to cost between £25 and £35) should usually be adequate.

• Check when you buy the policy how soon you have to notify the company if you need to make a claim. The policy may require you to phone or send a telegram as soon as possible – not when you get home.

• If you have to pay on the spot, get a receipt and send it to the insurance company with your claim form when you get home (see *Making an insurance claim*, page 381).

Aboard a crashing train or plane

Train and plane crashes often seem more terrifying than a car crash because they involve such large numbers of people.

In fact, your chances of being injured in a train or plane are far smaller than your chances of being hurt in a road accident.

If your train crashes

There is unlikely to be much warning before a train crash, but you might feel the emergency brakes go on, and in the seconds before final impact you may be able to take up a safer position.

• Get clear of windows and doors. Throw yourself to the floor, if necessary. Hang on to anything fixed to prevent yourself being thrown out of the carriage.

• Brace yourself against anything solid.

• Tuck your chin down onto your chest. This will help to protect your neck against the risk of whiplash injury.

• If you are sitting with your back to the engine, away from windows and doors, stay put.

• If you are not sitting with your back to the engine, away from windows and doors, move into this position if you can, but do not risk being caught unsupported when the impact comes.

• Do not try to jump out of the train, even if it careers for some distance off the tracks. While you remain in the train, the compartment will absorb some of the crash impact. If you jump out, your body hitting the tracks will receive the full force. There may also be a danger from a live rail or other hazards – broken equipment, for example. A broken train battery could create a pool of acid which would be indistinguishable from a rain puddle.

• Once the train has come to rest, assess the situation. In a busy area, or if the train is trapped in a tunnel, it may be best to stay put until official

---

RESCUE ON THE 5.54

Three people died when a London commuter train crashed into the side of a goods train outside Wembley on the evening of October 11, 1984. All three died because they were thrown through or against the broken windows of the first carriage, and crushed as it rolled.

Army Staff Sergeant Peter Kemp was saved from going the same way by the strength of 38-year-old Warrant Officer Colin 'Slim' Cheetham of the Royal Signals.

Staff Sergeant Kemp, then 39, escaped with cuts and cracked ribs. 'The carriage rolled over to the left and was dragged along the line,' he said later.

'The carriage window broke and all I could see was the railway line. Slim got behind me and got his arm under my tummy and was pulling me away from the window.'

A man in the same carriage who fell onto the window was killed.

---

help comes. Wandering about outside the train may expose you to further dangers, particularly since you are likely to be in a state of shock after a crash.

• If there is a live rail, do not get out of the train until you are told by rail staff that the current has been turned off.

• The most modern long-distance carriages have double-thickness glass which is unlikely to break even if the carriage turns over. If you need to get through the window – if the exits at either end of the coach are blocked, for example – break out using the hammers which are kept in red boxes at each end of the coach.

• Once you are outside, call the emergency services. If you are near a set of signals, there is often a telephone at the base of them. Use it to call the signal box. If there is a public call box or a house nearby, contact the emergency services by dialling 999.

If a train door swings open

Leaning out of a moving train to close a door is extremely dangerous – trains coming in the opposite direction pass within inches. A sudden jolt could also throw you out of the train.

• If you find a door open on a moving train, do not try to shut the door.

• Move well away from the open doorway, and get others to do the same.

• Notify a guard, or, if this is not possible, pull the communication cord. Do not take any other action until the train has stopped. Let the train staff deal with the problem. They will want to check the door lock.

If your plane crashes

Being frightened of flying is a common and understandable problem among air passengers. Doctors believe that the fear is often related to the fear of being helpless if things go wrong, or the fear of being in a confined space. Ask your doctor's advice if the fear is serious. Otherwise, keep reminding yourself that air travel is safer than motoring.

The riskiest part of any journey by air is the beginning and the end; six out of ten plane crashes happen on takeoff or landing.

So listen carefully when the cabin crew brief you on emergency procedures at the start of the flight, and make yourself familiar with safety features such as exits before the plane leaves the ground.

• Identify the nearest emergency exit to your seat. Memorise its position and how to open it – the instructions will be on the door. In the aftermath of a crash, you might have to find and open it in thick smoke.

• Read the emergency procedures card in the seat pocket in front.

• In the event of an emergency, follow the instructions of the cabin crew. They are highly trained in emergency procedures.

• If instructed, remove any spectacles, dentures

Emergencies on holiday and in the country

and high-heeled shoes you are wearing. Also remove sharp objects such as pens and pencils from your pockets.

• If there is smoke in the aircraft, protect your nose and mouth with a handkerchief. Wet the handkerchief, if possible. Keep near the floor when moving to the emergency exit.

• Escape slides inflate automatically when the door is opened. Jump onto the slide in a seated position.

• When you reach the ground, move well away from the aircraft. Do not attempt to go back for personal belongings.

• If you or someone else has been injured, tell one of the crew. They are trained in first aid, and have the equipment necessary for dealing with casualties.

• While waiting for outside help to arrive, try to keep up morale by chatting to and comforting other passengers.

HOW TO STAY COMFORTABLE IN THE AIR

• Choose your flight schedule carefully. If you are travelling east or west across time zones, plan to arrive early in the evening by local clocks so that you can get to bed shortly after arrival.

• Plan to arrive early at the airport and give yourself plenty of time to get there. More heart attacks occur at airports than during flight. This is due chiefly to passengers panicking on late arrival (see *If you miss your plane*, page 287).

• If you have a choice of seats, try to get as far forward in the plane as possible. The ride will be more comfortable there, which is why first-class compartments are always at the front. Noise and vibration tend to be worst near the tail. There is no evidence, though, that where you sit makes any difference to your safety in the event of a crash.

• Wear casual, loose-fitting clothes and shoes for the flight. Sitting upright for long hours may cause stomach, ankles and feet to swell, and make tight clothes uncomfortable.

• Carry a comfortable sweater to slip on or off. Temperatures may change even on a short flight. On a longer flight, climatic conditions may vary enormously. When it is winter in England, for instance, it is high summer in Australia. Think about climatic changes at refuelling stops, and dress appropriately for the weather. Make a note of the local time at these stops; a desert airport at night can be surprisingly chilly. Take a sponge bag, too, so that you can freshen up en route.

• Avoid smoking, or, if you are a compulsive smoker, cut it down. Smokers are more affected by high altitudes than non-smokers, because tobacco smoke hinders the body's ability to absorb oxygen. In flight, the oxygen level in the air inside the plane – which is usually pressurised to the equivalent of an altitude of 6000-7000ft (1830-2130m) – is lower than when on the ground.

• If you experience popping in the ears, do not worry. It is perfectly normal and occurs as air in the middle ear adjusts to the air pressure in the cabin. To clear your ears on the ascent, swallow; on the descent, shut your mouth, hold your nose and try to blow out gently. Try to avoid flying if you have a heavy cold or sinus problems, but if you have to fly, use a nasal decongestant.

• Make a point of drinking plenty of liquid during a long flight. Aim to consume 4-5 pints (2-3 litres) of liquid every 24 hours. At high altitudes, the aircraft cabin air is extremely dry, and you lose fluid which must be replaced if you are to avoid increased fatigue and dehydration. The best drinks are water and fruit squashes.

• Avoid alcohol, because it dehydrates the body. Coffee and tea also tend to dehydrate, so drink them sparingly.

• Aircraft meals help to relieve the boredom of a long international flight. But try to time your meals so that they conform to your normal eating pattern. For example, if your internal clock says it is 2am, it is best to avoid a meal because your gastrointestinal system has largely shut down for the night. If you do want something, drink water or a fruit squash.

• Sleep as much as you can on a long flight. Even dozing or taking short naps will help to minimise jet lag – the disorientation caused by crossing several time zones.

• Travel sickness (see page 284) is rarely experienced today on large jet aircraft. They rapidly penetrate bad weather and cruise high above it, so the effects of motion and acceleration are minimal.

• If you are prone to travel sickness, try to get a seat away from the windows and in the centre of the aircraft, where there is the least motion.

• If you use travel-sickness pills, take the first dose 30 minutes before takeoff, and others at recommended intervals thereafter. Remember, though, that some pills, such as antihistamines, cause drowsiness; they should be avoided if you plan to drive at the end of the flight.

Coping with a caravan tyre puncture

A caravan tyre may puncture when you are miles from a telephone. If you have no spare and no tyre inflators (see *Spare parts for everyday motoring*, page 225), you may be tempted to leave the caravan and seek help – leaving it vulnerable to thieves or vandals.

But there is a way to make an emergency repair on the spot.
- Jack up the caravan under its axle.
- Remove the wheel and undo the tyre valve to let the air out. Then stand on the tyre and tread out any air left in it (jumping on it will help).
- Use a jack handle or tyre lever to prise one edge of the tyre over the wheel rim.
- Having exposed the inside of the tyre, pack in any soft vegetation to hand – for example, grass, straw, bracken, heather, leaves or seaweed. Stand the wheel upright to check that the vegetation is packed solidly.
- Refit the tyre to the rim. To get the last part of the bead back over the rim, unhook the caravan and lay the wheel flat, in front and just to the side of the car. Drive across the edge of the tyre just behind the unfitted bead. Be careful not to drive over the metal rim of the tyre; you could crush it. Then refit the wheel.
- Hook up the caravan and drive slowly to the nearest telephone or garage to arrange a proper repair. Check the state of the tyre frequently and, if necessary, pack it with more vegetation.

SITING A CARAVAN SAFELY

On most caravan sites, pitches are allocated when you book in. But on some you are allowed to choose a pitch in an allotted field, and if you get a landowner's permission, you may be able to camp 'wild' on his property. Take care in choosing your site.
- Ask local people what direction the prevailing wind blows from, and look for firm, flat ground sheltered from it. Listen to local radio weather forecasts as well.
- Farm buildings, natural banks and thick hedgerows will all help to break the wind. Avoid tall trees, however – they could themselves be blown over in high winds.
- Avoid any area that looks prone to flooding – riverside meadowlands, for example.
- On sloping ground, use the corner steadies to adjust the height from front to rear and make the van as level as possible. Chock up the wheels to prevent the caravan rolling.
- If you park across the slope, dig a trench, if necessary, to lower the higher wheel. This is safer than jacking up the lower wheel because it keeps the caravan's centre of gravity nearer the ground and thus improves its stability.
- Check whether the clearance underneath the caravan affects the positioning of the waste-water container. If it does, you may have to dig a space for the container or turn the caravan round.
- Replace soil and turf before leaving.

Securing a caravan against theft
Protecting a caravan against theft is more like guarding a house than guarding a car.
- Fit secure locks and an efficient alarm system. Display conspicuously a sign warning that the caravan is fitted with an alarm – even if you do not in fact have one.
- Make sure that any gas cylinders are secure by locking their container. If they have no container, chain and padlock them to their carrier or fixing clamps.
- Lock the towbar into a cover (known as a hitchlock) so that the caravan cannot be towed away. If the cover has a padlock, make sure the padlock has an enclosed shackle so that it cannot be cut through.
- Make sure the corner legs cannot be raised, either by padlocking the steel collars that enclose the heads of the threaded rods or by locking each leg, using what is known as a 'steady' clamp.
- Whenever you leave the caravan, lay out a table set for a meal with plates, cups, cutlery, bread and so on. This will suggest an imminent return to any potential burglar.
- If you are leaving the caravan for a short period, hang washing on the line and leave a radio playing inside.
- Consider fitting a timeswitch or electronic trigger to turn the caravan lights on if it is unoccupied after dark.
- When you go away on day trips, ask a neighbour or the site warden to keep an eye on the caravan for you.
- If you plan to stay at one site for some time, get locking wheel nuts fitted, or use wheel clamps. Clamps also help to make the wheel into a stable, rigid support.
- Consider having each of the caravan windows etched or engraved with your postcode and the number of your house (or the first two letters of its name). This will make the caravan easier to identify if it is stolen, and may discourage a thief. The Caravan Club or a local police station should be able to advise on where to get the marking done. The Caravan Club's information office is at East Grinstead House, East Grinstead, West Sussex RH19 1UA; telephone (0342) 26944.

Emergencies on holiday and in the country

Righting an overturned caravan

If high winds topple a caravan onto its side, the safest course is to get expert help from a garage or motoring organisation. But it is possible to get the caravan back up on your own.

To use the technique, you need three fairly strong adults and at least 60ft (18m) of stout rope such as that used by climbers. You also need to practise the pulley knot shown here. It uses the rope to make a series of loops which act like pulleys, giving you extra leverage. Once you have mastered the knot, however, you can use it in any situation to move much heavier weights than you could otherwise handle: to help to free a car stuck in mud, for example.

• Remove as much equipment as possible from the caravan, and put it in the car. If the door is inaccessible, get into the caravan through an end window. Turn off any gas cylinders and disconnect the electricity as well.

• Raise the corner legs, or 'steadies', on the lower side. Put a block against the lower wheel, too, to stop it slipping. Lower the upper steadies slightly – not fully – so that they will make a three-point touchdown with the wheel.

• Tie the middle of the rope securely to the upper axle or a nearby part of the chassis. Then make the pulley knot shown here. Put the loop at the end of the knot round a sturdy stake driven into the ground at an angle.

• Throw the rope's other end over the caravan and wind it twice round a second stake to make a lowering line.

• Pull slowly and carefully on the free end of the rope. Ask at least two adults to pay out the lowering line gradually at the same time. Use as many adults as are available.

• Alternatively, you may be able to use the car either to help to pull the caravan up or in place of one of the stakes. Attach or loop the rope round the car's towing bracket.

• As the caravan comes upright, do not let it drop the last few feet; you could damage the axle and sub-frame. Let it down carefully.

HOW TO MAKE A PULLEY KNOT

1 *Attach the middle of the rope firmly to the caravan's axle or chassis. Throw one end over the caravan to make the lowering line.*

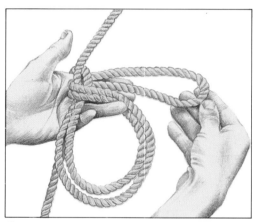

2 *Make a fold in the other rope about 2ft (600mm) from the fixing point, and bring the doubled section across and behind the rope.*

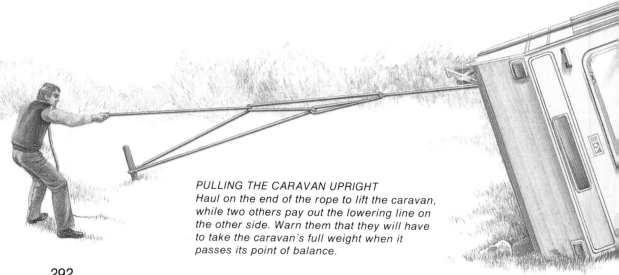

PULLING THE CARAVAN UPRIGHT
Haul on the end of the rope to lift the caravan, while two others pay out the lowering line on the other side. Warn them that they will have to take the caravan's full weight when it passes its point of balance.

3 *Bring the end of the folded section round the rope and push it through the loop to make a figure-of-eight pattern.*

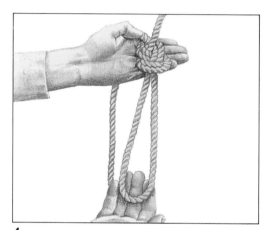

4 *Pull the figure-of-eight tight. This figure-of-eight is safer than a simple half-hitch because it will not shift under strain.*

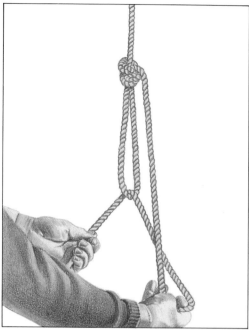

5 *Take a second fold in the rope and slip it through the loop to make a second loop. In use, the two loops act like pulleys, effectively more than doubling your strength.*

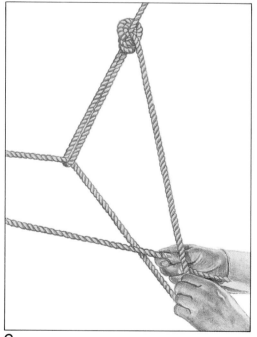

6 *Hook the rope's free end round a stout stake in the ground about 10-15ft (3-5m) from the caravan. Bring the end back to and through the second loop to complete the pulley knot.*

Camping out

Modern tents are compact, strong and light. But they can be as vulnerable as any other shelter – to wind, rain, snow and fire.

If you are caught in a burning tent
- Get out fast if your tent catches fire. As you go, beware of pieces of burning fabric – brush them off if they fall on you, and smother the flames with clothes or a sleeping bag. They will not be damaged if this is done decisively.
- Once outside, collapse the tent poles and, if necessary, the main guy ropes. Then stamp out the flames, if possible, or grab the tent by the end away from the fire, and pull it clear of your equipment inside.
- If the fire is too fierce to approach, though, let it burn. Equipment can be replaced; your life cannot.
- If the cause of the fire is a blazing stove in

the doorway, push or kick it clear before getting out and collapsing the tent.
- When the fire in the tent is out, pour water over the area round the stove to stop undergrowth catching fire.
- Try to keep the fire away from any foam rubber or plastic mat being used as a sleeping pad. Many of these materials give off poisonous fumes when they burn.

If the tent leaks
- If rain or melting snow finds its way into the tent, try to block up the holes by pressing warm candle wax or sticky tape onto the fabric from the inside or outside. Alternatively, run a finger down the inside of the tent from the site of the leak to divert the drips.
- If the leaks persist, protect clothes and sleeping bags with a waterproof anorak or a sheet of

EMERGENCY EXIT

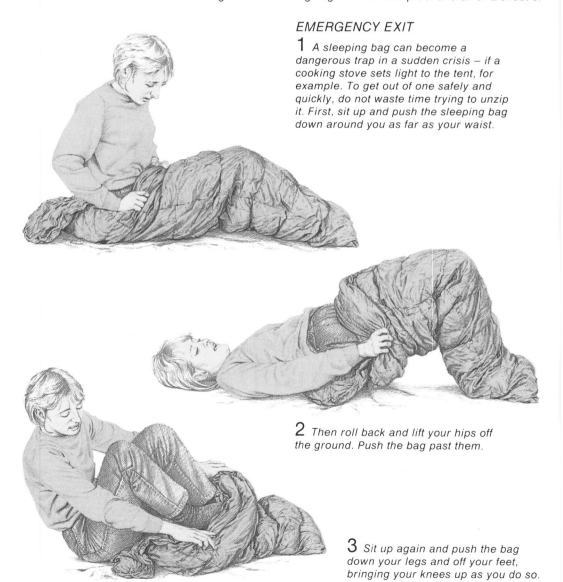

1 *A sleeping bag can become a dangerous trap in a sudden crisis – if a cooking stove sets light to the tent, for example. To get out of one safely and quickly, do not waste time trying to unzip it. First, sit up and push the sleeping bag down around you as far as your waist.*

2 *Then roll back and lift your hips off the ground. Push the bag past them.*

3 *Sit up again and push the bag down your legs and off your feet, bringing your knees up as you do so.*

PROPPING UP A COLLAPSED TENT
If your tent collapses in a storm, stay inside.
Stop it blowing away by sitting on the fabric.
Keep one pole in place to create space.

plastic. If you have a survival bag – a large plastic bag – climb inside it with your sleeping bag to keep dry and warm.

If the tent is flooded
The safest course of action in a flood depends on what your sleeping bag is made of. A down-filled bag loses its insulation properties if it gets soaked. The safest course then is to abandon tent and bag, and make for somewhere dry.
• If there is no shelter nearby, make a platform – of branches, say – and sit out the night in your driest clothes.
• In very cold weather, preserve body heat by not using the sleeves of the top one or two layers of clothes. Instead, button or zip the clothes up; then work them down over your head and body. Fold your arms under the cocoon, tucking your hands into your armpits.
• Sleeping bags which are filled with synthetic material retain warmth even when wet. The safest course then is to prevent any further water coming in – perhaps by digging a channel around the tent to divert the flow. Mop out the tent, wring out the bag and stay put.

If the tent blows down
• Repitching a collapsed tent in high winds is very difficult. In severe weather, if there is no other shelter – a car, say – stay inside the tent.
• Use the weight of your body on the edges of the tent or on the sewn-in groundsheet to stop the tent being blown away.
• Make some space inside by propping up the fabric with a backpack or one of the tent poles.

PITCHING CAMP
Setting up a campsite carefully can minimise the risk of things going wrong.
• Pick a site on firm, flat ground away from river banks and dried-up watercourses.
• Pick a spot that is sheltered from the wind. Test the site for concealed stones by lying down on the ground.
• Pitch the tent so that its doorway faces away from the wind. Pull the fabric and guy ropes drum-tight; on modern tents, there is no need to slacken ropes in rain.
• If rain is expected, dig channels under the edge of the tent roof and across any slope above the tent to carry water away.
• When high winds are likely, rest heavy stones on the pegs and flaps.
• Always keep some ventilation – especially if, in bad weather, you decide to do your cooking inside. If you start to feel drowsy, or a stove burns with a yellow flame rather than a blue one, it may mean that there is insufficient oxygen. Get out into the open at once.
• Anchor a stove to the ground with tent pegs to stabilise it while it is in use. When it is not being used, store it and any fuel containers away from the tent. Do your cooking outside if at all possible.

If you are threatened by a dangerous animal

Fierce dogs and angry bulls are the two most hazardous animals you are likely to meet in the British countryside. Both need to be treated with the utmost caution.

Be alert for danger from bulls. On average, two people die every year because of attacks by bulls, and 18 people are injured.

In most parts of Britain, farmers are not allowed to keep a bull in a field which is crossed by a public footpath.

Bulls that are less than ten months old, however, or ones that are not of a recognised dairy breed (such as Ayrshire or Guernsey), may be kept in such a field if they are with a group of heifers. A cow with a calf can also be very dangerous. Keep well away from all cattle.

If you are chased by a bull

• There are few circumstances in which it is wise to run from a bull. If the creature is a long way off, sudden movements will only excite its attention. Contrary to popular belief, bulls are not particularly enraged by the colour red – it is movement, not colour, which provokes them. Research suggests that bulls probably cannot distinguish very well between colours. So make for safety at a controlled pace, with your eye on the animal all the time.

• If the bull is close and starts to give chase, do not turn your back and run. The farmers' rule is simple: 'Never turn your back to a bull.' Instead, make quickly for safety, but keep your eye on the bull all the time.

• Try discarding an item of clothing: this may distract the bull long enough for you to make extra ground. But do not flap things at the bull or wave your arms.

• If you cannot reach and get over a wall or fence before the bull catches up with you, stop and face the danger. Do not square up to the bull in a threatening manner. Instead, be prepared to dodge to one side at the last moment. This is not as difficult as it might sound. A bull is an unwieldy animal, and once it has built up momentum in a charge it cannot easily change direction or come to a halt.

• Once you have dodged out of the bull's path, continue to make as quickly as you can for safety. But make sure that you keep your eye on the bull – and be prepared to dodge out of its way again.

If you are threatened by a fierce dog

• If you are menaced by an angry dog, do not look it in the eye. The dog will probably interpret this as a threatening gesture and it may become more aggressive as a result.

• Do not make any other kind of gesture which could suggest to the dog that you intend to kick or strike it.

• Stand still and order the dog off in a commanding tone of voice. Try shouting 'Leave!' or 'Stay!', for example.

• Alternatively, try to calm the dog by talking to it in quiet, soothing and friendly tones.

• Try both the commanding and calming approaches, if necessary, to see which of the two brings the better response.

• If the dog persists in coming at you, try to grasp it by the neck. Then push it backwards towards and through any door or gate which can be firmly closed.

• Do not grasp the dog by its tail. It will whip round and bite your hand.

• If the dog clearly intends to bite, offer it a forearm. If you are able to, cover your arm with a sweater or jacket. Then push your forearm down hard towards the animal's throat. This should weaken its grip. Keep pushing till it lets go. Do not try to pull your arm away from the dog's mouth. Its grip is very strong and by pulling you will cause a nasty, lacerated wound in your arm instead of a clean one.

• If you have been bitten by a dog, wash the wound carefully with soap and water, cleaning away all saliva. Seek medical attention quickly so that an anti-tetanus injection can be administered. (See also *Animal bites*, page 48.)

DOGS – STAYING OUT OF DANGER

Every year in Britain, more than 200,000 people are treated in hospital after being bitten by a dog.

You may meet a strange dog anywhere on holiday or in the countryside. In particular, be prepared for sudden barking if a footpath takes you through a farmyard. Farm dogs are not necessarily as fierce as they sound, but, like any other unknown animal, should be treated with respect.

Keep away from places where guard dogs are kept, and let your family know about the danger. A trained guard dog is a creature that has been reared to deter intruders. Some guard dogs are well disciplined. Many more are not, however, and all guard dogs are dangerous to strangers.

It is never wise to approach any strange dog, still less to try to touch it. Do not encourage children to do so either – in the false belief that children should be actively friendly to unknown animals. One happy experience with a stray dog may lead to a less happy one – with a creature that bites.

What to do if you encounter a snake

Most snakes are timid creatures which will attack only when startled or cornered. The adder, or viper, the only poisonous snake native to Britain, will usually hurry away before you get near it. Even if you are bitten, the bites rarely prove fatal. There have been barely a dozen deaths from snakebites in Britain during the past 60 years.

• If you see any snake, stop at once and move quickly to at least 20ft (6m) from it.

• If you do get bitten, clean the wound and bandage it firmly. Keep the injured limb low (see *Snakebite*, page 125).

Where snakes live

Snakes are cold-blooded, and most live in tropical or subtropical parts of the world. There are no snakes near the Poles. Snakes in cooler regions – including Britain – hibernate during the winter.

In Britain there are only two common snakes: the adder; and the grass snake. Adders live in almost any dry place, but they prefer sandy heathland or rough common.

Outside Britain, although many of the snakes encountered are harmless, all should be treated with extreme caution. If you go walking in areas where snakes are likely, keep to paths and wear lightweight boots (not sandals) to protect your feet and ankles – the commonest target of a striking snake.

HOW TO AVOID INSECT BITES

If you are stung by an insect in the British countryside, the consequences are unlikely to be serious. However, a sting may cause an allergic reaction, and a bee or wasp sting inside the mouth is dangerous to anyone. For first aid, see *Insect stings and bites*, page 110.

• To minimise the chance of getting bitten by insects such as mosquitoes and midges, use a repellent cream. One of the best active ingredients is diethyl toluamide, which is available from chemists as a gel, a stick or a spray.

• Apply the repellent all over the body. Also apply it to bedsheets or clothing, as appropriate. Repellents are washed off the skin in time by perspiration, but they last longer when applied to material.

• Avoid camping at the edge of a river, lake or stream. Waterside campsites are particularly prone to constant attack by midges in summer.

• Avoid hillside bracken beds, which house sheep ticks and a swarm of other insects. Stay on paths in such areas.

Emergencies on holiday and in the country

ADDERS AND GRASS SNAKES: HOW TO TELL THE DIFFERENCE

Adders, which are most often seen in spring, have dark zigzag markings, and grow to about 18-24in (450-600mm) long. Females are usually duller and browner than the males shown here.

Grass snakes, which live in damp grass and near slow-moving water, have no V-shaped marks on their heads. They are Britain's largest snakes, growing to 30-42in (0.75-1.1m). Despite their size, they are harmless

If you are caught in a lightning storm

When lightning comes to earth, it tends to strike the highest point around and to travel to earth along the line of least resistance.

Tall, isolated trees and buildings are particularly vulnerable. But people can be targets too, either because they are themselves the tallest object in the area, or because they are in contact with, or close to, something struck by lightning.

Every year in Britain, two or three people are killed by lightning.

• If your skin tingles and you feel your hair stand on end during a thunderstorm, it means that a lightning strike may be imminent.

• If you are in an open area, drop to the ground at once and lie flat. This lessens the risk that you will be struck.

• If you are near tall objects, such as trees or boulders, get away from them quickly if you can.

• Make for low, level ground and lie flat.

• If you cannot get away from tall objects, sit on something dry with your feet together. Keep your feet on the insulating material and off the ground. It is important that the material you sit on should be dry. Wet objects provide no insulation and thus no advantage because water is a good conductor of electricity.

• Hug your knees to your chest with both arms and tuck your head – the most vulnerable part of your body – well down.

• Do not put down a hand to steady yourself. This will make double contact with the ground and expose you to greater risks.

If someone is struck by lightning

A lightning strike is not necessarily fatal. Many people have escaped with only shock and minor burns.

Lightning is most likely to kill if it strikes the head and passes through the torso on its way to earth. In such circumstances it is more likely to cause heart failure or asphyxiation.

Lightning may also cause severe burns, broken bones – because of muscular spasms caused by the shock – and cuts.

In addition, the victim's clothing may catch fire and metal ornaments or watch straps may melt.

• If the victim's clothing is on fire, lay him down on the ground at once to keep the flames away from his face. Otherwise he could die from lack of air or from burns caused by breathing in the flames.

• If necessary – if, say, he is panicking and not responding to your instructions – trip him up or knock him over, taking care as you do this not to get burnt yourself.

• Put out the flames quickly by dousing them with water or wrapping the person in a heavy coat or blanket.

• Treat as for electric shock (see page 93).

• Get medical attention immediately – even if the victim appears to be unhurt.

• Reassure him and keep him warm and comfortable until help arrives.

SAFETY DURING A THUNDERSTORM

Your chances of getting struck by lightning during a thunderstorm are extremely small. Nevertheless, lightning is not entirely predictable and it is worth taking precautions to cut the risk still further.

• Get off high ground, such as the brow of a hill, and away from tall trees.

• Do not take cover in cave mouths, rock-face overhangs or recesses under boulders. They create spark gaps across which lightning can arc on its way to earth, striking anyone there. A deep cave is, however, safe; go right to the back.

• Keep well away from metal fences and other metal objects. Lightning does not have to strike directly to kill. Subsidiary flashes can arc out sideways from the main spark across several yards. In addition, the enormously high temperature of the bolt heats the air along its path explosively, causing shock waves. At a distance, these shock waves are audible as thunder. But close to, they are powerful enough to crush the lungs.

• If you are swimming or in a small boat, make for the shore at once. If you are in a larger boat, the crew should go below deck and the helmsman should avoid touching anything metal.

• Never fly a kite, ride a bicycle or ride a horse in a thunderstorm.

• If you are driving, stay in your car. It is one of the safest places to be. If lightning does strike, it will flash over the surface of the vehicle – which is virtually a metal cage – and run harmlessly to earth.

• In general, buildings offer good protection, but avoid isolated barns and huts.

• At home, unplug the TV at both the power socket and the aerial.

• Outdoors, rubber-soled shoes or wellington boots may offer some protection but they are no guarantee of safety.

• The traditional beliefs that you should close your windows and stay away from a fireplace during a thunderstorm are of only limited value. Closing windows is potentially useful only against ball lightning – a phenomenon so rare that nothing reliable is known about it. Ordinary lightning would not come through an open window anyway. Staying away from a fireplace was of more importance in the days of inglenooks when it was possible to sit directly under the chimney – and thus be in danger from falling debris if lightning demolished the stack.

Poisoned by a crop-sprayer

Crop-spraying with pesticides and fertilisers usually takes place on farms in spring and autumn. In Britain it is mostly done by tractor, but occasionally planes or helicopters are used.

Even in light winds, spray and dust can sometimes drift out of the field being sprayed and pose a threat to nearby workers, ramblers and picnickers. Many of the chemicals used by farmers are poisonous or corrosive if they are inhaled, and some can poison simply through contact with the skin.

• If you see a tractor or plane spraying, move well away from the area.

• Do not let dogs run on fields which are being sprayed with pesticide or sprinkled with fertiliser. They may pick up the chemicals on their paws, or swallow them.

• If the spray or dust falls on you or someone else, assume – for the sake of safety – that the spray is poisonous.

• Get out of the spraying area.

• Send someone for medical help immediately. Tell the doctor or ambulanceman the name of the pesticide being used – if you know it – or what crop is being sprayed. This will help doctors to decide which is the most appropriate treatment.

• If you do not know what chemical is involved, tell the doctor where the field is. With the help of local police, he will be able to find out quickly who owns the field and which pesticide or fertiliser was being used.

• Remove any contaminated clothing, and wash thoroughly any areas of skin that have been exposed to the chemicals. Use soap and water if possible.

• If chemicals have entered the eyes, flush them with clean water, under a running tap if possible, for at least ten minutes.

• Keep warm by wrapping up in a clean blanket or coat.

• If you have not been exposed to the spray yourself but are helping someone who has been, put gloves on before you touch any piece of his contaminated clothing. Otherwise the chemicals will get onto your skin too. If you do not have any gloves, wrap your hands loosely with, say, a jersey.

• If the person who has been sprayed loses consciousness, place him in the recovery position (see page 136).

• If he stops breathing, apply artificial respiration, the kiss of life (see page 50). If his face has been exposed to the spray, clean the area around his mouth and nose thoroughly first, and protect your mouth with a handkerchief.

Emergencies on holiday and in the country

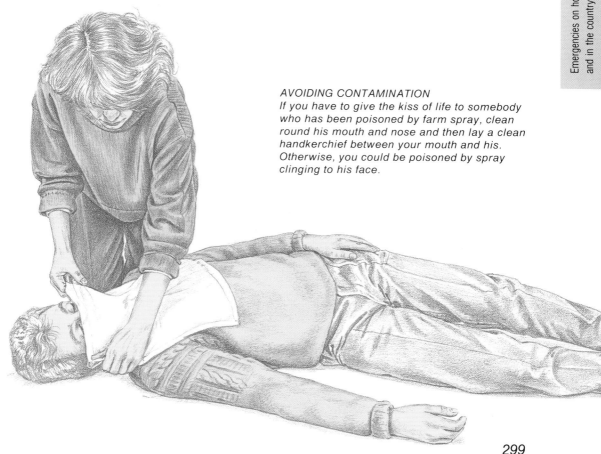

AVOIDING CONTAMINATION
If you have to give the kiss of life to somebody who has been poisoned by farm spray, clean round his mouth and nose and then lay a clean handkerchief between your mouth and his. Otherwise, you could be poisoned by spray clinging to his face.

Trapped in a bog or quicksand

Hazardous bogs, marshes and quicksands are found on both high ground and low. And they can be lethal to the unsuspecting walker. The principle of surviving is the same whichever you fall into: spread your body weight as widely as possible, and move very slowly.

• As soon as you realise that you are stuck, fall as gently as you can onto your back, spreading your arms wide as you drop. Spreading your weight in this way will enable you effectively to float on the surface.

• If you are wearing a pack or cape, leave it on. It may improve your buoyancy. If you have a stick, get it underneath you.

• Make all your movements – including getting your feet back to the surface – deliberate and *extremely* slow. You have to allow time for the mud or sand to flow around your limbs as you move. Quick movements only create pockets of vacuum in the mud or sand, which will tend to suck you deeper.

• If you are with a companion, lie still. Wait until he or she throws you a line, or holds out a pole to you. Use long, firm pulls to haul yourself out. Frantic jerks will be less effective and will tire you more quickly.

• If you are alone, stay on your back and use your arms and legs as paddles with a breast-stroke movement to propel yourself very slowly towards the edge.

• Use roots or large clumps of grass, if there are any, to pull yourself along.

• Do not hurry. It may take an hour or more to cover only a few feet in safety. If you need to rest. spread your arms and legs wide, and lie still. You will float.

DANGER SIGNS

A bog is an area of wet, spongy ground in marsh or moorland terrain. Some of the worst bogs in Britain are in parts of the New Forest and Dartmoor. Beware of flat, black expanses with no vegetation.

Beware too of bright green expanses covered with sphagnum moss. This is a treacherous vegetation which sometimes spreads like a carpet over a lethal mire.

If you have to cross boggy terrain, always keep to the highest ground where taller trees or bushes grow. Tread where possible on tussocks of heather – they indicate drier ground. If you are in any doubt about which way to go, throw heavy stones ahead of you as well to check the firmness of the ground. At the edge of a doubtful patch, try also stamping hard. If the ground ahead quivers, the patch is probably waterlogged; avoid it.

A quicksand is a bed of loose, wet sand which will swallow up any heavy weight. It is often difficult to spot, for a firm crust may cover the fluid below. The golden beaches of Morecambe Bay in Lancashire conceal notorious quicksands.

When exploring any unfrequented beach or unknown sandy area, carry a stick or pole as a probe, and toss stones ahead of you to test the ground.

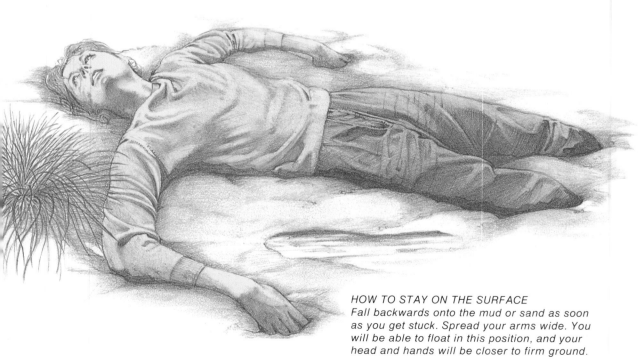

HOW TO STAY ON THE SURFACE
Fall backwards onto the mud or sand as soon as you get stuck. Spread your arms wide. You will be able to float in this position, and your head and hands will be closer to firm ground.

Exposure: the silent killer

Anyone who is exposed to the cold without adequate protection may suffer from a drop in the body's normal temperature, which can be fatal if left untreated. Doctors call the condition exposure or hypothermia.

It is blamed for the deaths of about five people a year on Britain's hills. But mountain rescue experts say that exposure could be the indirect cause of many more deaths because it saps the victim's strength and clouds his judgment, increasing the chances of some other accident, such as a fall.

. Most cases occur in the summer, when hill-walkers are least likely to be well prepared for sudden, biting winds and rain. The severity of the condition varies with age and general health. But exposure can kill even a vigorous healthy person in less than four hours.

Warning signs
Apathy and listlessness are usually the first signs of falling body temperature. Other symptoms are: abnormally cold skin; stumbling; shivering; cramps; slurred speech; abnormal vision; and erratic behaviour or irritability.

What to do
• If you notice any of the warning signs in yourself, change into dry clothes if your clothes are wet. Cover your head, face and neck as well as your body to minimise further heat loss. About 50 per cent of the heat lost by the body escapes through the head and neck.
• Find shelter quickly, and get into a sleeping bag or a plastic survival bag – a bag large enough to enclose a person completely.
• Consume warm, sweet drinks and food.

How to help a casualty
• If you notice the symptoms of exposure in somebody else, do not force him or her to keep moving or to walk quickly.
• Stop. Place the casualty in a sleeping bag – with a companion for extra warmth.
• If the symptoms are severe, leave the casualty's clothes on, even if they are wet. Changing clothes in these circumstances costs too much body heat for safety.
• Protect the casualty against the weather with a tent, a plastic sheet or any makeshift shelter. Use clothes, grass or anything else available to insulate the sleeping bag from the ground.
• If the casualty is conscious, give him warm drinks and food.
• Do not offer alcohol or massage: both tend to dilate the blood vessels near the skin. This draws body heat away from deeper organs at a time when it is crucial to warm the core of the body, not the surface.
• If the casualty loses consciousness, put him in the recovery position (see page 136). Never give an unconscious person anything to eat or drink. It could choke him.
• Once the worst symptoms have passed, treat the casualty as a stretcher case. Even if he appears fully recovered, do not move him without covering his head, neck and face.
• If you reach a house and the victim is conscious, put him in a warm, but not hot, bath. Keep the water at a temperature that is comfortable to the elbow.
• When the casualty begins to sweat, dry him, put him in a warm bed and keep him rested.
• Do not put an unconscious person in a bath. Instead, once you are indoors, take off any wet clothes he is wearing and put him in a warm bed. Place hot-water bottles (wrapped thickly in towels to avoid burning him) around his torso.

HOW TO AVOID EXPOSURE

• Get a good night's rest before spending a day in the hills. Victims of exposure often admit to having felt off-colour on the morning of the incident. Common causes are arduous overnight travelling – and drinking sprees – before setting out.
• Eat a good breakfast with plenty of fluids before you leave. Eat high-energy snacks such as chocolate frequently during the day.
• Always carry a plastic survival bag – a bag large enough to hold a person inside a sleeping bag – inside your rucksack.
• Wear warm clothing that gives full protection against the wind. Outer clothing should be fully waterproofed. Do not rely on jeans or showerproof anoraks – they are totally inadequate in severe weather.
• Carry a spare set of dry clothing.
• When walking, take off excess clothing if you get hot. It is important not to get soaked in sweat, because water draws warmth from the body faster than air.
• Never carry more weight than you can comfortably bear. In cold weather, it will make you more vulnerable to fatigue and exposure. For the same reason, go at a comfortable pace.
• Be alert to the risk of exposure in windy conditions even when the air temperature out of the wind is comfortable. As a rule of thumb to calculate this 'wind chill factor', subtract 1°F from the temperature for every 1mph of wind speed (1°C for every 3km/h). A strong breeze of about 30mph (48km/h) in an air temperature of about 60°F (15°C), for example, will have the same chilling effect as if there were no wind and the temperature was down at a freezing 30°F (-1°C). Use the Beaufort scale to estimate the wind speed (see *The wind and the sea*, page 268).

Emergencies on holiday and in the country

What to do if you get lost

What you should do if you get lost in the country depends largely on the circumstances. At night or in cold weather, the priority is to find warmth and shelter. On a sunny day, the priority is likely to be to find a main road or a telephone.

If you get lost on a clear day
• Once you suspect you are lost, stop and take stock of your situation. Going on blindly may only make the situation worse.
• If you have a map, check the key so that you know what its symbols stand for. You will probably have at least a rough idea of where you are.
• Look around you for landmarks that match the map.
• Try to find on the map the last position you were sure of, and try to trace your route since then by remembering any buildings, streams or other landmarks you have passed.
• Examine the contour lines on the map to get an idea of the shape of the ground in the area where you are lost. Widely spaced contour lines (which join places of equal height) indicate gentle slopes. An absence of contour lines indicates a plain or a broad ridge. Contours bending in a loop usually mark the spur of a hill or a valley.
• Check the scale of the map, too. It is usually given as a ratio figure – 1:50,000, say. This means that 1cm on the map equals 50,000cm (0.5km) on the ground. On this scale, $1\frac{1}{4}$in on the map equals 1 mile.
• Use a finger as a rough distance guide if you have no pen and paper. The index finger of most adults measures about 1in (25mm or 2.5cm) from its tip to the first joint. All Ordnance Survey maps are also marked with a grid of squares. On the 1:50,000 maps commonly used by walkers, each square represents an area of 1km by 1km. On smaller-scale maps, such as those often used by motorists, each square represents an area of 10km by 10km.
• Turn the map until the symbols on it are lined up with the landmarks they represent. Decide on the direction you want to travel to reach a main road or settlement.
• Check that there is nothing – a cliff, say, or a wide river – to bar the way to your chosen destination. If there is, work out a way to get round it.
• Look on the map and on the ground for a landmark to aim for. Check your progress on the map by watching out for more landmarks on either side of your path as you walk (see *How to use a map and compass*, page 306).

If you have no map
It is still possible to find your way to safety even if you have no map and no compass.
• Consider first retracing your steps to the last main road you passed.
• If going back is not practicable, look around you. If you can see a road – or something that indicates its presence, such as a building or telephone wires – head for the road.
• If you can orientate yourself by any landmarks, so that you know at least roughly where you are, aim for the nearest road, path, railway line or stream which you know will lead you to safety.

HOW TO CALL FOR HELP IN THE WILD

People on foot in open country are extremely difficult to spot from a distance or from the air. But there are a number of ways of improving your chances of being found.
• The internationally recognised mountain distress signal is six whistle blasts or torch flashes a minute, then a minute's pause – repeated as often as necessary.
• If you have wood and matches, light one or more fires. Once the fire is well alight, add damp wood or grass to make plenty of smoke.
• Wear brightly coloured clothing and a brightly coloured hat.
• Lay objects on the ground – branches, stones or clothing – to form the words HELP or SOS. Make the letters as large as possible – at least 20ft (6m) long. If there is snow on the ground, tread out trenches in snowdrifts to form the same words.
• In addition, wave a large flag made out of the most brightly coloured clothing you have.
• If you are being rescued by helicopter – on a mountain, say – let off a flare if you have one or light a small smoky fire near the pick-up point when the helicopter approaches. The smoke will show the pilot the direction of the wind, and help him to hold his position accurately while he is hovering.

Using a home-made heliograph
Heliographs – devices which use reflected sunlight to flash messages from one person to another – have been used by military signallers since the time of the ancient Greeks. They are easy to make at home before you travel – though they can be improvised on the spot – and, on a clear day, can attract attention from a distance of several miles. This is how to make and use one.
• You need a flat sheet of metal which is bright enough to show a reflection on both sides. A tin

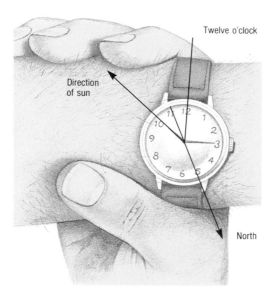

HOW TO FIND NORTH WITH A WATCH
Point the hour hand at the sun (ignore the minute hand). South in the Northern Hemisphere is halfway between the hour hand and the 12.

• Ideally, head for a feature, such as a road or stream, which you know cuts squarely across your line of travel. That way, you will still be able to find it even if you stray slightly off course.
• If no reliable landmarks are visible, decide what direction to head in, then orientate yourself by using the sun.
• The sun rises in the east and sets in the west.

At midday it will be due south in the Northern Hemisphere, and due north if you are in the Southern Hemisphere.
• If the sun is obscured by clouds, check its position by holding a nail file or knife blade on edge on a glossy surface such as a plastic credit card or a thumbnail. Turn the file until you see a faint shadow. The sun will be opposite it.
• If you are in Britain and you have a watch with hands, set it by Greenwich Mean Time (put it back an hour in summer). Elsewhere in the world, leave it on local time.
• Point the hour hand at the sun, and divide the angle between the hour hand and 12 o'clock in half with an imaginary line. If it is 4pm, for instance, the line will pass through 2 o'clock. The imaginary line will point due south in the Northern Hemisphere, due north in the Southern Hemisphere. In the Southern Hemisphere, point the figure 12 at the sun, and north is between the hour hand and the 12.
• If the clouds are too dense to find the sun, look for moss on trees and rocks. Since moss grows best in the shade, the most luxuriant growth will be on the north or north-east side in the Northern Hemisphere, on the south or south-east side in the Southern Hemisphere. This will give you a rough idea of your bearings. But confirm your direction from the sun as soon as there is a break in the clouds.
• If you have to stay put for a time, you can work out your bearings by placing a stick upright on flat ground. Mark the tip of the stick's shadow on the ground every hour or so. A line drawn through the marks will point due east and west.

lid rubbed clean will work, or a piece of tin foil.
• Make a small hole through the centre of the lid. Look through the hole until you can see the person or place you want to signal to.
• Now, holding the lid steady, look at the reflection of your own face in the back of the lid. You will see a spot of light on your reflected face from the sunlight shining through the hole.
• Tilt the lid until the spot of light in the reflection disappears into the hole. When it does, the flash is on target.
• Rock the lid slowly to generate a series of flashes. A series will be more readily noticeable than a constant beam, which could be dismissed as a chance reflection from water or a discarded piece of glass.
• Time the flashes, if possible, to match the international mountain distress signal – six flashes in one minute, followed by a minute's pause, followed by another six flashes in the next minute, and so on.

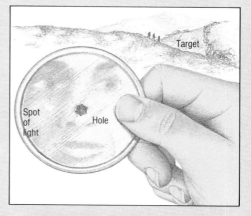

HOW TO AIM A HELIOGRAPH
Sight through the central hole on your target. Then tilt the lid so that the spot of light on your reflected face vanishes into the hole.

If you are caught in bad weather

• If you have survival equipment, such as a plastic survival bag – a plastic bag or a tube large enough to sit inside with your whole body and head protected – consider staying where you are and sitting out the bad weather.

• If you have no survival equipment and the weather turns bad with driving rain or high winds, the priority is to get down from high ground. It does not matter if you arrive in the wrong valley – so long as you do it in one piece.

• Check for danger spots on a map, if you have one. Steep-sided crags, for instance, are shown by hachures (knuckle-shaped marks). Plot a route around them.

• Use the direction of flow in streams to tell you which way leads downhill. But do not follow streams too closely; on hills, water sometimes carves deep ravines that could be dangerously steep. Instead, keep the stream within earshot and aim to follow its line.

• Avoid areas in a depression where there are tufts of spiky, light green grass. Tufts of this kind often indicate a bog or swamp.

• As you come down the hill, watch out for places that might offer or lead to shelter – a farmhouse, say, or a track. Make for them.·

If you are lost in mist or fog

• If mist closes in, line a map up with a compass and decide which direction to go in.

• Sight along the bearing you want to follow, using a straight-edge or a compass, and pick out some visible marker along the line – a rock, say, or a branch or fern.

• Walk to the marker, then use your compass again to identify another marker in the same direction.

• Repeat the procedure until you walk out of the mist.

• If you have no map or compass, stay put until the mist clears.

Caught in a whiteout

When the light reflected by snow is the same colour as the sky, the landscape loses all form. It has no horizon, no height, no depth and no shadows. Climbers and explorers call this weather condition a whiteout.

• Stop and wait for the whiteout to pass if you can. In a blizzard, find a snowdrift, scoop out a depression in the snow and burrow into it for shelter (see *How to make a snow-hole shelter*, page 317). Alternatively, enlarge the depression that often forms in snow around the base of a tree and shelter in that.

• If you have a plastic survival bag, sit inside it. Use a pad – a rucksack, say, or branches – to insulate your body from the cold ground.

• Put on as many layers of clothing as you can. Take your arms out of the sleeves of the top jacket or anorak. Button or zip it up, then work it down over your head and body like a tube.

• Cross your arms underneath the jacket and

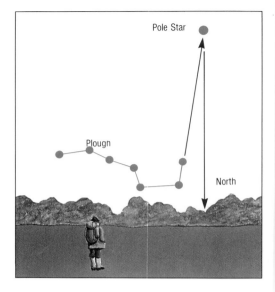

HOW TO FIND NORTH BY THE STARS
Look for the Plough, which can be at any angle in the sky. Its end stars point at the relatively faint Pole Star, which marks true north.

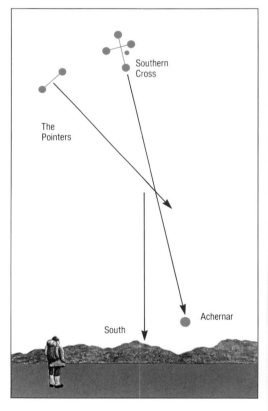

HOW TO FIND SOUTH BY THE STARS
Draw a line through the Southern Cross and three times its length. Due south is slightly to one side of the end of the line. Use Achernar and the Pointers to help to pinpoint the spot.

tuck your hands into your armpits to help to conserve warmth.

• If you have to move during a whiteout, use a map and compass to find your way. Toss snowballs ahead of you as you walk. Watching where they land and how they roll when they do will show you the direction of any slope. If they vanish altogether, it means you could be on the edge of a cliff.

Lost at night

• If there is a moon, moonlit grass or snow can give good visibility. In these circumstances, try to reach a road or any house or barn.

• If you have no compass, use the stars as a guide. In the Northern Hemisphere, Polaris, the Pole Star, which can be found using the constellation of the Plough, is always due north. In the Southern Hemisphere, the Southern Cross points towards the south, though not precisely.

• Another way of finding the Pole, in either hemisphere, is by using the constellation Orion. A line drawn between the middle star of Orion's belt and the centre of his head points due north (above his head) and south (below his feet).

• If visibility is too poor to travel by and you are on a mountain, find what shelter you can in the lee of a wall or rocks, and get inside a plastic survival bag if you have one.

• Members of a group can help each other to stay warm, even if they do not have survival bags, by sitting or lying huddled together. The middle position is the warmest, so change over from time to time.

If a child gets lost

An adventurous toddler or child, absorbed in his exploration of a beach, a picnic spot, a hillside or a funfair, can easily get lost.

• At the start of the outing, impress on the child the dangers of wandering out of sight. But fix some prominent place where you can meet should he or she nevertheless get lost.

• As soon as you notice the child's absence, make a quick search of the area where he or she was last seen.

• Go to the prearranged meeting place. If possible, have somebody wait there while you look around.

• If there is a public address system – as there often is at a funfair, say – find the people in charge of it and ask them to describe the missing child over the air.

• If all this fails, phone the police as soon as possible. Be ready with a detailed description of the child – his name, height, age, colouring, and what he was wearing.

• Once you contact the police, stay where you have arranged to meet them – even if there is a delay before they arrive.

HOW TO STAY OUT OF TROUBLE

Anyone who ventures into rough country on foot can minimise the risks of getting lost or stranded by following a few simple guidelines.

• Tell someone where you are going and when you expect to arrive. Check in when you do arrive, so that your contact does not call out rescue services unnecessarily.

• Estimate how long your journey will take. A fit adult can reckon to walk over open country at about 2½mph (4km/h), not counting rest stops.

• Add 30 minutes to your estimate for each 1000ft to be climbed along the route (50 minutes for each 500m).

• Telephone for a local weather report before you go, and dress accordingly.

• Walk in groups of at least four people. Then if one person is hurt – with a sprained ankle, say – another can stay with him while the other two go for help.

• If you have little experience of walking in open country, consider joining a walking club. The Ramblers' Association – whose headquarters are at 1/5 Wandsworth Rd, London SW8 2LJ; telephone 01-582 6826 – can provide information about clubs and groups near you, and give you their addresses.

What to take with you

• Carry a plastic survival bag – a large plastic tube or bag big enough to envelop completely a person in a sleeping bag.

• Carry or wear: a waterproof (not just showerproof) anorak and waterproof trousers; stout, comfortable boots; a spare sweater; and a warm hat and gloves. Also carry: food, including chocolate and dried fruit; an up-to-date large-scale map of the area and a compass; matches; a first aid kit; whistle and torch; and pencil and paper.

• In addition, take a first aid kit which includes a foil space blanket (see *What you need in a first aid kit*, page 44).

• For extended journeys, take a more comprehensive survival kit as well (see *Individual survival pack*, page 321).

• If your plans change for any reason after you set out, telephone those expecting you if at all possible. If necessary, contact the police and make sure that the emergency services are not alerted unnecessarily.

How to use a map and compass

With an accurate map and a compass, plus a pencil and a straight-edge (a ruler, say, a cigarette packet or the edge of a walker's compass), it is possible to navigate with a fair degree of precision across even totally unfamiliar country. And if you get lost, you can – provided there are two or three identifiable landmarks in sight – rediscover fairly quickly where you are.

Finding your position on the map

• Fold the map flat so that the arrows on it which identify north are visible. Large-scale maps (1:50,000 or larger) of the kind used by walkers normally have two arrows. One shows true north (the direction indicated by the Pole Star); the other shows magnetic north (the direction to which a compass points). The grid lines on Ordnance Survey maps are closely though not exactly aligned with true north.

• Lay the compass on the map, and turn the map until the compass needle and the arrow pointing to magnetic north are aligned.

• Once the map is lined up, look around you for clear landmarks – a church, say, or a known peak. Find the same landmark on the map.

• Lay the straight-edge on the map so that it touches the landmark symbol. Sight along the edge and turn it – *without turning the map* – until it points directly at the corresponding landmark on the ground. Draw a line along the straight-edge from the map landmark back towards the position of your eye.

• Repeat the procedure with a second landmark. Your position is approximately where the two lines on the map cross. Use a third landmark, if one is visible, as a check.

• Once you have worked out where you are, use the map to work out where you want to go. Lay the straight-edge along your intended line of travel and – again without turning the map – sight along the edge at the landscape ahead.

• Choose some easily recognisable feature along the line and use it as a beacon. When you reach it, use the map to replot your line of travel – avoiding any obstacles such as cliffs and bogs – then pick another marker to walk to.

• Whenever you use a compass, make sure it is well away from metal, which could affect it, and away from the magnetic fields generated by electric current, such as in pylon cables.

• It is possible to use a compass instead of a straight-edge to measure the direction, or bearing, of each landmark from your position, and to use a straight-edge only to draw the lines on the map. But it is easier, and just as accurate, to use a straight-edge for both jobs.

• If you use the compass method, remember to draw each line in the *opposite* direction from the bearing you measure. If one landmark is, say, exactly NE of you, draw the line SW from the corresponding spot on the map. To calculate a 'back-bearing' in this way, add 180 degrees to the bearing if it is less than 180 degrees; subtract 180 degrees if it is more.

Lining up the map with a compass
Find on the map the arrow showing the direction of magnetic north – it is usually on the top edge or the side. Turn the map until the arrow and the compass needle are exactly in line.

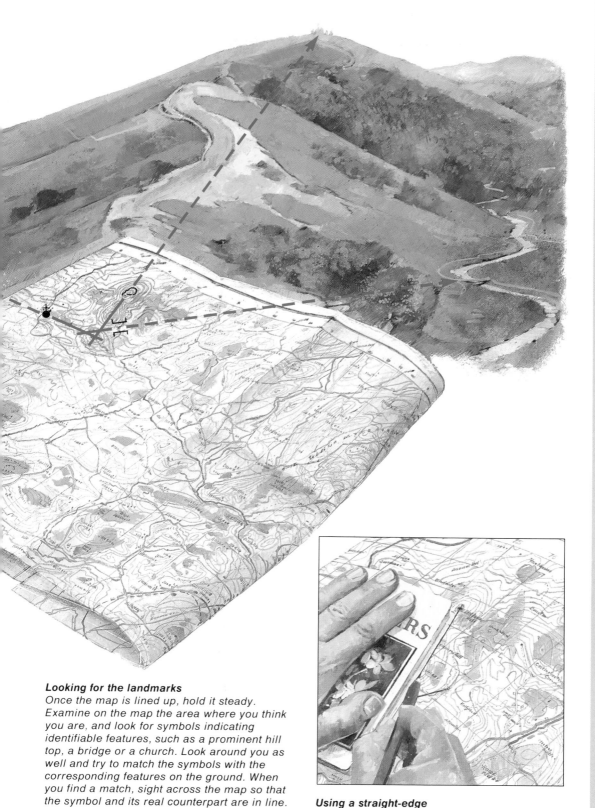

Looking for the landmarks
*Once the map is lined up, hold it steady.
Examine on the map the area where you think
you are, and look for symbols indicating
identifiable features, such as a prominent hill
top, a bridge or a church. Look around you as
well and try to match the symbols with the
corresponding features on the ground. When
you find a match, sight across the map so that
the symbol and its real counterpart are in line.
Your position is somewhere along that line.
Repeat the process with other landmarks and
your position is where the lines meet:
somewhere in the triangle they usually form.*

Using a straight-edge
*Any straight-edged object can be used as a
sighting instrument. Look along it the way a
golfer sights along a putter, or hold it and the
map up to eye level without turning the map.*

Skiing: coping with an accident

Ski resorts are well equipped to cope with accidents. If you break a leg on a well-used slope, emergency services are unlikely to be far away. But if you go skiing alone far from the normal routes, a broken leg may threaten your life unless you can reach shelter on your own.

• If you do break a leg, stop any bleeding by making bandages from torn strips of cloth. Use shirt-sleeves or underclothing. But do not use an outer garment; you must keep warm.

• Apply snow to the wound to reduce swelling.

• Put splints on either side of the leg, tying them above and below the fracture (see *Splints*, page 127). The task may be painful, but it must be done: tackle it with patience and determination. For splints, use ski sticks or any branches available.

• Do not try to walk across the snow. You are likely to sink in and do more damage. Instead, lie flat on your stomach on one or both skis and propel yourself with your hands.

• Follow a zigzag or diagonal path downhill, heading for anywhere help may be available.

• The best way to avoid the risk of having to find your own way to safety with a serious injury is never to ski alone. If you do plan a trip away from well-used routes, even with companions, consider setting your ski bindings looser than usual. It is easier to put a ski back on if you fall than to deal with a badly twisted ankle or a broken leg.

How to help an injured companion

• If a companion breaks a leg on a remote slope, apply emergency first aid (see page 98).

• Make an improvised litter using skis, ski sticks, and jackets or scarves (see page 115). Do not use the casualty's jacket for this purpose; he needs to be kept warm.

• Tow the litter slowly and carefully – on foot unless you are an expert skier. Head for the nearest well-used route.

ALONE WITH A BROKEN LEG
In August 1984, a 33-year-old Dutch maths teacher, Ton Peters, spent five days on a Scottish hillside with a broken leg. He missed his footing as he walked on Beinn nan Aighenan, above Glen Kinglass, and fell 40ft (12m) into a ravine, breaking his leg high up on the thigh. Realising that he was extremely unlikely to be found, he resolved to stay put until the pain in his leg had subsided, then try to climb out.

An experienced hill-walker, Ton was well equipped to survive. In his rucksack he had food for more than a week, pain-killing tablets, a tent, sleeping bag and a portable sleeping mat. He reckons the mat saved his life. Once he had dragged himself to a rock ledge, he was able to cover himself with the tent and sleeping bag (he could not put the tent up) and to lie on the mat. Without the mat to insulate him from the cold ground, he believes he would have died.

On the fourth night after Ton's fall, rain triggered a flash flood which swept all his gear away and washed him off his ledge. From his new position, Ton was later able to climb out of the ravine. In the morning, after a night of shivering agony in the open, he saw a car pull up at a house below. He shouted, waved his red anorak – and was spotted.

In hospital later, he said: 'If someone had told me before that I could endure all this and still live, I wouldn't have believed him. The main point is that you should never give up. You are stronger than you think.' There was one piece of equipment which Ton did not have: a whistle.

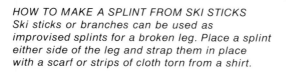

HOW TO MAKE A SPLINT FROM SKI STICKS
Ski sticks or branches can be used as improvised splints for a broken leg. Place a splint either side of the leg and strap them in place with a scarf or strips of cloth torn from a shirt.

If he had had one, he might have attracted attention much sooner – and his ordeal might not have come so close to costing him his life.

If you lose your skis

• Skis spread your body weight over the snow. If you lose them in a fall, but are unhurt, do not make for home simply by walking across the slopes. Walking through deep, soft snow will quickly exhaust you. If possible, improvise snow shoes. They spread your weight, and help to save energy too.

• Find two bushy pine branches, the thicker the needles the better. Place them on the snow with the natural curve down at the centre, rising forward and behind. The wider end of the branch should be towards the front and the stem behind your heel.

• Strap the branch onto your foot using improvised binding. Strips of cloth, laces or soft pine twigs will all serve for binding.

• Move downhill with care, and cross slopes diagonally or following a zigzag course. Use your ski sticks for support as you walk.

If your bindings break

Ski bindings can snap, making conventional skiing impossible. If this should happen, you can still get down a slope safely – and more quickly than would be possible on foot – by making an improvised hobbyhorse.

• Bind your skis together, using strips of cloth for lashing, and tie the ski sticks across the back end of the skis.

• Sit astride the skis with the tips behind you. Hold onto the ski sticks and lift them.

• Follow a zigzag path down the slope, controlling your descent with your feet.

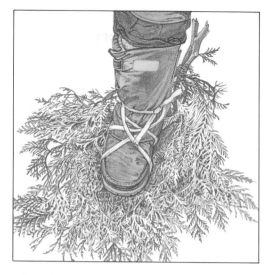

HOW TO MAKE A SNOW SHOE
If you have to walk through soft snow, make improvised snow shoes by tying bushy branches, stems backwards, to your feet.

HOW TO TOBOGGAN ON BROKEN SKIS
On firm snow, make skis with broken bindings into a hobbyhorse to help you to get down a slope more easily. Sit well back and lift your toes so that you plane over the snow.

Emergencies on holiday
and in the country

309

Crisis underground

Exploring caves can be extremely dangerous for the casual or ill-equipped. On average, cave rescue organisations in Britain are called out to help cavers in trouble about 50 times a year, and between two and three people die every year in Britain as a result of potholing accidents.

Mine workings are particularly dangerous because they often contain unmarked vertical shafts, whose entrances can easily be mistaken for deep shadows on the floor of a tunnel. Miners also used to store waste rock on timber platforms in the ceilings of tunnels. When the timbers rot, the rock can be left jammed precariously overhead and can be dislodged without warning by noise or an unwary hand. Old mines may also contain dangerous or even lethal con-

centrations of foul air or poisonous or explosive gases. Because of these hazards, never explore a man-made hole in the ground, or any hole which looks man-made.

If you get lost in a cave system

• If you think you might be lost, stop at once. Try to work out where you might have gone wrong.

• Calculate the time you have spent underground so that you can estimate roughly how long it ought to take you to get back.

• Mark where you are. Scrape a mark in mud on the floor or pile rocks to make a small cairn. If this is impossible, scratch on the wall with a knife or make a mark with soot from a candle flame.

• Try to retrace your steps.

• Keep looking back to recognise passages. A passage viewed from one direction on the way into a cave system can look very different on the way out.

• Leave markers as you go.

• Rest often to save energy. Switch your light off whenever you stop, to prolong the life of the batteries. Warming the batteries against your body will also make them last longer.

• If your path takes you deeper into unfamiliar territory, return to the last point you were sure of by following your markers, and try another route. Keep trying until you find the right one. Even in a honeycomb of passages you will gradually narrow the options.

• Shout, or blow a whistle, if you hear sounds that may be other people in the cave.

If you get stuck in a passage

• Relax completely. Taut muscles and fast, panicky breathing inflate your body and make escape more difficult. Go limp.

SAFE CAVING

• The only safe way to go caving or potholing is with experienced and properly equipped cavers, usually members of a specialist club. Public libraries often have lists of local caving clubs. Alternatively, contact the National Caving Association or the British Cave Research Association. Neither has a permanent head office, but a library should be able to help you to find their current addresses.

• Never go caving with fewer than four in a group. If there is an accident, one can stay behind with the injured person while two go for help.

• If you leave markers such as cairns on the way in as a precaution, remove them on the way out. Follow the cavers' rule: Take nothing but photographs – leave nothing but footprints.

• Tell someone of your plans so that help can be raised quickly if necessary.

• If you have to raise the alarm, dial 999 and ask the police to put you in touch with the local Cave Rescue Organisation.

• Check weather reports before you go. Rain can flood some caves very quickly.

• Wear warm clothing covered by a boiler suit – caves are chilly, muddy and usually damp all year round. Wear strong lace-up boots or wellingtons, and a plastic safety helmet.

• Take with you: a headlamp with a battery that will last longer than the trip is expected to take; spare batteries and spare lights or candles and matches; high-energy food – such as chocolate, glucose, fudge or raisins – and water; a map of the cave system; a first aid kit; a whistle; a watch with a luminous dial; and strong climbing rope.

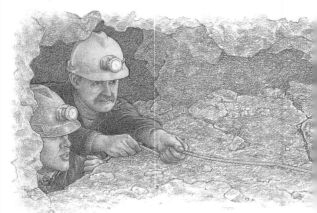

HOW TO GET OUT OF A TIGHT SPOT
If you get stuck underground and can find nothing to hold on to, get your companions to tie a loop in one end of a line. Put your foot in the loop and bend your leg. Tell the others to pull the line taut and anchor it, then push your leg down hard and heave your way out.

- Once you are breathing normally, try to wriggle out slowly. Tackle the task patiently, keeping as relaxed as possible.
- Use your whole body. It is often easier to push your way out with your legs than to pull with your arms.

If your light goes out

Inside a cave system, the blackness is total. And without light it is easy to become completely disorientated.

- Stop immediately. Crouch down and put one hand on the ground directly in front of your feet, the other hand directly behind you.
- Keep your hands still and turn round, using your hands as markers, so that you are facing towards the way out Do not turn any more or wander about.
- Sit down and wait for at least ten minutes to let your eyes adjust as much as possible to the dark. If you are not far from the entrance, a glimmer of light may become visible as your eyes adapt.
- While you are waiting, try to recall the caves and passages you came through.
- If there is a glimmer of light from the opening, crawl towards it slowly, on hands and knees, testing the ground in front of you as you go. Keep feeling in front of your face and body, too, to check for projecting rocks and boulders.
- If there is no light at all but the route you took was straightforward – few bends, no passages branching off, a floor without hazards – retrace your steps on all fours, keeping the route in your mind's eye. Feel your way along the wall of the cave.
- If you have come through a hazardous or complicated system, wait for somebody to come and rescue you. Your chances of finding your own way out safely are minimal.

A STONE'S THROW FROM SURVIVAL
Twenty times, a hundred times, a thousand times, Larry Ritchey threw a stone tied to a rope up into the patch of light that was his only chance of escape. Each time, it fell back.

Ritchey, a 35-year-old salesman, had been walking in the Cascade Mountains of the northwestern USA one November weekend in 1982. Suddenly, as he picked his way through deep snow, the ground gave way beneath him. He plunged 14ft (4.3m) into a subterranean stream flowing through a cavern about 10ft (3m) wide. The stillness of the air showed that there was no exit to the surface via the stream. And the rock walls were sheer. There was no chance of scrambling out.

Ritchey tied the stone to the end of his 30ft (9m) climbing rope and tossed it up through the hole in the cavern ceiling in the hope that it would catch on something. Again and again he threw, working his way round and round the lip of the hole. Three times the stone seemed to hold fast and then pulled loose as he tried to climb. But he never gave up, even after five days of failure. By the end of the fifth day he had no more food, the water was rising about him, and he was showing signs of hypothermia.

At last the stone caught again. This time it held. Ritchey hauled himself painfully back to the surface. He trudged and staggered 10 miles (16km) to a road and flagged down a car.

A search had been organised once Ritchey was overdue, but his shouts would never have been heard over the crashing of the stream, even had the rescuers come near him. What had saved his life was his own endurance – and the adage he had kept repeating to himself: 'If at first you don't succeed . . . .'

Emergencies on holiday and in the country

Survival in the wild

An injury, a breakdown, bad weather or sheer bad luck can turn an adventurous expedition into a fight for life. It can happen anywhere: on a moor or mountain, in a tropical rain forest or a barren desert. Wherever it happens, there are four immediate priorities. In order of importance they are: shelter; a signal; water; and food.

The ten pages that begin here describe how survival experts cope with these priorities in a variety of circumstances. All the techniques mentioned have been used in real-life emergencies and are part of the survival training used by such organisations as the Special Air Service (SAS). Some, however, are themselves hazardous and should be used only when their risks are outweighed by other dangers.

The first steps

• Wherever you are, the first step is to get out of the cold, heat, wind or rain so that you can make plans with thought and care.

• Next, let others know where you are by setting up a conspicuous signal. Use anything to hand for this. Spread out bright clothing that contrasts with the environment. Light a fire to make a smoke signal. Use a whistle if you have one. The internationally recognised distress signal is six blasts in a minute – then a minute's pause followed by another six and so on. Improvise mirrors to reflect the sun, or, at night, flash lights. There is no point in foraging for food and water before this task is done. Search parties may be in the vicinity already – and may miss you if no signal is set up.

• Finding water is more vital than finding food. An average person can survive for only a few days without water – and then only in a temperate climate. During the time spent finding and improving a shelter, setting up a signal and so on, you will have used up a significant amount of body fluid, which has to be replaced.

• Finally, find food. Under average conditions, an adult male can survive for at least a week without food before serious physical deterioration sets in.

• Nevertheless, start foraging early. Where necessary, test nearby vegetation for edible foods (see *The edibility test*, page 316).

Making and using a fire

Survival in the wild may depend on your ability to light a fire. Warmth, cooking, boiling water, drying clothes, signalling, warding off insects – all are essential needs. On any excursion into remote or difficult terrain it is vital to take an adequate supply of matches or a lighter. Waterproof matches are available; otherwise carry ordinary matches in a waterproof container.

Finding dry tinder and kindling

• Tinder must be bone-dry. Sources of tinder include dry grasses, stems, straw, leaves, twigs, bark fragments and splinters of wood. In wet weather, look especially under the bases of trees and under rock overhangs for the driest material.

• Even in wet weather, birch bark peeled from a tree makes good tinder since it contains highly inflammable oils. The resinous pitch in pine knots has the same inflammable properties.

• Where no natural dry tinder can be found, shred fragments of clothing. Tufts of cotton wool,

PREPARING FOR A JOURNEY IN THE WILD

No amount of preparation can remove all the risks from a journey through remote or rugged country. But preparation can considerably lessen the chances of things going wrong, and improve your chances of survival if they do.

• Learn to use a map and compass until you can navigate with confidence.

• Before setting out, inform relatives, friends or the police of your route, departure time, estimated time of arrival, and the number in your party. They can raise the alarm if you are held up. Never travel alone.

• Talk over your plans with people familiar with the area you are going to. They will often be able to give you valuable advice about local conditions.

• Wear clean, loose-fitting clothes that protect you against the weather. What you wear will depend on the climate.

• Wear next to the skin fabrics that will absorb sweat. In general cotton and wool are better than man-made fibres, but synthetic 'thermal' material is also good. Cotton is good in warm climates because of its sweat-absorbing properties, but it is not suitable for cold weather because it dries out slowly.

• In warm climates wear lightweight trousers. For cooler conditions the best clothing is breeches – made of tweed, corduroy or special synthetic fabric – and long socks. Do not wear jeans. When the fabric is wet it loses all its heat-retaining properties.

• Wear one or two pairs of wool socks. They absorb sweat and cushion the feet.

• Roughly 50 per cent of the heat that escapes from the body is lost from the head and hands. Wear a hat and gloves to help to conserve it in cold weather.

• Carry a survival kit (see pages 320-321)

unravelled bandages from a first aid kit and fluff from pockets all serve as valuable tinder.
• Blow gently on glowing tinder, and add bits of kindling sparingly as it ignites. Remember that split branches burn better than whole ones. Stack fuel loosely so that the air continues to circulate as you build the fire. Once the fire is going, add whatever wood is to hand.

Lighting a fire with a car battery
If you are stranded in a car but have no matches, there are two main ways that you can use the car to get a fire going. Never be tempted, however, to use petrol to light a fire or to keep one

going. Petrol burns explosively, and the flames or the blast can kill.
• If the car has a cigar lighter, twist a piece of paper into a spill, or use a piece of dry, frayed cloth or dry bark (birch bark is best).
• When the cigar lighter is red-hot, pull it out and touch it to the spill to light it. Then use the spill like a match to light the fire.
• Alternatively, if the car has no built-in lighter, use the car battery to light a fire.
• Disconnect the battery and remove it from the vehicle. Keep the battery upright when you lift it out to avoid splashing any acid onto yourself.
• Take two pieces of inessential wiring – from

HOW TO USE A BATTERY TO LIGHT A FIRE

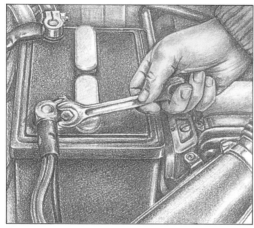

1 *Disconnect the terminals on the battery, and lift it out of the car. Take care not to touch both terminals at once with the spanner.*

2 *If you have no spare wire or jump leads, take out two pieces of insulated wire – the longer the better.*

3 *Bare the ends of the wires, attach one end of each to a terminal, and touch the free ends together. Catch the sparks in tinder to ignite it.*

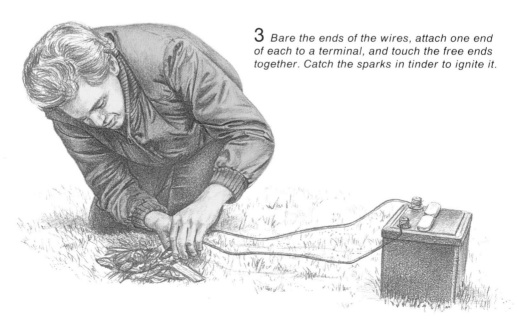

HOW A HUNTSMAN'S FIRE WORKS
The fireplace's funnel shape, which can be made out of logs, stones, earth or turf, acts like a natural flue. Use green logs or a metal grille to support cooking pans over the embers.

an interior light cable, say. Or use jump leads.
• Connect one wire or lead to each terminal. Then, carefully, touch the free ends together and catch the sparks in a pile of dry tinder.

How to build a fire

Before you light any fire, clear the ground around it of anything that might burn, and have something handy to put it out if necessary: water, perhaps, or branches to beat it out.

One particularly effective and simple fire is a type sometimes called a huntsman's fire. It makes an excellent cooking fire.
• Use logs, earth or stones to form a funnel shape about 12–18in (300–450mm) long. The wider end should point directly into the wind and be about 12in (300mm) across. The narrow end, pointing away from the prevailing wind, should be about 3–4in (75–100mm) across.
• Light the fire at the wider end.
• The hottest part of the fire will be a little downwind of the embers. So by moving pans towards or away from the narrow end, you can control the cooking temperature fairly precisely.
• Another way to make the funnel is to slice through the turf with a knife and roll back the turf on either side of the cut. The turf then forms the walls of the funnel, and the grass can be rolled back into place later, when you leave.

MAROONED IN AN ALASKAN WINTER
The Wortman family – 53-year-old Elmo, a disabled carpenter, and his three children – were on their way home from a visit to the dentist on February 13, 1979, when they were shipwrecked on the hostile coast of Alaska.

The family, who had travelled by boat to the

nearest dentist, across the border in Canada, were washed up on a bleak snow-covered island, injured and without food or shelter. They had with them matches, protected in glass bottles by Elmo in the last moments before the boat went down. With these, they were able to start a fire. Using salvage from the boat, the children – Cindy, 16, Randy, 15, and Jena Lynn, 12 – built a shelter. They rested two poles on a pair of large rocks and draped over them a sail, covering top, back and floor. The opening faced the fire to keep the crude shelter warm.

The Wortmans ate clams, mussels and seaweed scavenged from the shore.

With logs and some of the salvage from the boat – electrical wire, rubber tubing and plywood – they later improvised a raft, and managed to reach a trapper's cabin on a neighbouring island. From there, all were rescued on March 10 – weak and frostbitten but alive.

Keeping a fire going through the night

• To keep a wood fire burning overnight, reduce the draught of air by banking around the edges with earth or stones. Add slow-burning hardwoods or green logs.
• For maximum warmth at night, lie between the fire and any natural barrier such as a bank, rock wall or big log. This will reflect the heat back at parts of the body not facing the fire.
• If necessary, improvise a heat-reflector by rolling boulders or logs into position.
• Huddle together with any companions for extra warmth and to conserve heat.

HOW TO HOLD A POT IN PLACE
Stick a forked branch firmly into the ground, and prop another stick against it to hold a cooking pot securely in place over a fire.

Cooking in the wild

• Cook on glowing embers, not on flames.

• Cook all food – especially meat and fish – thoroughly before eating. This is particularly important in hot and humid countries where bacteria thrive. Cooking destroys harmful bacteria, and also neutralises some poisons.

• Boiling is usually the safest method of preparing food for eating. Boiling will also soften tough meat.

• If you are in doubt about whether any particular species of animal or plant is safe to eat, use the edibility test (see page 316).

How to cope with stomach upsets

You may succumb to severe stomach pains in the wild. Common causes are eating a poisonous plant, or drinking contaminated water.

• If you think that food or water is the cause of the pain, and you have no medicines for it, try to make yourself sick. Either put a finger down your throat or drink clean salt water.

• Alternatively, eat some carbon or chalk. Either is capable of absorbing poisons. Chalk may be available from nearby rocks; carbon can be any piece of charred wood from a fire.

• Crush the pieces and eat one or two tablespoons of the powdered chalk or carbon. Wash the powder down with plenty of clean drinking water.

If you suspect that water is contaminated

• Dirty or contaminated water should be boiled. To be completely safe, the water should be boiled for ten minutes. Alternatively, it can be purified chemically (see *Potassium permanganate – the all-purpose aid*, page 320).

• Filtering water will not purify it, but it will often improve the water's appearance and taste.

• If no proper filters are available, you can make your own equipment. For the container, use a canvas bag, a polythene bag, a large tin, a knotted shirt sleeve – or even a sock.

• Fill the bottom of the container with a layer of fine gravel. Above it place alternate layers of crushed carbon and sand – as many as will fit. Make each layer about 1in (25mm) thick. If no sand is available, use fine gravel instead.

• Make small holes in the container's base. Pour the water through, catching it in a cup.

• If you decide to filter the water, do the filtering before you boil or treat it chemically – not afterwards. The filter may otherwise contaminate the water again.

Using snow or ice

Where there is snow, there is water. But snow needs to be melted before consumption. Never eat raw snow. Because of the air it contains, raw snow causes diarrhoea and dehydration.

In general, ice is more valuable than snow, because it takes 50 per cent less fuel to melt it. When heating snow, much fuel is wasted warming the air trapped among the flakes.

Surviving in the jungle

Getting stranded in jungle is, in some ways, less of an ordeal than fighting to survive in other environments. Food and water, for example, are usually plentiful. And trees

HOW TO FILTER WATER

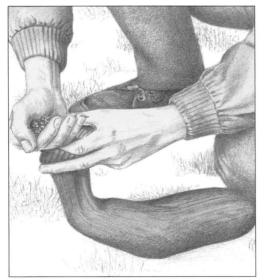

1 *Any tubular container with holes at the bottom – a clean sock, say – can make a filter. Put 1in (25mm) of gravel in the bottom.*

2 *Add layers, alternately, of sand and carbon (crushed burnt wood), then pour the water through. Boil the water afterwards to purify it.*

315

offer both fuel for fires and protection against the elements.

The worst enemy is generally anxiety: you cannot afford to be squeamish about anything that walks, crawls, swims or flies.

• Use what natural shelter you can find, or build a simple lean-to off the ground.

• When building a shelter, bamboo is an invaluable plant and found widely in tropical rain forests. It has innumerable additional advantages. You can make anything from a spear to a full-scale raft with bamboo. The canes can be used as firewood, and the tender shoots are both edible and nutritious.

• Filter and boil all water. Cook all food. Germs, like the vegetation, thrive in humid forests. When collecting food, beware of any brightly coloured plants, especially red and orange ones. They are often poisonous.

• Wash yourself whenever possible to discourage insects and prevent skin infections.

• Wash your clothes every day to stop sweat from rotting the fabric.

• Use fire to get rid of bugs, midges and other insects. Use an insect repellent, too – it also helps to ward off leeches.

• When travelling through thick jungle, movement is bound to be slow. Do not try to rush. It often helps to move backwards – if you get tangled in climbing vines, say.

• To find your way out of the jungle, locate any flow of water and head downstream. Follow a spring to a stream, a stream to a river, and a river to the sea if necessary.

• Sooner or later you will almost certainly come across other human beings, for waterways are the main lines of communication in tropical rain forests.

TWENTY-EIGHT YEARS IN THE JUNGLE
One night in January 1972, two hunters on the Pacific island of Guam came across a mysterious figure. He was wearing trousers and jacket made of tree and bark fibre, and he was heavily bearded. Brought in at gunpoint, he turned out to be Shoichi Yokoi, a former sergeant in the Japanese army. He had been hiding out in the jungle for 28 years – ever since the end of the Second World War.

Yokoi had fled into the jungle when US

THE EDIBILITY TEST

If you are stranded in remote country, you may be forced to live off the land, and that will mean trying to survive mostly by eating plants. The range of poisonous and non-poisonous plants is vast, and you may get confused trying to remember the different species. In an emergency, it is possible to find out which is which by using yourself as a cautious guinea pig.

Do not try this technique at home, however, and particularly do not encourage children to try it. Use it only in an emergency when the risk of making yourself ill is outweighed by the risk of starving.

• One person should test only one plant at a time, and each plant should be tested by only one person. And remember that just because you see birds or animals eating a plant, it does not mean that the plant is safe for humans.

• Choose a species which seems to grow plentifully in the area. But do not experiment with fungi. Unless you know that a fungus is edible, make no attempt to eat it or to prepare it for eating. Even boiling fungi does not always remove dangerous toxins.

• Having selected a plant, look for the colour of the sap by squeezing the leaf or stem between your fingers.

• Discard any plant that has a creamy or

milky sap – it is probably poisonous. (An important exception to this rule is the dandelion: the whole plant is edible and nutritious. It also helps to stop diarrhoea.)

• Rub the juices or sap around the tender parts on the inside of your bottom lip. At the same time, place a small piece of the plant – fingernail-size or smaller – on the tip of your tongue. Wait for 4-5 minutes. If you detect any stinging, burning or putrid sensation, discard the plant.

• If you detect none of these sensations, take a larger piece of the plant, roughly 2in (50mm) square. Chew it and swallow it. Wait for two hours. If you experience any stomach upset or feeling of nausea, discard the plant – it is probably poisonous.

• If you detect none of these symptoms, take a larger portion of the plant, roughly 6in (150mm) square, chew and swallow it, and wait a further two hours. If you feel no ill effects, the plant is probably safe to eat.

• Having identified the plant as probably safe, boil it and throw away the juices. Then, as a final precaution, boil it again before eating.

• As the days pass, repeat the test with other plants – trying out roots, fruits, berries and flowers as well as leaves and stems – so that you build up, in time, a varied diet.

troops recaptured the island in 1944. Fearing capture, he had burnt his service uniform and improvised clothing with the materials to hand. For shelter he dug out a cave in a bamboo thicket and left it only at night.

Through the entire period he survived on a diet of nuts, breadfruit, mangoes, papaya, fish, shrimps, snails, rats and frogs. When discovered by the hunters he was on his way to a river to set his traps for fish.

Yokoi was in good physical health (though bewildered by the world of TVs and space travel to which he was returned). His largely salt-free diet had, however, left him slightly anaemic. Salt is present in roasted meat, but not in boiled food. In an emergency, it can be obtained by boiling sea water and collecting the salt crystals left behind.

Surviving in the mountains

• Look for shelter in caves and overhangs. Besides offering protection from the elements, they almost always contain some water or moisture. But avoid them during a thunderstorm. They are dangerous if lightning strikes.

• Avoid any area which threatens landslide or avalanche, such as a scree slope.
• If you are trapped in a remote valley, the higher ground to either side may be safer than the basin.
• Use spare clothes or a bright groundsheet to mark your position.
• Try to attract attention by using a whistle or by calling out – sound travels far in mountains. Give the international distress signal – six blasts a minute, then a minute's pause, followed by another six and so on. This is more likely to be noticed than random shouts.

How to make a snow-hole shelter

• If you are in snow, and bad weather or fading light prevents you from travelling for the time being, you can make your own shelter in the form of a snow hole.
• Use natural snow cavities where possible. The heavily snow-laden branches of a tree, for example, may provide a promising shelter which needs little extra work. Otherwise, dig into the side of a drift.
• Test the drift for depth: about 5-6ft (1.5-1.8m) is best.

USING A SNOW HOLE FOR SHELTER
Once you have dug a snow hole, get inside and block the entrance tunnel. Keep a stick or pole handy to poke ventilation shafts through the roof, and keep them open. Burn a candle if you have one. Put heather or branches on the bench to insulate yourself from the snow.

• Once you have found a suitable spot, mark your position conspicuously. Dig out a small entrance low down, tunnel in about 2ft (600mm) and scoop out a cavity. It should be large enough to hold you in a sitting position. If there are more than three of you, it may be necessary to dig more than one hole, but otherwise share. Company and additional body warmth will make the ordeal easier to endure.

• Dig with a shovel or an ice-axe, or improvise using cooking pans, for example, or branches. Your hands alone will not be enough.

• Pierce an air shaft through the roof with a stick for ventilation. You may need more than one shaft if several people are in the hole. Keep the stick handy to clear the shaft in case it gets blocked by snow.

• Shape a rough bench for yourself within the cavity. Scoop out a small trench where the bench meets the back and side walls. This will prevent any melting snow from flooding your seat. Line the bench with bushy branches.

• Scoop out a well in the floor in front of your feet. Cold air travels downwards, and the well will help to ensure that the chilliest air collects below the level of your body.

• Once the snow hole is ready, get inside, block up the entrance and stay put until morning or until the weather clears and you can move on.

• Avoid falling asleep in a snow-hole shelter unless you are properly equipped with a sleeping bag and plastic survival bag. Keep your spirits up by singing, telling yourself stories – whatever it takes to keep you alert.

• Light a candle, if you have one. It will provide warmth and help to keep your spirits up.

BOYS AGAINST A BLIZZARD

Training, preparation and a determination to stay alive saved the lives of three teenage American climbers who became trapped on Mount Hood in Oregon by a terrifying blizzard. Once Gary Schneider and Matt Meacham, both 16, and 18-year-old Randy Knapp realised they could go no farther during their New Year hike in 1976, they dug a snow hole and settled in to wait out the storm. They were well equipped and had plenty of food, and they kept wriggling their toes and rubbing their feet to keep the circulation going.

They were rescued after two weeks when the storm died away. Each had lost about 2 stone (13kg) in weight, and Randy and Matt had minor frostbite. But all were well enough to go back to school within a couple of weeks.

Surviving in the desert

The vital need in a desert is to avoid dehydration. If you are stranded in a car, use its shelter to keep cool during the heat of the day. If you are on foot, find whatever shade you can – in a cave, say, or in the shadow of rocks.

• Improvise a headdress – a hat with a handkerchief, say, hanging from the back of it – to protect your head and the back of your neck from the sun. It is important to cover the back of the neck as well as the head to guard against heat stroke (see page 106).

• Set up a signal for rescue parties (see page 312), then take cover from the sun. Keep to the shade throughout the day. Move only at night.

• If you are stranded in a car, never leave it and try to walk out. Stay with the vehicle.

• An adult in the shade can make do on 4 pints (2.25 litres) of water a day. Try to drink in the early morning and evening. Drinking during the heat of the day can lead to excessive perspiration and loss of body salts.

• To obtain drinking water, collect water in a solar still or use a dew trap.

• Look, too, for a natural source of water in the beds of dried-up streams or rivers. Dig in damp

HOW TO MAKE A DEW TRAP
To collect dew in the desert, pile clean, smooth stones on plastic in a shallow hole. Each morning, collect the dew that drains from the stones into the plastic before the sun gets up and evaporates it.

MAKING A SOLAR STILL
To use the sun's heat to draw water out of the ground, lay a sheet of plastic over a tin set in a wide hole. Use a tube, if you have one, to suck out the water that collects in the tin.

patches or around the bases of plants. There may be moisture underground.

• Watch also the behaviour of wildlife. Wherever there are insects, flies, animals and birds, there is moisture somewhere nearby.

• For food, look for any vegetation around. Most desert plants have some edible part to them (see *The edibility test*, page 316).

Making a dew trap

During the night, water collects on shiny surfaces such as windows and metal, or on smooth stones and pebbles. The dew can be collected by wiping the surfaces with a cloth early in the morning and wringing it out into a container. It can also be collected in a dew trap.

• Dig a shallow hole and line it with plastic sheeting or some other non-absorbent material.

• Pile clean, smooth stones onto the sheet. The dew which collects on the stones will drain into the plastic sheeting.

• Early in the morning – before the sun evaporates the dew – remove the stones and collect the water.

• Sterilise the water before drinking it. The stones may be contaminated.

How to make a solar still

Another way to collect water in the desert is to suck it out of the ground with a solar still. A well-constructed still will collect up to $3\frac{1}{2}$ pints (2 litres) of water a day.

• Dig a hole at least 3ft (900mm) across.

• Place a clean can, or any other container with a wide neck, centrally in the bottom of the hole.

• If there are any leaves or shrubs near, put them loosely in the base of the hole. This will increase the water yield.

• Spread a sheet of plastic over the hole and anchor it round the edge with stones or other

heavy objects. Place a stone in the centre of the plastic so that its lowest point is right over the container, but not touching it. Condensation will collect on the underside of the plastic, trickle down the sheet and drip into the can.

• If you have a length of plastic tubing, place one end in the can and the other on the surface, protruding from under the sheeting. You will then be able to suck the water from the can without disturbing the still.

• There is no need to sterilise water from a solar still as long as the can and the plastic are clean. The process of collecting the water distils it and so makes it safe to drink.

Surviving on moorland

Wet, cold weather is the particular hazard of open moorland. If you get damp and chilled, you run the risk of exposure, so look for dry shelter immediately (see *Exposure: the silent killer*, page 301).

• Seek out places where animals are taking refuge from the elements – such as woods, copses, caves, overhangs and banks by streams. Try to share the shelter with them, or move them on and use the space yourself. Moorland sheep and cattle pens are also good for getting out of the wind.

• Collect rain or melt snow or ice for drinking water. But do not venture out unnecessarily in heavy rain, mist or snow.

• When conditions clear, head for the nearest place of safety (see *What to do if you get lost*, page 302).

SURVIVORS ON THE MOOR
In April 1981, five cadets from the Air Training Corps on a weekend exercise survived two days and nights of freak blizzards on Dartmoor.

Richard Stubbs, aged 16, his brother Russell, Roger Pheasant and Daren Green, all 14, and Stephen King, 15, ran into trouble on the Saturday afternoon as weather conditions worsened across the moor.

All five of them huddled into their single two-man tent, which they had pitched in a sheltered river valley. With just one sleeping bag between them, and only a single day's rations, they sang and told jokes to keep cheerful as the blizzard roared outside.

Temperatures were so low that the peas froze in the whistles of the rescue party called out to look for the teenagers after they failed to reach a checkpoint.

When the blizzard finally eased 50 hours later on Monday morning, the teenagers set off back, and were met, only 2 miles (3km) from the main road, by members of the 200-strong rescue team. The five teenagers were suffering from exposure and mild hypothermia but were otherwise unharmed. Inspector Rachel James, of Okehampton police, who was in charge of the rescue operation, said afterwards: 'The boys did everything right. They survived through sheer guts and determination.'

Potassium permanganate – the all-purpose aid
Potassium permanganate – a chemical normally sold as small purple crystals – is one of the most versatile items in any survival kit. It can be used to purify water, disinfect a wound, start a fire or signal distress.
• To purify water, add three or four crystals of potassium permanganate to 1 litre of water. Leave for 30 minutes. The chemical will stain the water slightly but the water will then be safe to drink or cook with.
• To clean cuts and abrasions, or treat fungal

MOTORIST'S SURVIVAL KIT

A survival kit – kept in the boot of the car, or under the back seat – is a valuable piece of equipment for any motorist preparing for a long journey in remote country.

The contents suggested here are not expensive to assemble: many of the items can be old or used materials from everyday life. You may never need to use the kit at all – but on the one occasion when you do, it could prove absolutely invaluable.

The clear polythene bag can serve as the container for the kit. It is important that the bag should be clear, because in an emergency you will not want to waste valuable time rummaging through an opaque container for a small item which is needed immediately.

Item	Uses
Large, clear polythene bag	Keeping things dry and together; shelter; flotation aid; cordage (when torn into strips); solar still; water container; emergency windscreen.
Nylon washing line at least 16ft (5m) long	Tow rope; lashing.
Blanket	Warmth; stretcher; cordage or bandages if torn into strips.
Sweater and socks (in various colours)	Warmth; improvised filters; distress signals.
Flexible water can	Water container; flotation aid.
Tins of food	Nourishment; cooking utensils (when empty); signalling (using metal lid as mirror – see box, page 302).
Waterproof matches	Firelighting.
Potassium permanganate	Disinfectant; firelighting (see text above).

infections, dissolve permanganate crystals in a glass of water one by one. Stop adding the crystals as soon as the water turns purple. Bathe the wound in the solution.

• To start a fire, take 1 part of sugar and 2 parts of potassium permanganate. Mix them dry and grind them together between two pieces of dry kindling. If the conditions are sufficiently dry, the kindling will burst into flames.

• As an alternative method of starting a fire, take a dessertspoon of potassium permanganate crystals and place it in a newspaper. Add a few drops of antifreeze and squeeze the newspaper into a ball. The chemical reaction will produce a flame within 30 seconds.

• To signal distress in snowy terrain, sprinkle potassium permanganate dissolved in water onto the snow. It will stain the snow a vivid purple as a marker for search parties.

• Mixing permanganate in water will also act as a temporary dye marker to help rescuers to spot you if you are adrift in a small boat.

THE ORDEAL OF SVERRE BØRNES

On October 17, 1982, during a storm off the Norwegian coast, the engine of Sverre Børnes's 16ft (5m) boat failed. Børnes, a 35-year-old engineer, was on a weekend trip to his island cabin, and had planned to do some hunting along the way. He managed to steer into a rock to stop being swept out to sea, but his boat sank, stranding him.

He salvaged his hunting rifle, and a tarpaulin which became his only shelter. For food, he scavenged limpets and seaweed. He also shot a seagull, which he plucked and ate raw.

Børnes's right foot had been badly cut as he scrambled ashore. Terrified that it would turn gangrenous from the cold and wet, he spent days pounding it with his fist to keep the circulation going – and saved it.

He was rescued after ten days – $1\frac{1}{2}$ stone (10kg) lighter, but otherwise fit and well.

INDIVIDUAL SURVIVAL PACK

Even a pocket-sized personal survival kit can carry enough equipment to stop a problem becoming a crisis. It should be carried as a back-up kit and separately from a rucksack – in an anorak pocket, say. Then, if you get parted from your gear for any reason, you can use it to find your way back to safety – or to stay alive until rescuers find you.

Item	Uses
Empty tin with lid (such as a tobacco tin)	Container for survival pack; cooking utensil; signalling device (when used as a mirror – see box, page 302).
Small compass	Direction finding.
Waterproof matches	Firelighting.
Small, square candle	Light; warmth; firelighting aid.
Cotton wool	Swab; packing; tinder.
Knife	Cutting; opening tins; cooking.
Thin nylon line	Repair of equipment; ties for shelter.
Foil space blanket	Warmth; shelter.
Potassium permanganate	Disinfectant; firelighting (see page 320).
Whistle	Signalling.

Natural disasters

Caught in an avalanche

A snow slope that starts to slide may come down slowly like a flow of wet concrete, sometimes halted by obstacles in its path.

Alternatively, it may hurtle down the mountainside as a 'slab' avalanche of broken chunks, preceded by a mighty blast of air.

In either case, the priority is the same: get out of its path.

• Assess the situation. Your first instinct may be to run downhill, but the avalanche is travelling downhill too – and it may be moving at as much as 100mph (160km/h).

• It is usually safer to head to the side. You may be able to get out of the path of the avalanche, or to reach higher ground.

• Get rid of any encumbrances such as a rucksack, skis and ski poles. They will make it more difficult for you to move if the snow engulfs you.

• Do not try to escape by skiing unless you are on the very edge of the avalanche's path where a sprint will see you clear.

• If you cannot escape and the avalanche overtakes you, clamp your mouth tightly shut and hold your breath. This will prevent snow from entering your throat and lungs, and so minimise the risk of suffocation.

• Hang on to the downhill side of any fixed object – a rock pinnacle, for example. Even if you are engulfed for a time, the avalanche may eventually flow past and come to rest farther down, leaving you free.

• If you are swept downhill, fight to stay on top of the avalanche. Swim *against* the tide and towards the nearest side, using breast stroke, dog paddle or back stroke.

• While swimming, you may need to use your arms to fend off rocks and snow slabs, but above all keep fighting for the surface.

If you are buried by an avalanche

• Summon every effort to break out immediately the avalanche begins to slow up, because avalanche debris begins to set hard within minutes of coming to rest.

• Wrap both arms around your head to create as much of a breathing space as possible.

• To find out which way up you are, collect saliva in your mouth and dribble it from your lips. If the spit travels towards your nose, for example, you will know you are upside down.

• When you know which direction to aim for, try to break out of the snow.

• If you cannot break out, conserve your oxygen by moving as little as possible and breathing slowly. It is possible to survive under snow for some time until rescuers reach the scene.

SAFETY IN AVALANCHE COUNTRY

• When skiing or walking in mountainous areas, listen regularly to weather reports. Conditions can change very suddenly and it is better to cancel or cut short a planned excursion than to endanger your life and the lives of your rescuers.

• Never venture onto a mountain slope soon after a heavy snowfall. Avalanches often happen after successive falls of snow have built up in layers. The upper layers may then become unstable, and the weight of a single skier – or even the vibrations of a shout – may be enough to trigger a slide.

• Be particularly careful during intervals of warm weather or once a general thaw has set in during the spring.

• Be alert for the first signs of an avalanche: sounds of cracking ice; snowballs rolling down the hill; a dull roaring sound; or clouds of white dust farther up the hill.

• Obey all warning notices and avoid crossing risky slopes.

• If you have to cross a dangerous slope, do not go alone. Travel in a party and cross one at a time so that there is always someone to go for help.

• Continue to cross singly until all are safely over. Just because one person negotiates the slope successfully, it does not mean that the slope is safe.

• On long ski tours or walks in high hills, always take a professional guide. Touring parties should work to a timetable so that the alarm can be raised quickly if they do not reach their destination.

Precautions against avalanches

Helicopters, dogs and mountain rescue teams provide emergency services in areas where avalanches are common. For skiers and walkers, there are specific aids that may save life if disaster strikes.

• An avalanche bleeper is a small, portable electronic device which sends out a signal enabling rescue parties to locate victims buried in the snow immediately.

• Avalanche cords are thin, red or orange nylon lines which are easily seen against snow. They are 60-100ft (18-30m) long. Tie one round your waist and trail it behind if you have to cross any slope that looks remotely hazardous. The cords are sometimes crimped at intervals with arrowed metal tags to show the direction of the victim and the depth at which he is buried. Make sure you tie the correct end around your waist.

Escaping a volcanic eruption

Whether dormant or active, a volcano may erupt without warning. In a violent cataclysm, clouds of ash darken the sky, shattered rocks hail from above and molten lava floods down the slopes. Clouds of poisonous gas may also be released from the crater or from fissures on the flanks of the mountain.

A volcanic eruption is a catastrophe on such a large scale that it may seem impossible that any action one person could take would make any difference. Luck, of course, plays a large part in determining who survives and who does not, but decisive action may tip the balance of luck in your favour.

• If you are near a volcano and you notice any of the symptoms of an imminent eruption (see box, this page), leave at once. Travel is likely to be much more difficult – because of panicking refugees and the breakdown of services – if or when an eruption begins.

• If you are caught in an eruption, leave the area immediately.

• Use any transport available. Be prepared, though, for wheels to stick in deepening ash. You may have to abandon the vehicle. If necessary, run, heading where possible for the nearest road out of the area.

• If you are threatened by lava flows, climb to high ground.

• Try to protect your head. Flying rocks are a serious hazard, and a hard hat or crash helmet is ideal. However, any kind of headgear, padded out with newspaper, will provide useful protection.

• Improvise a mask against toxic fumes, using whatever material is to hand. A wet scarf or handkerchief over nose and mouth will help to filter out dust and gases.

• Put on close-fitting goggles, such as swimming goggles, if you have them, to protect your eyes.

• Wear the thickest clothing possible for protection.

• In some areas of volcanic activity there are shelters designated for emergency use. If there is none near you, avoid taking cover in buildings unless you are under imminent threat from advancing lava. Though walls may survive the impact of flying debris, roofs are likely to be crushed.

• If you find yourself in the path of what scientists call a *nuée ardente* (glowing cloud) – a red hot cloud of dust and gases which can roll down the side of the volcano at more than 100mph (160km/h) – there are only two known means of survival.

• The best way is to take cover in a strong, brick underground shelter. Alternatively, jump into a river and hold your breath underwater. A small *nuée ardente* normally passes over in less than 30 seconds.

• If a period of calm follows an eruption, continue your escape from the area. Further – and more violent – eruptions may follow.

FIRE AND ICE *Ash and rocks caved in the roof of this house during an eruption which partly buried a fishing port on the island of Heimaey off Iceland in 1973.*

WARNING SIGNS

A volcanic eruption may occur anywhere where the earth's surface is deeply fissured. There is an especially well-defined volcanic belt around the Pacific, but many volcanoes exist elsewhere. Vesuvius near Naples, Etna in Sicily and Hekla in Iceland are European examples. Most volcanoes are in areas which are also prone to earthquakes.

Some volcanoes are constantly rumbling, but even a volcano dormant for centuries may suddenly burst into life. The warning signs ahead of a major eruption may last for weeks, and can include:

• Increasing seismic activity, ranging from barely noticeable tremors to substantial earthquakes.

• Loud rumbling noises from the volcano or the ground.

• The smell of sulphur coming from local rivers. The water may also feel warm.

• A cloud of steam hovering over the mountain top.

• Falls of acidic rain, which may sting unprotected skin.

• Fine pumice dust hanging in the sky like heavy talcum powder.

• Periodic emissions of hot ash and gases from the volcano's throat.

If any of these symptoms occur from a nearby volcano, the safest course is to leave the area at once.

Natural disasters

How to stay safe in a hurricane

Hurricanes are the world's largest and wildest storms. Racing winds of up to 190mph (300km/h) can destroy houses, tear down power lines and uproot trees.

Hurricanes – known in some parts of the world as typhoons and cyclones – also bring torrential rain and may cause tidal waves which crash inland, washing out roads and flooding large areas. You are unlikely to be caught entirely unawares by a hurricane. In a high-risk area, warning broadcasts and steadily increasing winds will give time to make preparations.

• When a hurricane is imminent, keep well away from the shore, rivers, and any low-lying areas which may be swept by storm tides. Head for high ground. Try to get as high above the possible flood level as you can.

• If you have access to a car, top it up with petrol and drive at once out of the danger area. Aim to get out of the storm's predicted path or well inland – hurricanes weaken as they pass over land.

• If a hurricane strikes before you can escape, stay indoors. The wind and rain make travel extremely dangerous, if not impossible, once the storm begins.

• Take shelter in the largest and most solidly constructed building available. The safest place is usually under the stairs or in a cellar.

• Take with you stocks of food and drinking water. Avoid foods that need cooking, refrigeration or dilution. Supplies of power and water may be disrupted for days.

• Lock doors and windows securely. Close any window shutters. Put bands of sticky tape across windows in a star pattern to reduce the risk of flying glass if the wind shatters the panes. Keep well away from all windows – even if they are taped, pieces of glass can still fly about.

• If you are caught on high or open ground as the winds reach hurricane force, lie flat on the ground. Crawl on your stomach into the lee of anything – a boulder, a belt of trees or an outcrop of rock – which will break the full force of the wind. If you are sheltering close to trees, however, take care in case there are falling branches or the trees are in danger of being uprooted.

• Shortly after the winds reach their fiercest, there may be a period of calm. This occurs as the central 'eye' of the hurricane passes overhead, bringing a patch of clear sky and respite from the winds.

• Stay in a sheltered spot. In less than an hour the hurricane will resume, this time with the winds blowing from the opposite direction.

• If you are sheltering behind a rock or trees when the 'eye' reaches you, move to the other side during the period of calm.

What to do if a tornado strikes

Tornadoes are whirling funnels of air which descend from the base of a storm cloud. They are usually about 80-160ft (25-50m) across.

Where the funnel touches the ground it causes great destruction.

The winds in the funnel may be spinning at more than 200mph (320km/h). But the tornado itself moves forward at about 30-40mph (50-65km/h), so the storm is over in minutes.

Tornadoes most often strike over the prairies of North America, but occasionally small tornadoes occur in Britain.

• Buildings in the path of a tornado can explode, because the normal air pressure inside is much higher than the exceptionally low pressure in the storm's centre.

• If your house is in a tornado's path, open all the doors and windows on the side away from the approaching storm to help to equalise the air pressure inside and out.

• Keep the windows and doors tightly closed on the side from which the tornado is approaching. If the wind gets in, it may lift off the roof or blow out the walls.

• Take other precautions as for hurricanes.

WHERE HURRICANES HAPPEN

Hurricanes form over tropical and subtropical seas. Winds swept in from the Atlantic may reach close to hurricane force on mountain tops in Britain, but true hurricanes are almost unknown in this country. The storms go under different names in different parts of the world: typhoons in the Pacific, cyclones in Australia and hurricanes in the Atlantic. But they are all essentially the same.

Around the calm 'eye', winds race at 75-190mph (120-300km/h), and the area they cover is an average of 100 miles (160km) across. Outside the spinning mass of air, gale-force winds – over 40mph (65km/h) – may sweep an area four times as great.

The most violent hurricanes tend to occur in well-defined regions: the southwest Indian Ocean; the Bay of Bengal; the Arabian Sea; off the north coast of Australia; in the West Indies and Gulf of Mexico; and in the west Pacific.

Hurricanes are also common in the south-eastern and southern United States. There the hurricane season lasts roughly from June to October, and as soon as the weather bureau issues an alert, a comprehensive disaster organisation goes into action. The hurricane is located and its movement forecast. Threatened areas are identified and the inhabitants are warned in repeated radio and television broadcasts.

Earthquake!

An earthquake is unlike a hurricane or flood in that no reliable advance warning can be given, although small tremors in an area prone to earthquakes may be a sign that a larger shock is coming. The immediate risk during a quake is from falling debris.

• If you are indoors when tremors begin, do not rush out into the streets.

• Take cover beneath a strong desk, table or bed. If no heavy furniture is available, stand in a doorway – the frame will provide some protection.

• Keep away from windows. The vibrations of the shock or movement in the building could shatter them.

• If you are outdoors when the earthquake strikes, keep away from tall buildings, trees, power lines and any other high structure which might collapse.

• Run into an open space as far from any high structure as possible. If there is no such space, take cover in a doorway.

• Do not take refuge in cellars, subways or underground tunnels. The exits could become blocked by debris, or the tunnels themselves could cave in.

• If you are in a car, stop the vehicle and dive for the floor, crouching below seat level if possible. If you are in an open area and the earthquake is severe enough to throw you off balance, lie flat.

• When the initial tremor is over, stay put. Several further tremors may follow the first one at unpredictable intervals. Wait until police or rescue teams give the all clear.

• In the aftermath of a major earthquake, fires may start from overturned cookers and broken power lines, and pollution could result from shattered sewage pipes. Water is likely to be in short supply, too, or cut off entirely because of broken mains. Check your own home for signs of damage, and listen to radio or TV broadcasts for official instructions and warnings.

• If you have to go outside, keep well away from houses or any other structures which may have been weakened by the shocks. They could collapse without warning.

Earthquake zones

Certain areas of the world are more prone to earthquakes than others. The main areas are: the Pacific coast of North and South America; Japan; South-east Asia; Indonesia; the east coast of China; central Asia; and a band which stretches across the Mediterranean from Italy to Iran.

But there is nowhere in the world that is entirely safe. Even the United Kingdom has experienced earthquakes, though the tremors have been small compared with those in other parts of the world. In many of the cities in very unstable areas, such as Tokyo and San Francisco, modern buildings are constructed on earthquake-resistant rafts.

WHEN THE EARTH MOVED *A bungalow, crumpled and half swallowed by the earth, and trees tipped at crazy angles, testify to the force of a quake which devastated the city of Anchorage, Alaska, on Good Friday 1964. The earthquake measured 8.6 on the Richter scale.*

SHAKING BRITAIN

It has been estimated that more than 1000 earthquakes have taken place in Britain since the first known tremors in AD 103. And some have been serious enough to cause deaths.

In 1382 the bell tower at Canterbury Cathedral in Kent was demolished, and in 1580 a quake centred on the Strait of Dover killed people as far away as London and Belgium. The city of Swansea has been damaged by earthquakes four times since 1700. London had two more small but damaging quakes in 1750.

The worst calamity of modern times was the great Colchester earthquake of 1884. Occurring at 9.18am on April 22, it shattered more than 1200 buildings. Church steeples tottered in East Anglia, many people were made homeless and three were killed.

In April 1984, the worst tremor in Britain since 1884 rocked Newtown in central Wales, shaking houses, cracking walls and overturning furniture. Measuring 3.3 on the Richter scale, the quake was felt over an area of 400 square miles (1030 square kilometres). The next month a tremor measuring 2.7 was felt over most of Leicestershire, Nottinghamshire and parts of Lincolnshire.

Natural disasters

Trapped in a forest fire

A forest fire can spread at enormous speed, defying every attempt to contain it. In a large blaze, burning leaves and twigs, blown ahead of the flames, can enable the fire to leapfrog across the countryside faster than a galloping horse, and to jump even wide natural barriers such as rivers and roads. So, before you try to outrun the fire, quickly assess the situation. There may be better courses of action.

• Aim for a road or a river – these are the best escape routes. Otherwise, head for a ploughed field or an expanse of rocky scree – anywhere which has little vegetation. If possible, aim diagonally away from the fire to try to get out of its path.

• If the flames block your escape route, get into the middle of the largest open area you can reach.

• Avoid dry bracken beds and other areas of dead vegetation – they may be tinder-dry and practically explode on contact with the flames.

• If you are in a car, stay in it. The risks of the petrol tank exploding are less than the risks of being burnt by the fire's fierce heat or suffocated by smoke.

• If you are on foot, get as low as you can when the flames come close. Thick smoke and lack of oxygen can suffocate.

• If the ground is soft enough, scrape a hole and lie in that. If there is a stream or pond, wade or swim to the centre.

• Cover your head and body with a blanket or coat, wet if possible, to protect your skin from the hot air.

• Stamp out nearby sparks or smother smouldering clothes after the main fire front has passed.

• Once the main fire has gone past you, look for a way out upwind through areas where the blaze has died away.

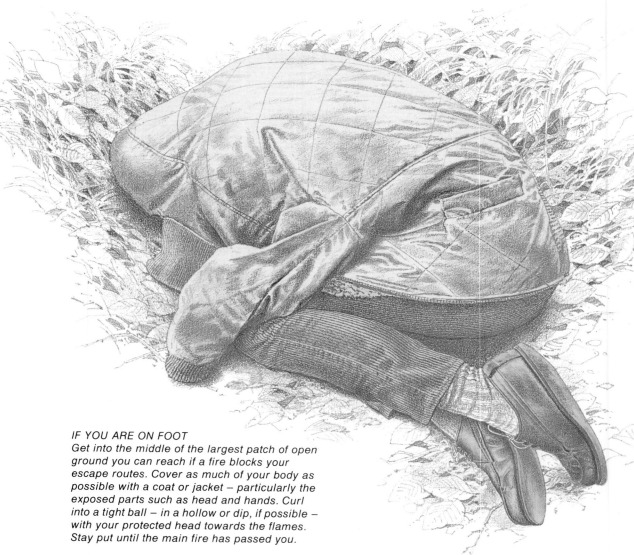

IF YOU ARE ON FOOT
Get into the middle of the largest patch of open ground you can reach if a fire blocks your escape routes. Cover as much of your body as possible with a coat or jacket – particularly the exposed parts such as head and hands. Curl into a tight ball – in a hollow or dip, if possible – with your protected head towards the flames. Stay put until the main fire has passed you.

TOWERING INFERNO *Silhouetted against a wall of flame, an Australian fire-fighter guides a water tanker during a bushfire that raged through the Blue Mountains, west of Sydney, in November 1968. Vehicles are one of the safest places to be in a forest fire. Despite the risk of the petrol tank exploding, you are much safer inside a car than on foot.*

WHEN FIRE RISKS ARE HIGH

Forests are most vulnerable to fire when dead vegetation dries out. Most forest fires occur in plantations of conifers where the forest floor is always carpeted with dead wood rich in flammable resin. Fires can start even during a winter frost, when moisture evaporates into the dry atmosphere. In Britain the worst period is usually late spring and early summer. But a long, dry summer can extend the period of maximum fire hazard. So-called forest fires can also blaze on heath and peaty moorland.

• *Never* discard cigarettes, cigars or pipe tobacco unless they are totally extinguished. Careless smokers are the main cause of forest fires – the tiniest fragment of glowing ash can set acres of woodland ablaze.

• Keep picnic stoves well away from any vegetation in summer. Fires can start on roadside verges as easily as anywhere else. Use stoves only in designated picnic areas.

• Keep alert when farmers burn fields of dead vegetation such as stubble or heather. The fires are usually carefully controlled by the use of firebreaks (broad paths of empty ground across which flames cannot travel). But accidents do happen. If you see a field burning dangerously close to the edge of a forest, keep away and raise the alarm.

• If you see any uncontrolled fire burning in the countryside, find the nearest telephone. Dial 999 and tell the police where you are and what you have seen. If no telephone is immediately to hand, you may be able to locate one by following telephone lines to a farm or house.

Natural disasters

How to cope with a small fire

If a small patch of dried grass or heather catches fire, you may be able to smother it. Fire beaters are often kept at strategic points in forests, and along forest boundaries. They look like brooms or long-handled rubber-bladed shovels, and are for public use in an emergency.

• If you are in a group of people, send two of them for help before setting to work on the fire.

• Lift the beater and press down hard on the burning vegetation to smother the flames. Do not wave the beater quickly. It will only fan the flames and spread sparks.

• Work with the wind behind you, moving inwards from the fire's edges, so that you are not caught in the path of the flames if the fire flares up.

• A branch, a sack or a picnic blanket can also be used as an improvised beater to help to smother the flames.

• Work as hard as you can to contain the fire, always shovelling ash and debris inwards.

• If the fire becomes uncontrollable, make immediately for safety. Move upwind so that you stay out of the fire's path, and raise the alarm as quickly as possible.

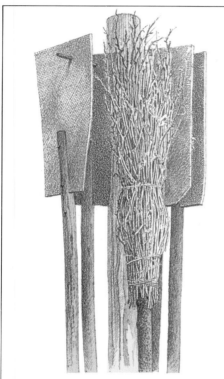

FIREFIGHTING EQUIPMENT
Emergency beaters are kept at strategic points in woods owned by the Forestry Commission. There are two main types: a birch broom; and a spade-shaped beater with a rubber blade.

USING A FIRE BEATER
Do not wave a beater quickly or thump it down hard on a fire. You will only fan the flames. Lay it over the fire. Press it down firmly to smother the blaze, then rub out the embers.

What to do if you are caught in a flood

Major floods tend to occur in river valleys, on coastlands and in other low-lying regions. If you live in an area prone to flooding, keep alert during and after storms and periods of prolonged rainfall. Many areas have a system of flood warnings which may include notices or boards informing of the degree of flood alert, and siren signals. Learn the system in your area. Contact the police in good time when danger threatens. They will advise you on what action to take.

• If a flood threatens your home, turn off gas and electricity at the mains at once to lessen the risk of fire from flooded wiring.

• If you have time, take up carpets and collect all valuables, putting them on an upper floor for safety.

• If there is no time to spare, place valuables for safety on any raised surface such as a table, cupboard or shelf.

• To keep water out of your home, first block all gaps under the outside doors. This is best done by lining the *outer* edge of the threshold with sandbags. The police may have provided bags. If not you can make your own. Ideally, the bags should measure 6in (150mm) round by 12in (300mm) long, but you can improvise by using any plastic bags filled with soil, sand or gravel. If nothing else is available, pack the cracks tightly with old carpets or blankets.

• Sandbag ground-floor windowsills on the outside in the same way if the water seems likely to rise that far.

• If the flood water continues to rise, take any food in the house upstairs. If you live in an isolated area it may be two or three days before anyone can reach you. The essentials are drinking water, food, warm clothing and materials for heating water. If you have no portable stove, candles can be used as heaters. Take a gas-filled cigarette lighter or dry matches with you.

• In a very severe flood, you may be forced onto the roof and have to improvise a raft for escape. As the waters rise, gather up any equipment which can be used to signal for help, such as a torch, whistle, flags, bright coloured sheets or blankets, oily rags (for flares) and a mirror.

• Before going outside for any reason, eat and drink as much as you can to build up your energy reserves. Put on your warmest clothing and footwear – they will help to preserve body heat even if you are immersed in water.

• Take ropes or sheets to tie yourself to the chimney-stack, to prevent you from slipping down the roof.

• To improvise a raft, assemble whatever buoyant materials are to hand: an air bed, wooden beams, chests, planks or even a wardrobe. If you have no rope for lashing a raft together, use bedsheets.

• Use the raft only as a last resort, and test it to see that it floats before climbing aboard. Take some sort of paddle with you, and your signalling equipment.

KEEPING WATER OUT OF THE HOME

1 *To stop water getting into a house, lay sandbags along the outside thresholds of the doors. If necessary, improvise by rolling up plastic shopping bags partly filled with soil.*

2 *If the flood seems likely to rise as far as the windows, pack more bags along the sills outside. If you run out of bags, pack any gaps tightly with strips of old carpet or blankets.*

Natural disasters

How to cross a flooded river

If you are trapped by a river in flood, take the utmost care when attempting a crossing. Even a small stream, swollen by fast-flowing water, may be strong enough to sweep you away.

• Make absolutely sure that the crossing is necessary before starting. It may be possible to make a detour to a bridge or to go upstream where the river may divide into smaller tributaries which are easier to negotiate.

• Remove your socks, then put your boots or shoes back on to give you a firm footing on the stream bed. Once across, you will be able to empty your footwear of water and replace your socks to help to keep your feet warm and dry.

• If you are carrying a rucksack, adjust it so that it rides high on your back. Do not discard the contents. The weight will provide stabilising ballast when you cross. As a precaution, however, undo the waist strap so that you can jettison the pack quickly in an emergency.

• Use a walking stick, or any other strong staff available. A staff about 6ft (1.8m) long is best. It will act as a third leg for stability, and you can also use it to probe for depth. Hold it on your upstream side so that the current does not tug the base away from you.

• Aim either straight across or diagonally downstream. But walk sideways, facing upstream so that your knees are braced against the current. If you face downstream, your knees may fold under the pressure of water from behind.

• Sidestep through the water, shuffling one foot at a time and moving each leg only when you are sure that the other is firmly planted.

• Do not cross your legs as you sidestep – you may lose balance.

Crossing with a rope

The safest way to cross a flooded river, if you are not alone, is with a rope.

• One person should cross the river holding

CROSSING A FLOODED RIVER ALONE
Sidestep across a flooded river, facing upstream. Use a long stick to probe the water for depth, and to improve your stability. If you are wearing a rucksack, keep it on. But undo the waist strap so that you can throw the pack off quickly if you fall.

one end of the rope. If the rope is long enough, he should tie it around his body. His companions should secure the other end of the rope by tying it to a tree or rock. If this is not possible, hold the rope so that if the first person slips he can be pulled back.

• When the first person reaches the far bank he should secure his end of the rope.

• The others should cross one by one, holding onto the rope with one hand and using a staff to steady themselves.

• If the rope is not long enough to cross the river, the group should tie themselves together in a line. Each should have a staff. Only one person should move at a time. While he is moving, the others should be braced against the current in case he slips.

Crossing in a group

Three or more people who have no rope can help each other by crossing in a group.

• Form a file, one behind the other, in a direct line down the current, all facing upstream. Each person should hold the waist or shoulders of the one in front. First, the leader takes a small step sideways, then the second, then the third and so on. While one person is moving, the others should be braced in case he slips.

• Alternatively, the whole file can move as one person. Everyone behind the leader should hold the person in front, and all take a step sideways at the same time.

• Three people can also cross with linked arms. The middle person faces upstream, and the other two face each other sideways on to the current. Only one person moves at a time.

Choosing a crossing point

• Look for a section where the river has broadened out. The flow should be slower and shallower there.

• Avoid crossing at a bend. Although the current may be slow and the river shallow on the inside of the bend, the water will be deeper and more powerful towards the outside bank.

• Large rocks and boulders can provide valuable handholds as you wade past them. But do not try to use them as stepping stones – the surface may be slippery or the base unsteady.

• Avoid crossing near submerged trees, high or slippery banks, and above rapids or weirs.

• Avoid stretches where a stream approaches a lake or valley basin. In flood, the stream will deepen and flow most powerfully here. It is best to head upstream until you come to a point where the flow is divided.

Natural disasters

CROSSING WITH A ROPE
If you have only a short rope, tie yourself and your companion together. While he moves, stand braced against the current paying out the rope. Keep the rope fairly taut so that you will not be jerked off your feet if he is swept away.

Crime

If you are attacked in the street

Escape if you can. Fight if you have to. These are the cardinal rules for dealing with an attacker. Precisely what you do depends on your strength, your confidence and your assessment of the assailant's intentions.

Faced with an armed mugger who wants your cash, it may be safer to hand it over rather than to risk getting seriously injured in a fight.

Faced with a potential killer and no way to escape, on the other hand, there may be nothing to lose by fighting. In each situation, be alert for any opportunity to escape or disable your attacker.

The techniques shown here need some practice, but not extensive training. All are dangerous – some are lethal. Never use them in earnest except in an emergency.

If you fight, never give a warning. Strike swiftly and as hard as you can. Be ready to repeat the blow or follow up with a different one. Scream or shout as you fight. Keep on until you can escape or your assailant collapses.

THE STOMACH JAB

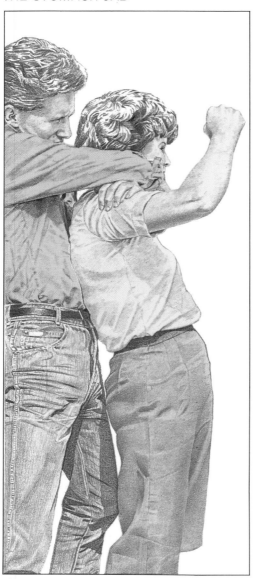

1 *If an assailant attacks you from behind, with his arms about your neck, the stomach jab is an effective deterrent. Twist your body slightly, clench your fist, and raise your arm. . . .*

2 *Jab backwards with your elbow into the attacker's stomach as hard as you can, aiming to wind him. This should force him to relax his grip enough for you to break free.*

THE SCRAPE AND STAMP

1 *If the stomach jab fails to break his grip, lift a foot and scrape the edge of your shoe down the front bony part of his shin. High-heeled shoes are particularly effective.*

2 *Stamp hard on the attacker's foot – a stiletto heel under the weight of an 8 stone (50kg) woman presses down with a force of more than three-quarters of a ton per square inch.*

THE FINGER TWIST
If he grabs your throat, grasp his little fingers and wrench them up and away from your neck. This will cause extreme pain and will probably break his fingers.

Crime

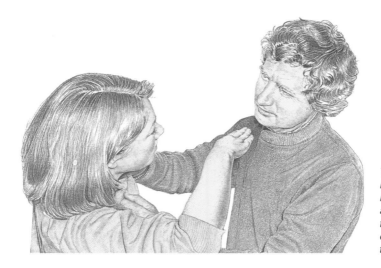

THE THROAT JAB
Hold the fingers of one hand rigidly straight and jab them into his throat, using either the ends of the fingers or the edge of your hand.

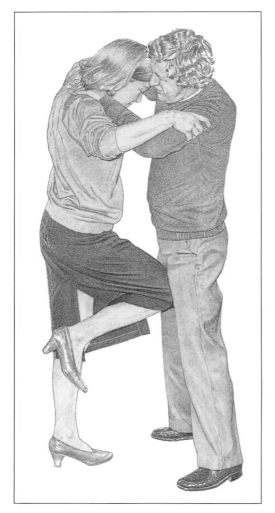

THE KNEE IN THE GROIN
Move in close and bring your knee up sharply into his groin. This will not work, though, if he is wearing a coat or if he twists away from you.

THE EYE JAB
Drop anything you are carrying to free your hands. Make a V with two fingers and poke them hard into the attacker's eyes.

338

How to escape

If you are approached by a suspicious-looking stranger, take evasive action early.

• Scream as loudly as you can.

• Run for the nearest well-lit street where other people are likely to be about.

• Alternatively, run to the nearest house that looks occupied and hammer on its door.

HOW TO AVOID A MUGGER

• Walk with friends if possible, and stay with them all the way to your front door.

• If you are dropped off at home by a car, ask the driver to wait until you are inside.

• Stay in well-lit streets at night, and avoid lonely alleys or waste ground.

• Walk on the street side of the pavement, or in the road if necessary, so that an attacker lurking in a doorway or alley has farther to come to reach you.

• Walk with confidence, even if you do not feel it. An air of purposefulness is often enough to deter an attack.

• Carry a torch after dark. Flashed in an attacker's face, it could dazzle him and give you time to escape. It could also be used as a club.

• On a familiar train route, try to sit in a carriage which will pull up near the exit at your station. You will save yourself a lonely and potentially dangerous walk along what may be a dimly lit platform. If you do not know where the exit is, sit near the middle of the train; that way, at worst, you will have to walk only half the length of the platform.

• On a road, walk facing the traffic. That way, a car cannot pull up behind you unobserved. Do not hitchhike.

• If you have a bag, hold it in your right hand or over your right shoulder, away from the road. Some muggers work on motorcycles or scooters, snatching handbags as they ride by.

• Carry a cheque book and cheque card separately. If you keep one in a bag, keep the other in a pocket.

• Keep your keys in your pocket, not in a briefcase or handbag. Then, if a mugger steals the bag, you can still get home.

• Do not put your name and address on keys. If they are stolen, they could be passed on to a burglar. Instead, attach to the key ring a tag marked with your postcode. The code will be useless to a thief, but will help to identify the keys if you lose them and they are later handed in to the police.

USING AN UMBRELLA

1 *An umbrella or a walking stick makes a powerful defence weapon. Hold it in both hands and jab its end hard into the attacker's face . . .*

2 *. . . or stomach. If you have no weapon, feel for his testicles. Grasp and twist them violently. The pain can knock an attacker unconscious.*

Crime

If you are threatened with rape

On average in Britain, a rape takes place every six hours. Nearly 1500 rapes are reported around the country each year – and a much larger but unknown number of rapes and attempted rapes are thought to go unreported.

Scotland Yard experts recommend that anyone at home who thinks she might be in danger from a prowler should contact the police, via a 999 call, sooner rather than later (see *Intruders in your home*, page 182).

The police say they are always happy to help to allay people's genuine fears, even if the fears turn out to be unfounded.

If you are attacked by a mugger or a rapist, at home or in the street, police experts say that the best advice is to run away if you can, and to fight only if you have to (see *If you are attacked in the street*, page 336).

If you are followed in the street

• If you think you are being followed, cross over the street to check your suspicions. Listen or glance back to see if the other person crosses the street after you.

• If you decide that you are being followed, go into any place where there are other people – a launderette, say, or a pub. Alternatively, knock at the first house which appears to be occupied.

• Tell the occupants you believe you are being followed and ask to use their phone. Call the police and give them a description of the person who was following you.

• Avoid using a phone box on the street to call for help, particularly in a quiet road. You could be trapped in the box by an attacker.

If you are accosted

If you are approached by someone whose motives are plainly sinister, and you cannot get away at once, you can use any or all of a number of ways of dealing with him.

Which is best depends on the circumstances and on your own strength and confidence. None of the methods described here can guarantee your safety, but all have been used successfully by women to escape a would-be rapist.

• If you have time before the person accosts you, try to get some hard object in your hand – a comb, perhaps, a bunch of keys, or a bottle or can of spray.

• If you pick keys, dangle them between your fingers and close your hand over them so that the ends of the keys stick out from your fist.

• Keep your improvised weapon concealed until the attack starts. Then use the weapon – suddenly, without warning and as hard as you possibly can.

• Jab the end of the comb into his face or drag the teeth across underneath his nose. Scrape the keys across his face. Or spray into his eyes. At the same time, scream as loudly as you can.

• Keep using the weapon until the attacker lets go, then run to the nearest well-lit street or the nearest occupied house and get help.

• If you have no weapon, scream at the attacker to leave you alone. Use forceful language when you do this – as loud and forceful as possible. It may upset the fantasy a rapist often weaves around his intended victim, and make him abandon the approach.

• At the same time as you shout, use a hand-

STAYING OUT OF DANGER

Most of the precautions you can take to avoid being attacked by a thief also apply to protecting yourself against the possibility of rape (see *How to avoid a mugger*, page 339).

If you live alone, though, or if you have to go out alone – particularly if you have to be out after dark – consider taking some additional precautions.

• Consider, for instance, buying a hand-held gas screech alarm. Carry it in your hand, not in your handbag where it may be difficult to reach in an emergency.

• If you live in a flat, use only your initials – not your full first name – on the tab beside your bell at the front door. That way, a stranger cannot tell whether a man or woman lives there.

• If you live alone, add another, fictitious name to the tab. A flat that appears to be shared is far less likely to be picked out as a target by a rapist or a thief.

• Fit a stout chain to the door, and a peep-hole viewer, and make a habit of using both to check visitors.

• Do not open your door unless you are certain that it is safe.

• Arrange with your friends to use a special pattern of rings or knocks as a recognition signal, but even then make sure of your visitor's identity before opening the door. A thief or a rapist might have overheard the signal and could be copying it.

• Gas and electricity companies will also agree to use a private codeword chosen by you to confirm the identity of meter readers. To arrange a codeword, contact your local gas or electricity office.

• If you are on your own when someone comes to the door, pretend that you have company. As you approach the door, call out loudly to your fictitious companion something like: 'Okay, Harry, I'll go.'

held alarm if you have one, aimed into his face.

- If the attacker grabs you so that flight is impossible, and he is too strong to fight, pretend that you welcome the approach.
- Aim to buy time until an opportunity arises to escape. For instance, invite him back to your flat or house. Make the invitation sound convincing. Use earthy language to encourage him in the belief that once you get home you will be more than eager to do what he wants.
- Wherever you actually live, guide him towards a well-lit street with people in it. Then run towards the people yelling for help.
- Alternatively, try to persuade the attacker that you would love to spend the night with him, but in a few days' time. Give him a bogus telephone number to encourage him to believe you. Invent a plausible reason for the delay – tell him you have a heavy period, for example, or that you are suffering from a venereal disease.
- Once he hesitates, keep talking. Suggest, perhaps, going for a drink together in the meantime. Again, once you are close enough to other people to call for help, break away and run towards them, shouting for help as loudly as you can.
- As soon as you get away from the attacker, dial 999, ask for the police and give them a detailed description of him (see *How to give a description to the police*, page 183).

If you are assaulted

- If you are attacked, get medical help as soon afterwards as possible. Do not wash or tidy yourself up before doing this. A medical examination will help to prove that you were forced to submit, and may be necessary to ensure that your attacker is convicted.
- Report the attack to the police and give them as detailed a description of the attacker as you can.
- The police will also want to make a forensic examination, which could involve an internal investigation, possibly by a male surgeon. This could be a traumatic experience if you are still suffering from shock. Later you might have to face your attacker in a police identity parade and, if the case comes to a trial, give very detailed evidence to a court in public. Many women find this an extremely painful experience.
- If you feel you cannot face the questions that the police will be obliged to ask, or the subsequent legal processes, consider getting advice and help from the nearest Rape Crisis Centre. The centres, which are staffed by women, exist in most large towns and cities. The phone number is listed in directories under 'Rape', but the address is not listed in order to ensure privacy. If no number is given in your local directory, you can find the nearest centre by telephoning at any time of day or night either of two numbers: London (01) 837 1600; or Birmingham (021) 233 2122.

Pestered by a drunk

A drunken stranger is more likely to be a nuisance than a danger. Nevertheless, the unpredictability of his behaviour and sudden switches in mood can be extremely frightening.

- Ignore a drunk, if possible, and keep out of his way. Do not invite his notice. On a train, for example, get off and move to another carriage as soon as you can – ideally before he notices you. In the street, cross to the other side of the road before you reach him.
- If avoidance is impossible, assess his mood and character. If he seems harmless and merely wants to chat, humour him until he goes away or until you are able to leave.
- Try not to appear embarrassed, because this may encourage him.
- In the street, do not stop; just say 'Goodnight' in response to his opening conversational gambit, and walk quickly by.

If he becomes aggressive

- Should he be either aggressive or maudlin, make a fuss and try to attract the attention of other people.
- Shout at him to go away, using language as forceful as you can make it. He is less likely to continue pestering someone fierce and firm than someone scared and submissive.
- If he is persistent and you are in a confined space such as a train, walk through the connecting doors between the carriages and find the guard.

If he attacks you

- If he makes a grab for you or attacks you, make as much noise as possible to attract other passengers.
- As a last resort, pull the communication handle – but only when the train reaches a station, not before. Pulling the handle will lock the doors on a tube train, but will quickly bring the guard along.
- Defend yourself if you have to. Hold him at bay by swinging something such as a handbag (see *If you are attacked in the street*, page 336).

Avoiding trouble on a train

- To cut down the risk of being pestered by someone on a train, always pick a carriage well occupied by both sexes. Avoid carriages where there is only one person – a man or a woman – or where there are groups of youths, such as football supporters.
- At night on a train, try to sit in a carriage which will stop near the exit at your destination. Drunks sometimes seek out railway stations, either in the hope of finding company or simply for shelter. Picking the right part of the train will save you a walk down what could be a lonely and shadowy platform.
- If you are not sure where the exit is on the platform at your destination, try to sit near the middle of the train. That way, you will at worst have to walk only half the length of the platform.

Crime

When a crowd turns ugly

Being part of a large, good-humoured crowd – at a public occasion, say, such as the New Year revel in Trafalgar Square, London – can be exhilarating. But if the mood of the crowd turns sour for any reason, anyone caught in the crush, as a participant or simply as a bystander, can be seriously hurt or even killed.

Danger is most likely to arise in situations where people's feelings become inflamed for some reason – at or after football matches, for instance, at protest meetings and demonstrations, and on picket lines. Panic, however, can turn any crowded place, such as a cinema or discotheque, into a potential death trap.

If you are on foot
• If you find yourself in the path of an obviously unruly or frightened crowd, walk away from it and get well out of its way. Do not run, though, because this may attract the crowd's attention.

• If you have no time to get right away from the scene before the crowd overtakes you, go into the nearest shop, knock at the door of the nearest house and ask for help, or tuck yourself into a convenient doorway.
• Stay put until the crowd has gone by.
• If you get caught up in the crowd, remember two overriding priorities: stay away from glass shop fronts; and stay on your feet. If you get pushed through a plate-glass window or trampled by the crowd, you are unlikely to escape without serious injury.
• Hang onto something fixed, such as a lamp post, if you can, and let the crowd surge on past you. Once the crowd clears, move calmly but briskly away from the scene.
• If you are swept along by the crush, create space for yourself by grasping one wrist in front of you with your other hand and bracing your elbows away from your sides. This will protect

IF YOU ARE SWEPT ALONG BY A CROWD

1 *In a crush you cannot escape from, create space for yourself around your chest so that you can breathe. Grip one wrist with the other hand and brace your arms in front of you with your elbows well out to the sides.*

2 *Stay on your feet and stay away from glass shop fronts for safety. If necessary, lift your feet off the ground so that your toes do not get trampled, allowing yourself to be supported by the people around you in the crowd.*

you from being squeezed by the people around you, and possibly fainting from sheer inability to breathe. Bend forwards slightly at the waist at the same time to create extra room for your lungs to expand.

• If necessary, bend your knees as well and lift your feet completely off the ground to avoid getting your toes trodden on. The crush of people will support you.

• Be ready to put your feet down again as soon as the crowd begins to open up.

• If you are pushed to the ground, try to get against a wall.

• Roll yourself into a tight ball facing the wall with your hands clasped around the back of your neck. This will help to protect the most vulnerable parts of your body.

• Do not panic; a street crowd is likely to sweep on past you within a few seconds.

If you are in a car

• Never drive through a crowd, particularly if it is in an angry or hostile mood – or if it looks as though it could become hostile. You could be seriously injured if the mob turns on the car and breaks the windows or turns the car over.

• If you find yourself in the path of a crowd, do not stop to watch it. Turn into a side road, reverse or turn round, and drive away calmly.

• If you cannot get away from the approaching crowd altogether, park the car, lock it and leave it. Take shelter in a side street, a shop, a house or a doorway.

• If there is no time even to park the car, stop it – in the middle of the road if necessary – and turn the engine off.

• Lock all the doors and stay quiet inside the car until the crowd has gone by.

STAYING OUT OF TROUBLE

• At public events where there are large numbers of people, check the exits as you go in. But remember that the safest way out may not be the same as the way you came in. If a fire breaks out in a crowded place – in a football grandstand, say, or a disco – look around for alternative escape routes. At a football match, the safest place might be on the pitch, not trying to fight your way out through narrow turnstiles.

• Stay behind at the end for at least 15 minutes to allow the main crowd to disperse.

• After a football match, never wear a scarf which identifies the team you support. Tuck it out of sight on your way home. Otherwise you could be picked on by rival fans. Most injuries occur after a match, not before or during it.

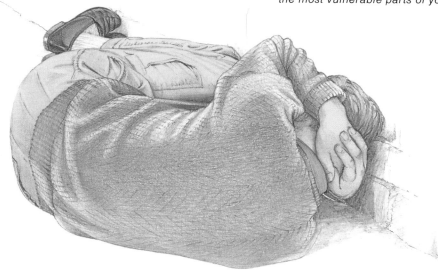

IF YOU ARE PUSHED TO THE GROUND
Try to get beside a wall if you lose your balance and go down. Tuck yourself into a tight ball, facing the wall. Clamp your hands together around the back of your neck. Your fingers, back and legs may get hurt, but you will protect the most vulnerable parts of your body.

Crime

How to deal with an obscene telephone call

Obscene calls are unpleasant and may be upsetting, but they are extremely unlikely to lead to personal contact or a physical attack.

• Never give your number when answering the telephone, the police advise – just say 'Hello'. This is because, in most cases, nuisance callers do not bother to find specific numbers in a directory. Usually they ring a combination of numbers at random until a woman answers. As a result, they are unlikely to know your number, or to remember what they dialled, unless you remind them by saying it.

• If you have not had a similar call before, ring off without making any reply as soon as you realise the nature of the call. Check with everyone else in your home to find out if it has happened before.

• Attempting to dissuade the caller by blowing down the phone with a whistle, or using something that makes a screeching noise, is not usually much good because the full effect of the noise is not transmitted.

• If the calls become persistent, tell the police. They may know of similar calls, and may decide to monitor the line or the exchange.

If nuisance calls continue

• If the calls continue after you have informed the police, try to keep the caller talking and listen for clues that might help the police to track him down. For example, note whether you hear rapid pips – indicating that the call is from a pay-phone – or whether there is background noise such as machinery or traffic.

• If possible, while the call continues get someone to ring the police on another phone. The police may then be able to trace the call.

• To keep the caller talking while police try to trace the call, try to lead him on with his sexual fantasies. A caller of this type usually wants to talk to someone who seems submissive and whom he feels he is dominating.

• If you find the calls disturbing, or are afraid your child might answer an obscene call, you can do a number of things that might solve the problem while the police investigate. The main options are listed below. To get detailed advice on any of them, contact the Customer Services Manager at your local British Telecom Sales Office.

• Arrange, for instance, for the telephone exchange to monitor your calls. There is usually no charge for intercepting calls (and there is never a charge if the police request it) but you may have to go on a short waiting list.

• Change your telephone number to reduce the chance of the same caller bothering you again. In 1985 the fee for changing a number was about £13. But the fee is sometimes waived if the change is being made because of nuisance calls.

• Install a plug and socket system. In 1985 this cost about £30, depending on the number of plugs. When the phone is pulled out of the plug, the caller can still hear it ringing but you cannot hear it at your end. The caller will think that you are out or have decided not to answer, and may give up dialling your number.

• Do not simply take your phone off the hook. This can create chaos at the local exchange and can cause faults on the line.

• If you make many more phone calls than you receive, arrange for the phone to be adjusted so that you can make only outgoing calls.

• Agree a code with friends and relatives who are likely to phone you. Ask them, for instance, to let the phone ring three times, hang up and dial again. Then you will be sure that you are not answering an unwanted call.

AVOIDING UNWELCOME CALLS

Obscene telephone calls are usually made by men who are on their own for long periods and who have access to a private telephone. They are rarely made from public call boxes, because the callers are usually secretive, and may call while indulging in some sexual aberration.

• If a caller asks you to confirm your number, do not do so; just ask what number is wanted. If it is not yours, do not give your number. Say: 'Sorry, wrong number', and ring off. If it is your number, ask who wants to know.

• If your children are likely to answer the phone, make sure they do not give the number. Obliterate it from the telephone dial if necessary.

• If you are uneasy about having your name and number published in the telephone directory, apply for an ex-directory number. You can then expect calls only from people to whom you have given your number. This does not prevent a random obscene call, but as long as you do not mention the number when answering, a repeat call is unlikely.

• If you are having a new phone put in, or if you simply ask for your existing number not to be listed in future editions of your telephone directory, an ex-directory number costs no more than an ordinary number. But if you want to change your existing number for an ex-directory one, you may have to pay for the change of number; in 1985 this fee was about £13.

• If you are a woman and want your name put in the directory, make sure that the entry gives only your surname and your initials – not your first name. Do not put Mrs, Miss or Ms either.

Caught up in a robbery

Every day in Britain, there are more than 70 robberies – thefts involving violence or the threat of it – and in about one in ten of them the robbers are armed. Their targets are most commonly places where valuable goods, such as jewellery, or large amounts of cash are stored or handled: banks, for instance, security vans, payroll offices or shops.

Burglary and housebreaking are far more common crimes. For details on how to cope with them, see *Intruders in your home*, page 182.

Most major robberies take place during the day, when the scene of the hold-up may be crowded with people. The thieves rely on speed and the terror they create to make their getaway.

If you are caught up in a robbery – at home, as a bystander when robbers burst in, as an employee of the firm that is being attacked, or, in rare cases, as a hostage – Scotland Yard crime prevention experts recommend that you should not 'have a go' at the raiders. Cash, they point out, can be replaced; life cannot.

What you can do, they say, is use your eyes and ears to help to ensure that police catch the thieves afterwards.

At home or in a shop
• If robbers – whether armed or not – burst into your house or into a shop where you are a customer, do not try to run away. By doing so, you make yourself the focus of the robbers' attention and could be killed or injured.
• Stay quiet. Do what you are told quickly and quietly. Do not argue.
• Make a mental note of everything you see and hear – including even the robbers' accents. Write it down as soon as possible, so that you do not forget details in the confusion after the raiders leave.
• Dial 999 as soon as you can after the raid, and pass on your information to the police (see *Making a 999 call*, inside back cover; *How to give a description to the police*, page 183).
• If you are on the street and notice a robbery taking place – through a shop window, say – but you are not in danger yourself, do not go inside.
• Dial 999 at once. Do not put down the phone once you have raised the alarm. Keep talking. If you are close to the scene, you may well be able to pass on to the police an immediate description of the getaway car and the direction it heads in when the robbers leave.
• If you cannot get to a phone, make written notes of what you have seen as soon as possible. Sign and date the notes – this makes them powerful evidence in any subsequent court trial.
• Take the notes to the nearest police station as soon as possible.

In an office
If the office, shop or factory where you work is raided by thieves, police recommend that you follow the same guidelines as those suggested for people who are caught up in a robbery at home or out shopping.
• Do not try to be a hero. Stay quiet and do what the robbers tell you. Observe, and make notes when the robbers have gone.
• Contact the police as soon as possible.

If you are taken hostage
The chance of your being taken hostage by robbers is very small. But it can happen.

The stress involved in being grabbed and threatened with instant death can be enough to drive every thought out of your head and create blind panic. But if you give way to panic, you only increase the danger you are in. Remember that anyone who takes a hostage does not intend to harm him or her. The intent is to use the *threat* of harm to force others to do what the robber wants.
• Do not struggle. Do not try to run away.
• Do what you are told.
• Remember everything you can about your captor – his approximate age, build, type of voice, appearance, clothes and so on.
• As soon as you are released, make a written note of what you recall and dial 999 at once.

GUARDING AN OFFICE

There are a number of precautions that can be taken in offices to prevent a raid. For high-risk targets, for instance, a silent alarm can be connected directly to the nearest police station and triggered by a concealed button in the office. Reinforced doors and windows can make it difficult for thieves to get in.

Staff training can help as well. If, for instance, the cash-handling area is protected by a door that is kept locked from the inside, thieves may take a member of staff hostage to gain access. In this situation, a pre-arranged code – such as '*George*, can you let me in?' – could alert staff inside without arousing the thieves' suspicions. Police can then be contacted while other members of staff stall the thieves by, say, pretending that the mythical George has the key but he is not available for the moment.

Modern electronic locking systems can also have a code built in to warn staff of an attack.

A detailed security plan will depend on the size of the business being protected and the layout of the offices. Managers and staff can get free advice and help with training by contacting the Crime Prevention Officer at the nearest police station.

Crime

What to do if a bomb goes off

A terrorist bomb is one of the least predictable and most terrifying emergencies anyone can be involved in. Faced with the sights and sounds of dozens, perhaps scores, of injured people, it is easy to feel helpless. Nevertheless, your help could be invaluable. The advice here was compiled with the help of crime prevention experts from Scotland Yard.

• If you have a camera, use the whole of the film on taking photographs of the scene. Concentrate particularly on taking pictures of people leaving the scene immediately after the explosion. The pictures could help to identify a bomber.

• Do not, however, put your own safety at risk – from falling debris, say – while you are taking the photographs.

• Dial 999 and ask for the police. They will alert other emergency services.

• Give what help you can to the injured until the emergency services arrive and take over (see *Treatment priorities*, page 198).

• If you feel you cannot help at the scene, leave the area quietly. Try not to run; you could start a panic and add to the casualty toll.

• Make a note of everything you remember as soon after the incident as possible.

• Take your notes – and your film if you had a camera – to the nearest police station.

If you see a suspicious package

• Do not, under any circumstances, touch a package or container that you think might be a bomb. Many terrorist bombs contain anti-tampering devices which can trigger an explosion as soon as the container is moved.

• Do not shout 'Bomb' or anything else that might cause panic.

• Move away from the package and encourage others to do the same.

• If you are on a moving train, do not pull the communication cord or handle. Stopping the train between stations only makes it more difficult for bomb disposal experts to reach the scene, and for passengers to get away to safety.

• Find the nearest person in authority and tell him of your suspicions. If you are on a train, find the guard, for instance; otherwise find a policeman, traffic warden or station porter. Alternatively, dial 999 from the nearest telephone and ask for the police.

• If you see someone placing a suspicious package and making off, make a written note of what he looks like on anything handy (see *How to give a description to the police*, page 183).

• If you have a camera, take a picture of him – if you can do so safely – and of the package. Even a fuzzy back view of the bomber may help to identify him. And if the package later explodes, knowledge of what it looked like to start with could give police valuable clues in finding the terrorists who masterminded the operation.

• If you think the package might have been left by accident, call to the person: 'Is that yours?'

If he denies it, act on the assumption that the package is a bomb.

• Get well clear of the package and make sure that others do so too.

• Alert the police at once by dialling 999.

HOW TO RECOGNISE A LETTER BOMB

Letter bombs, like other types of terrorist bomb, are almost always disguised to look entirely harmless. Conversely, some hoax devices are deliberately designed to look like bombs in order to cause maximum panic. There is thus no reliable way of identifying a bomb.

Nevertheless, Scotland Yard experts do recommend looking for these warning signs among letters and parcels: any signs of wires or batteries; grease marks; or a smell of almonds.

More generally, they recommend that you look for the unusual. Is the package oddly bulky, for instance? Is it wrapped or sealed in an unusual way? If you are not expecting a package, do you know anyone living in the area where this one was postmarked?

If you find a suspicious letter

• If you do come across a letter or package that arouses your suspicions, do not try to open it – letter bombs are designed to withstand postal handling and to explode on opening. Do not press, squeeze or prod it.

• Do not put it in another container. Do not put it in sand or water. Do not let anyone else do any of these things.

• Look for the name of the sender on the back. Phone the sender and check whether the package is genuine. If the package is not addressed to you, but to someone else in your home or office, ask the person to whom it is addressed if he or she is expecting a package.

• If these checks do not allay your suspicions, leave the package where you found it. Clear the room.

• Lock the door and keep the key so that nobody can walk unknowingly into the danger zone.

• If there are glass windows in the room, tell colleagues and passers-by outside to stay well clear of them to avoid being hit by flying glass if the bomb goes off.

• Contact your firm's security officer, if there is one, or the manager, or dial 999 and ask for the police.

If your plane is hijacked

Hijacking is not a common occurrence, but it does happen. In the 1980s, about 20 aircraft a year have been hijacked around the world. The planes affected have varied from light craft to huge jumbo jets. In all, up to 4000 passengers have experienced the ordeal each year.

The most vulnerable airports are those with the poorest security – often in Third World countries. Hijackers can more easily smuggle in weapons and make their presence known after take-off, or shoot their way on board.

At the start of any hijack, the hijackers, the crew and the passengers are all likely to be in a highly charged, emotional and excitable state which can lead to violence.
- Do not be aggressive. Try to melt into the background. Otherwise you may be singled out and put yourself and others at risk.
- Hide or dispose of any possessions – such as military identification papers – which, if found, might arouse the hijackers' hostility.
- As time passes, the situation will improve. Experience has shown that a rapport gradually builds up between passengers and hijackers. You may be asked to help with meals, clearing up and attending to the needs of others.
- Accept the more relaxed mood – but do not argue with your captors' political views.
- The hijack may last for days, and you may have to fly through a wearisome series of airports as the hijackers seek political sanctuary. Be alert for evidence of tension among fellow passengers, and reassure them where possible.
- Make allowances, too, for any symptoms of stress among hijackers and crew.

Surviving the ordeal
- If you are confined in a grounded aircraft, problems of heating and cooling may arise, especially if the aircraft has no ground power. Desert areas, for example, are hot by day and cold by night. Under these conditions, it may be worth asking the hijackers if you can remove the aircraft emergency windows for ventilation by day, and replace them for warmth at night.
- At night, if the hijackers agree, distribute all available blankets and get everyone bedded down if possible.
- Be prepared for sanitation problems. The toilet arrangements on most aircraft are self-contained, chemical recirculation systems. They will quickly fill, become offensive, and may have to be drained by opening a valve outside the aircraft. Water for washing may be in short supply, or may not be available at all while the aircraft's engines are switched off.
- In the prolonged crisis of a hijacking, passengers may do unaccountable things. Some will become depressed and withdrawn. Others will become hyperactive, nervous and unpredictable. Children, however, may present fewer problems than anticipated – and can be a useful contact with your captors.
- Try to keep your mind occupied with things other than the hijacking. Crossword puzzles, packs of cards, books and magazines will all help. A vacant mind, obsessed with the situation's dangers, tends to panic and take rash action.
- Try to keep fit – this is essential to a healthy frame of mind. Opportunities for exercise may be limited, but take every opportunity to get sleep. Even cat-napping is beneficial. If you are deprived of sleep, you will not think straight.
- Take fluid whenever possible – it is more important than food. A healthy person can go without food for a month or more, but in high temperatures body fluid is lost quickly in the form of sweat and urine. While on the ground, an average individual not taking exercise needs at least 2 pints (a little over 1 litre) of water every day – at high altitudes 4-5 pints (2-3 litres) is needed daily. Do not drink alcohol, though, because it dehydrates the body.
- As any deadline given by the captors approaches, tension is bound to increase. Try to calm any passengers showing signs of hysteria.
- If the aircraft is attacked by rescuing forces, get down on the floor and stay there. Try to make yourself as small as possible; roll into a ball between the seats. There may be flashes of light, explosions, shooting and cries of terror. Do not stand up until given the all clear.
- When this happens, leave the aircraft as quickly as possible. It may have been wired with explosives, or fuel may be leaking from punctured tanks.
- Outside the aircraft the rescue services will meet all your needs, providing medical attention, clean clothing, washing facilities and – best of all – a bed. Accept their assistance. The Press may be asking for interviews, but the airline staff will protect you from their approaches if you wish.

After the hijack
- Be prepared to face difficulties in the days that follow the ending of the hijack. You will feel completely drained physically and mentally. The experience may leave deep mental scars which may take weeks or months to overcome.
- Be prepared especially for feelings of guilt. Some people may be disappointed with their own performance during the emergency. They may feel that they lacked bravery, panicked easily or behaved irrationally under stress. Others, however, may have surprised themselves by discovering unsuspected strengths of character.
- Because the cause of a hijack is usually faulty airport security, hijack victims cannot normally claim compensation for their ordeal from the airline they were flying with. It may also be impracticable to pursue a claim against the airport responsible. It is, however, possible to buy insurance against the risks of being hijacked, and the cover is often included in holiday insurance packages.

Crime

Drink and drugs

Spotting and coping with a drink problem

Though moderate and occasional drinking among friends is unlikely to prove harmful, alcohol *is* a drug.

Its damaging effects become more obvious when it is taken persistently or in excess.

Through abuse, alcohol can cause hallucinations as terrifying as those of LSD; like barbiturates, it can cause fits during withdrawal; and like heroin, it can induce coma and death.

Medically speaking, alcohol is a sedative with tranquillising and hypnotic effects. Though a drinker may experience some initial elation, alcohol depresses rather than stimulates the central nervous system.

For this reason it belongs to the most dangerous category of abused drugs – those most likely to kill through overdose (see *Drug abuse: the risks*, page 355).

Alcohol as a drug

WHAT THE DRINKER FEELS Mild consumption of alcohol tends to free the drinker from inhibitions, reducing tension and anxiety. The drinker may feel relaxed, confident, euphoric or inspired. Large amounts induce excitement, agitation, nausea and vomiting. The drinker may *feel* alert both mentally and physically, but become confused, walk unsteadily and have difficulty in speaking clearly.

WHAT OTHERS SEE Alcohol reduces restraints and responsibility. These effects are often more evident to others than to the drinker. He or she may become impulsive and over-talkative, behaving in a grandiose, offensive or sometimes violent manner.

Judgment and concentration are affected progressively as more drink is consumed. The drinker may stagger and slur his or her speech. Accidents are a serious risk.

OVERDOSE SYMPTOMS Do not automatically assume that because a person *appears* drunk, he is *drunk*.

Other conditions – including diabetes – can produce similar symptoms, and so can numerous other drugs (see *Drug identification and emergency treatment*, page 356).

After excessive drinking, the drinker may lapse into a stupefied state, leading to coma. In severe cases, he may stop breathing.

How to treat an overdose

• If the patient stops breathing, start artificial respiration at once (see page 50).

• If the patient is unconscious but still breathing, use your finger to clear any obstruction from the mouth and throat.

• Do not, however, try to induce him or her to vomit. Vomiting can kill an unconscious or comatose patient.

• Turn the patient onto his stomach, with his head facing sideways, in the recovery position (see page 136).

• Loosen his clothing and ensure that the airway is still clear. Be especially careful to check

---

DRINKING – THE LONG-TERM EFFECTS

Besides the immediate risks associated with drunkenness, alcohol can also cause long-term damage. The liver and the central nervous system are especially vulnerable. Liver damage results from the poisonous action of the drug, while mental deterioration appears to result from organic changes which alcohol causes in the brain.

• Heavy drinkers tend to develop a fatty liver. Most will recover fully if they give up drink. A minority, however, develop more dangerous liver complications such as hepatitis (inflammation) and cirrhosis (replacement of healthy cells by fibrous tissue). With abstinence, the liver may recover from hepatitis, but the damage done by cirrhosis is irreversible. The condition can kill – but abstinence will at least check the progress of the disease.

• Other physical disorders include gastritis (inflammation of the stomach lining), pancreatitis (inflammation of the pancreas) and anaemia (a reduction of the oxygen-carrying haemoglobin in the red blood cells).

• Damage to the central nervous system may lead to polyneuritis, which is also known as polyneuropathy. This is an inflammation of the nerves which may result in some degree of paralysis.

• The symptoms of brain damage may include loss of memory, pathological feelings of jealousy and persecution, delusions and hallucinations. Additionally, alcoholic dementia may occur. This is an irreversible deterioration of the intellect, with confusion, incoherence and numbed understanding resembling the symptoms of senile dementia. Heavy drinkers who escape these penalties are, however, no more likely than non-drinkers to lapse into senile dementia in old age.

• Women should drink modestly – or, if possible, not at all – during pregnancy. Little is known about the effects of alcohol on an unborn child, but experts believe that heavy drinking restricts growth and may also lead to mental retardation.

that the tongue has not fallen back to block the windpipe.

• Call an ambulance if the patient is unconscious or if he cannot be roused. Other danger signs include an uneven or slow pulse rate, pale colour and continued difficulty in breathing. If any of these occur, call an ambulance at once.

• Call an ambulance if the patient has sustained an injury, if he vomits persistently or if he remains in a state of excitement or agitation.

• Call an ambulance if the patient is a diabetic, or if you suspect that any drugs have been taken in combination with the alcohol.

Withdrawal symptoms

Alcohol is an addictive drug, and with heavy drinking over a long period the body develops a tolerance for large doses.

The drinker may lose all pleasurable effects from drinking, and may come to rely on alcohol simply to stay 'normal' – to cope with the minor stresses and anxieties of life.

Often, a serious alcoholic problem is not detected until supplies are cut off or drastically reduced. When this happens, a serious withdrawal crisis may result. The symptoms resemble those experienced by withdrawal from barbiturates and tranquillisers.

• An alcoholic may exhibit anxiety, sweating and shaking before the onset of a withdrawal crisis. So-called 'morning shakes', often experienced by alcoholics, are in fact withdrawal symptoms which usually occur after sleep and are relieved by the first drink of the day.

• Delirium tremens (often known as the DTs) is a particularly severe complication of alcohol withdrawal. Typically, it begins some two to four days after the last drink was taken and may follow a convulsion, or fit, 12 to 36 hours after the last drink.

• A patient suffering from delirium tremens begins trembling uncontrollably, and becomes feverish and intensely agitated. Vividly realistic hallucinations may occur. These are usually visual and often terrifying.

• Whether or not delirium tremens develops, the withdrawal crisis may last for three days or longer before stopping, often abruptly.

• The withdrawal crisis may be so intense that there is a serious risk of accidental injury, and of complications, such as pneumonia, setting in. For these reasons, a heavy drinker should *not* stop drinking suddenly without first seeking medical advice. Friends and relatives should encourage him or her to enter a hospital or specialist clinic for expert treatment.

How to deal with an alcoholic

There is no single cause of alcoholism. The disease may arise, for example, from a psychological problem.

But it can also arise from a particularly stressful occupation, or simply from the company of hard-drinking friends who may themselves be dependent on alcohol. Similarly, alcoholism may appear in a variety of forms. Some people go for long periods without touching a drop – then go on prolonged 'binges' in which they find it impossible to stop drinking.

Other people seldom get truly drunk, but they keep topping up with small quantities of alcohol from morning to night.

Whatever the cause or the pattern of drinking, remember that *you* cannot stop an alcoholic drinking. The drinker himself – or herself – must make the decision.

However, there are a number of things you can do to encourage positive thinking about the problem and assist the recovery process.

What not to do

• Do not start drinking yourself. Husbands and wives of chronic alcoholics are subject to the extra stress and tension of living with a drinker and sometimes they succumb to the same disease as their spouses.

• Do not put your own mental and physical well-being at risk. Make sure that you safeguard your health and constructive attitudes.

• Do not nag, lecture, preach or get involved in angry slanging matches. All hostile approaches tend to belittle the drinker. They may provoke violence, or drive the drinker deeper into a sense of personal worthlessness for which drink has already become the remedy.

• Do not try to bargain with the drinker's emotions in an effort to make him or her stop drinking. Do not, for example, ask the drinker to demonstrate love for you by giving up alcohol. Similarly, do not threaten to leave – unless you are prepared to carry out your threat.

• Do not throw away any bottles you may find hidden about the house. You risk provoking violence and destroying such bonds of trust as still exist. An alcoholic will usually find some means of obtaining further supplies. And if he cannot find more drink, the enforced abstinence may only precipitate a withdrawal crisis with which you are unable to cope.

• Do not try to cover up for the drinker's habit by protecting him from its consequences. This mistake often takes the form of paying debts run up by the drinker. If money is owed, let the alcoholic face the problem. By smoothing the path, you act only as an 'enabler', indirectly encouraging the drinking habit.

• Do not be misled by glib promises. If a resolution to give up drinking is made, make sure that it is backed up by definite action such as seeing the family doctor, joining Alcoholics Anonymous (see page 354), or both.

• Do not give up hope. Ultimately, most alcoholics who face up to their problem and accept qualified help do well. The addiction can be ended. Out of every three alcoholics, about one eventually recovers completely, and another can be greatly improved after treatment. So never be satisfied with doing nothing.

Drink and drugs

What you can do to help

• Recognise that alcoholism is a sickness. No good is served by considering it a sign of weak will or self-indulgence.

• Join Al-Anon (see page 354). This is a fellowship for the families and friends of drinkers. Learn as much as possible about the disease, and attend meetings regularly.

• Encourage the drinker to join Alcoholics Anonymous (AA). Make the suggestion with tact, and offer to go to open meetings with him – attendance carries no obligation, and he will not be asked for his full name.

• Leave literature such as AA pamphlets lying about the house. The drinker may resent lecturing, but may nevertheless look at leaflets when you are not there.

• If the drinker shows any interest in giving up, encourage him to see the family doctor. In some cases, an alcoholic may not have acknowledged the scale of the problem to himself. Often, there will be reluctance to see a doctor, but greater readiness to speak to an understanding clergyman. The church minister may then persuade the drinker to seek medical advice.

• Strongly encourage any hobbies or activities which interest the drinker, so long as they keep him away from alcohol. Try to steer him away from playing darts in a pub, for instance.

• If a crisis occurs, for example through overdue debts, let the drinker face the problem. If he asks you for help, suggest that he contacts Alcoholics Anonymous; the organisation is skilled at advising on specialised problems.

FOUR STAGES IN THE DEVELOPMENT OF AN ALCOHOLIC

Stage one –
the pre-alcoholic phase

Anyone who answers 'yes' to any of these questions – particularly question 4 – should make an effort to control his drinking habits, as they could lead to serious problems.

1 Does he drink to feel at ease on social occasions?
2 Does he drink to forget worry or anxiety?
3 Does he feel more efficient or confident in his work when he is drinking?
4 Does he need to drink more than he used to in the past to obtain the same effect?

Stage two –
the warning phase

The answer 'yes' to one or more of the following questions shows that the drinker is well on the road to alcoholism. He should cut down his intake sharply. Most people can manage to do this without outside help.

1 After a period of drinking during which he was not obviously drunk, does he find it difficult to remember things he said or did?
2 Does he drink surreptitiously or secretly?
3 If he thinks there will not be enough to drink at a party, does he 'top up' with alcohol beforehand?
4 Does he arrange appointments so that they do not interfere with the opening hours of pubs and bars?
5 Does he gulp his drink?
6 Does he look for work in jobs where there is easy access to alcohol?
7 Does he ever drive after he has had several drinks?

Stage three –
the crucial phase

Every 'yes' in answer to these questions is a warning that the drinker must cut down his intake drastically, or in certain cases stop drinking altogether. He may need encouragement to do so from his family or friends, or to seek medical advice. He is not necessarily yet a fully fledged alcoholic, but he will be unless he changes his habits immediately.

1 Does he continue to drink after initially deciding to have 'just one or two'?
2 Does he frequently suffer from hangovers?
3 Does the idea of 'a hair of the dog' as a remedy for a hangover appeal to him?
4 Does he suffer from morning shakes?
5 Does he have a drink first thing in the morning?
6 Does he neglect his meals because of his drinking?
7 Does he feel guilty about his drinking?
8 Does he prefer to drink alone?
9 Does he lose time from work because of drinking?
10 Does his drinking harm his family in any way?
11 Does he need to drink at a definite time each day?
12 Does he need to 'top up' with a drink every few hours?
13 Does he carry drink with him, for example, in his car or briefcase?
14 Does his drinking make him irritable?

Where to go for help with a drink problem

If you are trying to overcome a drink problem of your own, keep in touch with your doctor.

Remember, though, that a chronic alcoholic should on no account try to give up drinking suddenly without taking medical advice.

In a specialised treatment centre, you may be given vitamins and possibly anticonvulsants (to guard against fits).

Additionally, the family doctor may suggest tablets to cope with a drink problem.

• Accept medical advice, but keep strictly to the prescribed doses.

• Remember that as an alcoholic you may be prone to excess and to the dangerous belief that four tablets are better than one.

• Also remember that no tablets can 'cure' alcoholism. They offer only a temporary aid, not an alternative, to the help which organisations such as Alcoholics Anonymous can provide.

• Under certain conditions, the doctor may recommend alcohol-sensitising tablets, such as Antabuse or Abstem. These are deterrent drugs which, combined with alcohol, induce unpleasant effects such as headache, nausea, vomiting and breathing difficulties. They are available only on prescription.

• Psychotropic drugs (which alter the taker's mood) are occasionally recommended. They should, however, be avoided unless your doctor strongly advises them. Psychotropic drugs can themselves be addictive and they may prove harmful, by weakening your determination to stay off drink.

15 Has he become jealous of his wife since he started heavy drinking?
16 Does his drinking cause physical symptoms, such as stomach pains?
17 Does drinking make him restless, or prevent him from sleeping?
18 Does he need a drink to be able to sleep?
19 Does he lose self-control after drinking?
20 Does he show less initiative, ambition, concentration or efficiency than before?
21 Has his sexual desire decreased?
22 Is he particularly moody?
23 Has he become more isolated and lost friends?
24 Have his wife and children had to change their way of life – for example, by not going out, or not inviting guests – because of his drinking?
25 Has drinking made him harder to get on with, or otherwise changed his personality?
26 Does he tend to drink with people of a different background to his own, or in places where he hopes he will not meet friends and acquaintances?
27 Does drinking affect his peace of mind?
28 Does he feel resentful, self-pitying or that everyone is treating him unfairly?
29 Is drinking jeopardising his job or damaging his reputation?

Stage four – the chronic phase

The answer 'yes' to any one of the first three questions means that there is a strong likelihood that the drinker is an alcoholic. The answer 'yes' to any one of the last five questions means that he is an alcoholic. He needs help *now* or he may do himself irreversible mental or physical harm.

1 Has he ever seriously considered suicide when drinking?
2 Does he feel incapable of coping with life, whether or not he has been drinking?
3 Does he suffer from any of the following conditions, all of which (in the absence of any other cause) are complications of heavy drinking? Vomiting blood; passing blood in the stools; severe abdominal pains; unsteadiness of gait when not drinking; pain in the calves; epileptic-like fits; hallucinations (delirium tremens, or 'DTs'); or severe tremors or sweating at night.
4 Does he go on alcoholic 'binges', drinking for several days in succession?
5 Does he get obviously drunk on much less than in the past?
6 Is he unable to take any action unless he has fortified himself with a drink beforehand?
7 Does he feel unable to give up drinking, even though he has been warned it is going to kill him?
8 Does he return to uncontrolled, excessive drinking again and again, even though he has tried to cut it down or give it up altogether?

Drink and drugs

Staying on the wagon

If you discover yourself to be heavily dependent on drink, you may need specialist care to cope with withdrawal symptoms. Afterwards, friends, relatives and advisers can help you to stay off drink. But remember that, ultimately, the responsibility for recovery is yours.

• At all costs, stay away from the *first* drink. If you allow yourself one, others will almost certainly follow.

• Stay in close touch with a specialist organisation (see box, this page).

• Build up your own network of non-drinking friends whom you can contact whenever you feel the need for support.

• Keep in close touch with your doctor. The doctor may suggest special tablets (see page 353) to help to deter you from drinking.

• Do not let the prospect of keeping off drink for the rest of your life become an obsession. Tackle the problem a day at a time: the days will mount to weeks, months and years. In time, abstinence will become part of your daily life.

• Do not be discouraged if, for some time after giving up drink, you still experience occasional cravings. Feeling like a drink is not the same as having one. The longer you stay sober, the less you will be troubled by cravings.

• Try to fill the gap created by giving up drink. Keep busy, exploring any activities which interest you. Cultivate new friends and new hobbies.

• Look closely at your own emotional make-up. Certain attitudes may have led you into alcoholism, such as feelings of guilt, inadequacy or self-destructive urges. If you can acknowledge and overcome them, the urge to drink may greatly diminish. Professional help through analysis or therapy may be useful in this context.

• Do not give up hope. Alcoholics who *really* want to get better usually do so.

Things to avoid

• Keep away from pubs, bars and other drinking places. If you have drunk heavily for long, you most likely have particular haunts and drinking companions – avoid them at all costs.

• Avoid keeping drink in your home. Only when you are certain that you have conquered your problem should you risk keeping alcohol.

• Avoid stressful situations which have encouraged drinking in the past. Learn when to call *'HALT'*. The letters of the word are a simple reminder of the states in which you are most vulnerable – when you are *H*ungry, *A*ngry, *L*onely, *T*ired or *T*hirsty.

SPECIALIST ORGANISATIONS THAT CAN HELP

ALCOHOL CONCERN
305 Grays Inn Road,
London WC1X 8QF (01-833 3471)
Alcohol Concern has information, education and advice centres throughout Britain. It replaces a number of earlier bodies including the National Council on Alcoholism, and the Alcohol Education Centre.

REGIONAL ALCOHOLISM UNITS
The National Health Service maintains some 35 rehabilitation units for alcoholics. The units provide specialised services for both inpatients and outpatients, as well as organising home visits and sometimes arranging for alcoholics to visit or stay in hostels and day centres. The units are distributed throughout the country. Addresses are available from the Department of Health and Social Security. Ask your family doctor whether referral to a unit might be helpful.

MEDICAL COUNCIL ON ALCOHOLISM
1, St Andrew's Place, London NW1 4LB (01-487 4445)
The council is a voluntary body set up to inform doctors about the problems of alcoholism. It can also advise alcoholics and their families on where to go for specialist help.

ALCOHOLICS ANONYMOUS
General Service Office, Po Box 1, Stonebow House, Stonebow, York YO1 2NJ (0904 644026)
The AA organisation will help anyone who has a drinking problem and who wants to do something about it. Its services include advice, support and the companionship of alcoholics who have stopped drinking. Closed meetings are held for alcoholics alone; open meetings are for families and friends as well. Centres are maintained throughout the country, and details can be obtained from the General Service Office.

AL-ANON FAMILY GROUPS UK AND EIRE
61 Great Dover Street,
London SE1 4YF (01-403 0888)
Al-Anon specialises in helping the families and friends of problem drinkers. Information about regional centres can be obtained from the London head office.

SALVATION ARMY
101 Queen Victoria Street,
London EC4P 4EP (01-236 5222)
The Salvation Army maintains hostels for homeless men and women throughout the country. Information can be obtained from the London headquarters.

Drug abuse: the risks

The abuse of any drug – including alcohol – may warp behaviour patterns, increase the risk of accidents and cause long-term distress among the user's friends and relatives. Most drug-related emergencies are caused by overdose, and in this area the greatest hazards arise from strong sedatives.

Sedatives are drugs which tend to induce sleep and damp down muscle activity. When taken in excess, they may slow the whole body system to the point where the user goes into a coma. In extreme cases, the drugs can kill by stopping the patient's breathing.

Even if a patient who is in a coma goes on breathing, he or she may choke to death on vomit, or suffocate because the tongue falls back and blocks the windpipe.

The drugs most likely to induce coma are: opiates such as heroin and morphine; strong tranquillisers; barbiturates; alcohol; and the inhaled fumes of solvents, glues, lighter fuel and similar volatile fluids.

Death through coma is less likely to result from the other main types of drugs abused. They include: stimulants such as cocaine and amphetamines; hallucinogens such as LSD; cannabis; and mild tranquillisers.

The risk of accidents
Whatever the risk of overdose and coma, all drugs are more or less intoxicating, depending on their strength and the dose taken. They can therefore seriously impair judgment and behaviour, creating risks of dangerous accidents on and off the roads.

An LSD user, for example, might imagine that he can fly – and might jump to his death from a window in that belief.

Strong forms of cannabis can cause a confused mental state with hazardous disorientation lasting for several days.

Massive amphetamine stimulation causes a 'blocked' mental state in which the user loses his grip on reality and may commit crimes without regard for the consequences.

The risk of injection
Any drug injected by an addict carries serious risk to the user, in addition to the risks of the drug itself.

Unskilled injection may result in ulcers on the skin, collapsed veins or a potentially lethal internal blood clot (a thrombosis).

Addicts also often become victims of infectious diseases such as AIDS, septicaemia and hepatitis. The diseases are caused by handling hypodermics carelessly, sharing syringes or needles, or by using impure water to dilute the drug in the syringe.

In general, injection into a vein is the most dangerous way of taking any drug, because the whole dose acts immediately on the body. Amphetamines, for example, have only a moderately harmful effect if they are swallowed, because digestion spreads the effect of the dose over several hours. If the same dose of an amphetamine is injected, though, the intensity of the resulting 'hit' makes the drug as dangerous and addictive as heroin.

Heroin itself is the most potent of all the widely abused drugs. It is usually heated on silver foil and the fumes inhaled, but may be injected. The body develops a tolerance for larger doses. But if the addict goes off the drug for a time, the tolerance is lost. As a result, a single injection of the addict's former dose can kill.

The risk of impure drugs
The dangers of taking pure drugs are multiplied in practice because those which appear on the black market have often been adulterated with other substances in order to increase the supplier's profit.

The additives or impurities may themselves be poisonous or contaminated with disease organisms, or they may be quite unsuitable for the use to which the drug is put. For example, a desperate addict may inject impure heroin (suitable only for smoking) with unpredictable toxic effects. Equally, an additive may induce nausea and vomiting – with lethal consequences to a drowsy user.

A grim variety of junk products circulate on the black market and are passed off as pure drugs. Users generally have no way of knowing quite what it is they are taking, or how strong it is – or, as a result, what doses of the substance their body can tolerate.

The risk of mixing drugs
Users themselves may mix drugs into cocktails with disastrous consequences. For example, a sedative or alcohol may be taken to try to 'come down' from a stimulant.

But drugs – even those with opposite effects when taken singly – do not necessarily counteract each other when they are taken in quick succession.

In some circumstances, they can combine to increase intoxication – with unpredictable and possibly tragic results.

The margin of safety
Different drugs affect the body's chemistry in different ways. LSD, for example, rarely produces an overdose, probably because it acts like a trigger on the brain. Once the chemical trigger has been pulled, extra amounts have little effect. Taking two or three times the normal dose, therefore, may not significantly alter the user's experience.

With glues and solvents, however, there is a very narrow margin of safety between the dose the user needs to achieve a 'high', and a dose that could threaten his life. While a single dose may only intoxicate, a double dose could be enough to stop the breathing and kill.

Drink and drugs

355

Drug identification and emergency treatment

The ten-page section that begins here covers, in alphabetical order, all the drugs which are most commonly abused in Britain.

Each entry describes what an individual drug looks like, and illustrates its most common forms – which may be a form in which it is usually prescribed by doctors, or the form in which it is most often sold on the black market. The entry goes on to explain what it is commonly called by users (since a parent's first knowledge of a drug problem in the family may be a youngster's chance remark).

Each entry also explains what a user feels when he or she is 'high', what someone else might notice, and tells you how to recognise and treat an overdose. For first aid details on how to treat an overdose of an unknown drug, see page 92.

The size of a dose is no guarantee of immunity from an overdose because drugs do not always act on different individuals in the same way. A single aspirin may cause acute stomach pain in some people. Others are hypersensitive to cocaine and may collapse in life-threatening shock immediately after sniffing the powder. There is, therefore, no amount of any of these drugs that can be taken in complete safety.

Age, weight and general health also play a part in determining what effect a given dose will have. Other factors being equal, an older or less healthy person runs a greater risk of suffering from an overdose than a fit person in his late teens or early twenties.

Similarly, the bigger the user, the more diluted the dose becomes in his body. So someone who is physically large and heavy is likely to be less affected by a given dose (again, other things being equal) than someone who is small and slight.

How the drug is taken makes a difference, too. A dose that is injected has a far more dramatic effect – and thus carries a greater risk of overdose – than the same quantity sniffed, smoked or eaten.

Moreover, a user who buys drugs on the black market has no reliable way of knowing what he is getting, or how strong it is. The drug is likely to have been 'cut' – in other words, adulterated – to an unknown degree in order to boost the pusher's profit.

The additive may itself be poisonous, or it may be a cheaper drug whose effects may magnify the effects of the drug it has been mixed with, affecting in an unpredictable way the chances of an overdose (see *Drug abuse: the risks*, page 355).

EMERGENCY SYMPTOM SORTER

A person who has taken a drug overdose may be in no condition to identify the drug involved, or may be unwilling to admit to taking a drug at all. This list shows the major overdose symptoms and the drugs that are most likely to cause them. For more details and for how to treat the overdose, look under the entry for the appropriate drug. For more details on alcohol, and on how to treat an alcohol overdose, see page 350.

Symptom	Possible causes
Apparent drunkenness	Amyl nitrite barbiturates glues tranquillisers
Coma	Alcohol barbiturates glues, heroin morphine methadone opium tranquillisers
Drowsiness	Barbiturates cannabis tranquillisers
Extreme restlessness	Amphetamines cocaine

Symptom	Possible causes
Fast pulse and fever	Amphetamines cocaine
Flushed skin	Amyl nitrite
Hallucinations	Cannabis, cocaine glues, LSD
Hysterical outbursts	Amphetamines cocaine, LSD
Severe headache	Amyl nitrite
Terror	LSD
Twitching and fits	Amphetamines cocaine
Violence	Amphetamines, LSD

Amphetamines (and other stimulants)

Amphetamine sulphate powder.
Pills and powder all about actual size

WHAT THEY LOOK LIKE When prescribed by doctors, amphetamines and other stimulants come in the form of tablets or capsules. Shapes and colours vary greatly. Many of these legally issued pills – which may be prescribed as slimming drugs because they suppress the appetite – find their way onto the black market.

A white powder, amphetamine sulphate, is also sold on the black market. Often, the powder is adulterated with chalk or talcum, and it is sometimes passed off as cocaine.

TRADE NAMES Dexedrine, Durophet.

WHAT THEY ARE CALLED Speed, pep pills and uppers are among the slang terms loosely used by drug-takers to cover the whole range of stimulant drugs.

Black bombers, blues, and hundreds and thousands take their names from the appearance of specific capsules and tablets. Bennies and dexies are slang contractions of trade names. Similarly, 'sulphate' refers to amphetamine sulphate.

HOW THEY ARE TAKEN Tablets and capsules are swallowed. Amphetamine sulphate powder may be sniffed, swallowed or (more rarely) dissolved in water and injected.

WHAT THE TAKER FEELS The short-term effects include heightened mental and physical activity. Users may feel no need for sleep, and may lose their normal inhibitions.

The drugs cause dryness in the mouth, so users often feel a strong thirst.

Excessive or repeated doses result in a sense of detachment from reality, sometimes accompanied by delusions. As the stimulation wears off, a depressed reaction sets in. The 'hangover' may be severe and persistent, leading to craving for another dose. The drugs become habit-forming, and addicts often experience acute craving, depression and anxiety when supplies are cut off.

WHAT OTHERS SEE Moderate stimulation produces talkative, erratic and restless behaviour. The user may sound hoarse, and may drink much more than normal.

Larger doses 'block' an awareness of reality. The user may stop communicating with other people, and may become accident-prone. Users also lose awareness of the consequences of their actions and may commit crimes or become violent.

With the craving for renewed supplies, an addict may plead for money, and there may be evidence of pilfering at home.

OVERDOSE SYMPTOMS In an overstimulated or 'blocked out' state, there may be extreme restlessness, irrational acts, outbursts of frustration, hysteria and delusions.

Physical symptoms can include a faster-than-usual pulse rate, fast breathing, twitching and even fits. If persistent, the whole body temperature may rise.

How to treat an overdose

• Make sure that no more stimulants – or any other drugs – are taken.

• Keep the patient away from bright lights, loud noise and fast movement – all will intensify the crisis.

• Try to calm the patient and keep a constant watch on him or her to prevent accidents. With a violent patient, some physical restraint may be necessary.

• Seek medical advice by telephoning your doctor or a hospital. If the patient is taken to hospital, doctors may administer a stomach washout to remove any drugs not yet absorbed. In severe cases, the overdose takes several hours to wear off, and the doctor may give a sedative or tranquilliser.

Drink and drugs

Amyl nitrite

Actual size

WHAT IT LOOKS LIKE Amyl nitrite is a clear liquid contained in a small glass ampoule. The container is usually sheathed in a cotton cocoon. The drug is used medically to treat angina, a heart condition.

TRADE NAMES None.

WHAT IT IS CALLED Ammies, sniffers, snappers, amps and nitrite amps.

HOW IT IS TAKEN The glass ampoule is crushed so that the volatile liquid soaks into the cotton covering. The vapour is then inhaled.

WHAT THE TAKER FEELS Users experience an intoxicated 'high'. However, the state often requires several ampoules to attain, and it is often accompanied by a pounding headache.
Large doses produce hallucinations.

WHAT OTHERS SEE Users appear drunk, elated or confused. The skin is often flushed, and the user may complain of a headache. The liquid also has a distinctive ether-like smell which may linger about the user.

OVERDOSE SYMPTOMS An excessive dose results in intensified symptoms. The headache may cause anguish and the skin can appear brightly flushed.
Staggering, incoherence and other symptoms of intoxication all become worse.
In a very severe case, the user may suffer temporary collapse and may have difficulty in breathing.

How to treat an overdose
• Apply artificial respiration at once if the patient stops breathing (see page 50).
• If artificial respiration is necessary, get medical help at once.
• Otherwise, stay with the patient to prevent accidents happening while he is intoxicated.
• Wait for the drug's effects to wear off. They should do so within about 30 minutes, provided no other drugs are involved.

Barbiturates

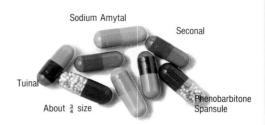

Sodium Amytal
Seconal
Tuinal
About ¾ size
Phenobarbitone Spansule

WHAT THEY LOOK LIKE Most barbiturates take the form of tablets, or coloured capsules containing white powder. Phenobarbitone, one of the most commonly prescribed barbiturates, comes in the form of a white tablet or a half blue, half clear slow-release capsule called a Spansule.
Occasionally, barbiturates reach the black market as loose white powder.

TRADE NAMES Sodium Amytal (blue capsules), Amytal (white tablets), Seconal (orange-red), Tuinal (half red, half blue). Luminal (white tablets) contains phenobarbitone. Ampoules of white powder are usually Pentothal, which is used by doctors as an anaesthetic.

WHAT THEY ARE CALLED Barbs, downers and sleepers.
Specific capsules often get their names from their appearance: blues, bluebirds, yellows and yellowjackets, for instance. Slang terms (phenobarb, ammies) come from chemicals.

HOW THEY ARE TAKEN Capsules and tablets are usually swallowed. Users often take them with alcohol – a combination which can prove fatal. Pentothal is injected.
Attempts are also made to inject powders extracted from capsules and tablets and dissolved in water, but most barbiturates are dangerously unsuitable for this use. The powder is caustic, only partially dissolves and may burn or cause serious ulcers.

WHAT THE TAKER FEELS The sensations felt by users who take even mild doses of barbiturates resemble drunkenness, but users are more prone to accidents and they progress more easily into drowsiness.
Barbiturates are addictive, and withdrawal symptoms include acute anxiety, headache, abdominal cramps, pains in the limbs and fits.

WHAT OTHERS SEE Users exhibit the typical symptoms of drunkenness, including slurred speech, stumbling, confusion and drowsiness.

OVERDOSE SYMPTOMS Heavy doses produce drowsiness deepening into semiconsciousness and coma. Breathing may stop, especially after the injection of a large dose.

How to treat an overdose

• Dial 999 and ask for an ambulance at once, stating clearly that you believe the emergency has been caused by an overdose of barbiturates.

• Provided the patient is conscious and cooperative, induce vomiting by putting your fingers down his or her throat.

• If the patient is not conscious or if he or she is not cooperative, however, do not try to make him or her vomit.

• Prevent any more drugs or alcohol being taken, and keep a close watch to prevent accidents.

• If the patient is comatose or unconscious but breathing, clear any obstruction from the mouth and put the patient in the recovery position (see page 136).

• If breathing has stopped, start artificial respiration immediately (see page 50).

• When medical help arrives, a stomach wash-out will be urgently needed to remove any unabsorbed drugs from the patient's body. The patient will need to be admitted to hospital.

Cannabis

Herbal marijuana

All about actual size

Resin

Cannabis oil

WHAT IT LOOKS LIKE In herbal form, cannabis – which comes from the hemp plant, *Cannabis sativa* – resembles a coarse tobacco. The dried leaves are greenish-brown, often chopped up with stems, seeds and flower parts.

The sap of the plant is also dried to extract cannabis resin, which takes the form of a greenish, brownish or blackish block, stick or lump, or a coarse brown powder.

Very occasionally, the drug appears in liquid form, either as yellowish-brown cannabis oil, or as cannabis tincture (a practically obsolete medical preparation).

TRADE NAMES None.

WHAT IT IS CALLED The herbal form is often known as grass, pot, marijuana, Mary Jane, weed, bhang, dagga or ganja. Resin is commonly referred to as hash, hashish, dope or resin. Other slang terms – such as Thai sticks, Moroccan gold, Lebanese gold and Nepalese black – derive from the drug's place of origin and its colour.

Cannabis cigarettes are described as joints, spliffs or reefers. The butt of a used joint is often referred to as the roach.

HOW IT IS TAKEN Cannabis is usually smoked in joints (often made with larger-than-usual cigarette papers) or in pipes to produce an immediate effect. In herbal form, it may be smoked on its own. Alternatively, in any form, it may be mixed with tobacco.

Sometimes, powdered resin is added to cake mixtures, which are cooked and eaten. The drug's effects are then more delayed.

WHAT THE TAKER FEELS The drug is unpredictable. A user, especially one who is already depressed or worried, may become withdrawn and experience deepening anxiety.

Drink and drugs

Large or repeated doses may produce deep drowsiness, or provoke delusions or hallucinations resembling those of an LSD trip. The skin is especially prone to imaginary creeping or crawling sensations.

WHAT OTHERS SEE Evidence of cannabis smoking may be present in the form of discarded butts, cigarette papers or torn strips of cardboard (used to make improvised cigarette filters).

Additionally, cannabis smoke has a distinctive smell, resembling that of burnt grass or a garden bonfire.

The eyes of a user are often red. He or she may appear unusually relaxed and distant, mildly confused or prone to senseless laughter.

Judgment is impaired, and users may appear clumsy and accident-prone.

Cannabis rarely produces a hangover, but habitual users may become anxious and urgent in their search for more drugs when supplies are cut off.

OVERDOSE SYMPTOMS Large doses produce intensified symptoms of drowsiness, disorientation or hallucinations. The symptoms may cause distress, but are not normally life-threatening. Nevertheless, intoxication may create serious accident risks, especially if the user is driving or operating machinery. Large or repeated doses can also produce 'cannabis psychosis' – a state of mental disorder and delusion which may take several days to pass.

How to treat an overdose

• Restrain the user from taking any more cannabis. Try to calm and reassure him. Take care to prevent accidents, remembering that, in severe cases, his judgment may be impaired for several days.
• If the user has persistent delusions or his behaviour becomes severely disordered, seek medical or psychiatric advice.

Cocaine

Single-dose packet; actual size

WHAT IT LOOKS LIKE A fine white powder. On the black market it is often sold in individual doses, folded in small pieces of paper or plastic. Because pure cocaine is extremely expensive, most doses are heavily adulterated with inactive powders such as chalk or talc. Some doses may contain no cocaine at all, but consist of cheaper amphetamine, often mixed with lignocaine (a local anaesthetic).

'Crack', a more powerful and addictive form of cocaine, is made by 'cooking' it with water and baking soda.

TRADE NAMES None.

WHAT IT IS CALLED Coke, crack, snow, lady snow, C, big C, princess and sniff. Individual doses are referred to as snorts.

HOW IT IS TAKEN The powder is most commonly sniffed ('snorted'). Alternatively, it may be dissolved in water and injected into a vein, a practice known as mainlining. The drug may also be mixed with tobacco and smoked, a practice known as freebasing. Wads of coca leaves – whose effects are much weaker than the powder's – are chewed. 'Crack' is usually smoked.

WHAT THE TAKER FEELS The drug counters drowsiness and prevents sleep. Large doses may give rise to hallucinations.

A depressed reaction sets in as the effects of the drug wear off. Depression is relieved by a further dose, and so the drug becomes habit-forming.

WHAT OTHERS SEE The user's mood may visibly brighten and his behaviour may become more uninhibited. He may seem mildly intoxicated or become accident-prone. Behaviour can also become erratic and may extend to violent outbursts if the user is frustrated.

Physically, cocaine tends to dry out the lining of the nose, and some users develop sniffing as a nervous tic.

An intensely depressed hangover is often experienced on the morning after taking the drug. Cocaine addicts develop powerful cravings with severe withdrawal symptoms if supplies are cut off. Frantic drug-seeking behaviour may result, often leading to crime to raise money.

OVERDOSE SYMPTOMS A few individuals are hypersensitive to cocaine; even a small dose may cause sudden collapse through an allergic reaction known as anaphylactic shock.

In any individual, an overdose may produce hysteria, delusions, physical tremors, muscle twitching and fits. Pulse, breathing rate and body temperature may also rise.

How to treat an overdose

• If a user collapses suddenly, call a doctor or ambulance immediately. Urgent medical care will be needed to treat anaphylactic shock (see *Dealing with an allergic reaction*, page 110).
• Otherwise, an overdose is rarely life-threatening. Prevent any more drugs being taken and try to calm and reassure the patient. Keep him or her away from bright lights, loud noise or fast movement, and keep watch to prevent accidents.
• The effects decline spontaneously over a few hours. A stomach wash-out is not necessary unless other drugs have been taken. If the overdose symptoms persist for longer than a few hours, however, or if they are very severe, get medical help.

Glues, solvents and lighter fuel

WHAT THEY LOOK LIKE Many household and industrial products are based on solvents which give off intoxicating vapour.

These freely available products include a wide range of glues, thinners, varnishes, paint strippers, spirits, dry-cleaning fluids, nail varnishes and nail-varnish removers. Petrol and lighter fuel have similar properties.

WHAT THEY ARE CALLED Glue, thinner, sniffer, spirit, evo and other contractions of familiar trade names.

HOW THEY ARE TAKEN Glues and solvents are either sniffed or inhaled by the mouth. Sometimes the vapours are obtained directly from the tube, tin or aerosol spray.

More often the vapours are inhaled from a plastic or paper bag into which the glue has been poured, or from a cloth which has been soaked in the fluid.

WHAT THE TAKER FEELS A rapid intoxication which relaxes and sedates like alcohol, and which may include hallucinations. Drowsiness or drunken stupor may follow.

WHAT OTHERS SEE Mild intoxication resembling drunkenness, with staggering and slurred speech. However, the use of solvents is often readily identified by the pervasive smell of the vapour inhaled.

Spilt glue, impregnated cloth or discarded plastic bags are all signs that a product may have been abused.

OVERDOSE SYMPTOMS Severe intoxication may lead rapidly to coma. In severe cases, breathing may stop. This is a particular risk if the patient falls forward and continues to inhale vapour while unconscious.

Drink and drugs

How to treat an overdose

- Remove the source of the vapour at once.
- In a room, open doors and windows.
- Clear any obstruction from the patient's mouth, and apply artificial respiration at once if breathing stops (see page 50).
- If the patient is unconscious or comatose, put him or her in the recovery position at once (see page 136).
- Then dial 999 and call an ambulance.
- If the patient is conscious but disorientated, watch him closely. If his condition deteriorates or fails to improve within five minutes, call an ambulance.
- Keep watch to prevent accidents while the patient remains under the influence.
- Take special care to avoid fire risks. Many glues and solvents are flammable – or even explosive – as well as intoxicating. This is a special risk where petrol or lighter fuel have been used: even a sparking light switch could ignite the vapour.

Heroin and morphine

Single-dose 'deals' of black market heroin; actual size

WHAT THEY LOOK LIKE Heroin and morphine are usually sold in powdered form. Both are prepared from opium, and although the refined powder is white, it often appears brownish-yellow because of impurities. Heroin (a derivative of morphine) is the stronger of the two, and probably the most dangerous drug in illegal use. Both drugs are usually 'cut' (meaning adulterated) with an inactive powder for sale on the black market.

Less commonly, the drugs may be sold in solution in glass ampoules, or, very occasionally, as small white tablets.

TRADE NAMES None in general use.

WHAT THEY ARE CALLED H, horse, smack and shit are among the slang terms for heroin. Morphine is usually known as M or morph. An individual dose is referred to as a fix or a hit.

HOW THEY ARE TAKEN Heroin and morphine are usually smoked – a practice sometimes called 'chasing the dragon'. They may be swallowed, or taken by injection, with the powder dissolved in water. Addicts generally inject directly into a vein, a practice known as 'mainlining'. Alternatively, the drugs may be injected under the skin, a practice known as 'skin popping'.

WHAT THE TAKER FEELS Users of either drug lose touch with reality, and feel drowsy. Some people, however, experience only unpleasant effects after taking heroin.

Heroin and morphine are both addictive, and habitual users tend to stop feeling any pleasurable effects. The drugs become necessary simply to remain 'normal', or to escape from harrowing withdrawal symptoms.

WHAT OTHERS SEE Signs of intoxication are often slight. The user may seem merely withdrawn into a private world, and have tiny, 'pinpoint' pupils. Larger doses produce more marked drowsiness.

Scars of injection, known as 'tracks', may be visible on the user. These are commonly found on the inside of the forearms and the front of the elbows. There may also be ulcers, or the scars of healed ulcers.

Discarded syringes, needles and ampoules, or foil and tube (used for sniffing the smoke from the drug), may indicate that the drugs are being used. If supplies are threatened, the user is likely to exhibit acute withdrawal symptoms and to become frantic and violent. He or she may turn to crime in the search for more.

OVERDOSE SYMPTOMS Deep coma, in which the patient is breathing but cannot be woken. The pupils of the eyes are reduced to mere pinpoints. Breathing may also stop.

An overdose is a particular risk when an addict has been off drugs for some time: in hospital, for example, or in prison. A single injection within days of discharge can kill, because the body can no longer tolerate doses to which it was previously accustomed.

How to treat an overdose

• Dial 999 and call an ambulance at once.
• If breathing stops, immediately clear any obstruction from the mouth and throat and apply artificial respiration (see page 50).
• Continue until breathing restarts, or until medical help arrives.
• If the patient is breathing but unconscious, check that the airway is clear and place him or her in the recovery position (see page 136).

LSD (and other hallucinogens)

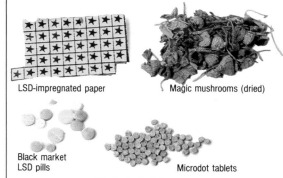

LSD-impregnated paper　　　Magic mushrooms (dried)

Black market LSD pills

Microdot tablets

All about actual size

WHAT THEY LOOK LIKE Lysergic acid diethylamide (LSD) and other chemical hallucinogens usually come in the form of tablets or capsules. Shapes, sizes and colours vary greatly, and include tiny microdot tablets (each about the size of this letter 'o', or even smaller) and squares of transparent plastic.

More rarely, LSD may be sold in the form of a colourless liquid, which is dropped onto sugar lumps, biscuits, paper or blotting paper for consumption.

In the picture above, for instance, each star on the sheet of yellow paper contains enough LSD for one 'trip'.

Mescalin, obtained from the Mexican peyote cactus, is sold in small, dried, brown portions of the plant.

Some fungi – often sold in dried form – contain hallucinogens, as do the seeds of some varieties of the morning glory plant.

TRADE NAMES None.

WHAT THEY ARE CALLED LSD is commonly known as acid. Doses are referred to as tabs (from tablets).

Other chemical hallucinogens are known by their abbreviated names, such as STP, DMT and PCP (also known as angel's dust).

Portions of the mescalin cactus are known as buttons, or mescal buttons. Hallucinogenic fungi are known as magic mushrooms.

HOW THEY ARE TAKEN Almost all hallucinogens are swallowed. Very rarely, LSD is injected.

WHAT THE TAKER FEELS Users experience a hallucinated 'trip', or sequence of disordered sensations. It starts about 30 minutes after the drug has been taken, and may last for four or more hours, depending on the dose.

Sense impressions are distorted, and users may experience highly coloured dream sequences. Sometimes, these are nightmarish and include terrifying imagery and visions.

Drink and drugs

WHAT OTHERS SEE Few physical symptoms are visible. The user appears to be in a daydream or trance, but may describe his or her experience more or less coherently.

The user may be prone to accidents through being detached from reality. Some imagine that they have acquired the power to fly, or to walk on water – with obvious dangers.

On a so-called 'bad trip', the user may cower from illusory terrors or try hysterically to escape them. Violent behaviour may result from imagined threats.

OVERDOSE SYMPTOMS True overdoses are very rare. However, excessive quantities of any hallucinogen will intensify or prolong an experience. The most common emergency results from the persistent terrors of a bad trip.

Some hallucinogens can be poisonous. They include magic mushrooms, PCP and impure LSD. The user's behaviour may become grossly disordered, and there may be symptoms of poisoning such as nausea, vomiting or physical collapse.

How to treat an overdose
• If poisoning is suspected, call an ambulance immediately.
• If the patient is unconscious, clear any obstruction from the mouth and put him or her in the recovery position (see page 136).
• If the patient is experiencing the horrors of a bad trip and remains conscious, there is no immediate need for medical help.
• Stay with the patient to prevent accidents and stop him or her taking any further drugs. Some physical restraint may be necessary if the patient is violent.
• Keep him or her away from bright lights, loud noises and fast movement. Where possible, keep him in dim lighting and try to talk him down, calming and reassuring him until the worst is over.
• If the crisis lasts longer than four hours, seek medical help. Call the doctor to the patient. Do not take the patient to the doctor, or you risk stirring up the horrors again.

Methadone

Linctus

About half actual size

Ampoule

Pills

WHAT IT LOOKS LIKE Small ampoules containing a clear solution. The drug may also be sold as a linctus or coloured syrup, or in the form of small white tablets.

TRADE NAME Physeptone.

WHAT IT IS CALLED Meth, phy or linctus.

HOW IT IS TAKEN The drug may be injected, either in a vein or under the skin. In drug clinics, it is widely used to treat heroin addiction since it may reduce heavy craving and dependence.

Linctus and tablets are swallowed. In clinics they are used to try to break the heroin-injection habit.

WHAT THE TAKER FEELS Methadone has effects similar to those of heroin and morphine. The effects last somewhat longer, however. Methadone itself is addictive, and may produce withdrawal symptoms.

WHAT OTHERS SEE The observable effects and signs of methadone abuse are the same as those of heroin and morphine abuse.

OVERDOSE SYMPTOMS The same as those of heroin and morphine.

How to treat an overdose
• Treat as for an overdose of heroin or morphine (see page 363).

Opium

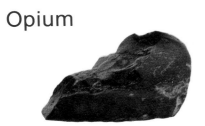

Actual size

WHAT IT LOOKS LIKE Raw opium (pictured above) appears in the form of blackish or brownish dried sap from the opium poppy. Refined opium is much paler in colour and often powdered. It was once widely used in medical preparations such as tinctures and cough linctus. But most have been phased out because of the dangers of creating dependency.

TRADE NAMES None.

WHAT IT IS CALLED Poppy.

HOW IT IS TAKEN Raw opium is generally smoked, in an opium pipe. It may also be swallowed. Refined opium may be smoked, swallowed or (in some forms) injected. All forms are addictive.

WHAT THE TAKER FEELS The effects are similar to those of heroin and morphine, which are both derived from opium. The sensations are generally milder, though.

WHAT OTHERS SEE Dreaminess, drowsiness and detachment may be evident, though less marked than in heroin or morphine users. Injection scars will not necessarily be present.

There may be evidence of smoking in the form of an opium pipe with a sweet, heady smell. Some experts, however, say that the smoke smells like burning old socks.

OVERDOSE SYMPTOMS An excessive dose may produce effects similar to those of heroin and morphine, but there is less risk that the patient will fall into a coma or stop breathing.

How to treat an overdose
• If the patient appears comatose – breathing, but incapable of being woken – treat as for heroin and morphine (see page 363).
• In milder cases, the patient can be allowed to recover on his own.
• Keep him under observation to ensure complete recovery, and to prevent any other drugs from being taken.

Tranquillisers

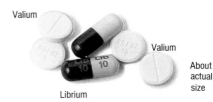

Valium

Valium

About actual size

Librium

WHAT THEY LOOK LIKE Tablets and capsules of various shapes and colours. Some are also sold as syrup or in ampoules.

TRADE NAMES Librium and Valium are known as 'mild' tranquillisers. In normal doses they tend to relieve stress without inducing sleep. Largactil and Sparine are stronger tranquillisers, and are sometimes prescribed for mental disorders. They have a sedative effect, and may induce drowsiness even in a normal dose.

WHAT THEY ARE CALLED Like the stronger sedatives (see *Barbiturates*, page 358), tranquillisers are known as downers because they tend to relax rather than stimulate.

HOW THEY ARE TAKEN Tranquillisers are usually swallowed.

Drug users often take them in dangerous combinations with alcohol, or in order to 'come down' after taking stimulants. Occasionally, the drugs are injected.

WHAT THE TAKER FEELS An easing of mental agitation and emotional stress. The drugs are mildly intoxicating, but more strongly so – sometimes much more strongly so – when they are taken with alcohol.

WHAT OTHERS SEE The characteristic symptoms of mild drunkenness, which may include staggering and clumsiness. Large doses, or smaller ones taken with alcohol, lead to greater confusion, drowsiness, slurred speech and uncoordinated movements.

Habitual use of tranquillisers may create a dependency, so that users exhibit anxiety when supplies are cut off.

OVERDOSE SYMPTOMS Excessive doses may lead to coma, though this is less common than with barbiturates.

How to treat an overdose
• Treat as for an overdose of barbiturates (see page 359).

Drink and drugs

365

Coping with a teenager on drugs

Drug abuse may come to light before an emergency arises. Your suspicions may be aroused, for instance, by an unexpected change in a teenager's behaviour patterns or by his or her poor performance at school.

Faced with evidence of drug-taking, it is best not to overdramatise the situation. Bear three major aims in mind:
• Try to keep on good terms with the user, who will often be the only person able to tell you what is going on.
• Try to establish some firm facts about the drug or drugs being used. Are they smoked, swallowed, injected or inhaled? Do they stimulate or relax? For how long and how often have the substances been taken?
• Consult your family doctor, who may be able to advise on the most sensible policy for coping with the problem. If the situation is serious, your doctor may refer you to a drug clinic or to a hospital where specialists will advise on treatment.

How you can help

Drug abuse among teenagers is widespread in Britain. Sometimes a youngster succumbs to temptation simply to be 'one of the gang'. In this case, a full explanation of the dangers may be enough to stop him or her using drugs again.

Often, however, the problem has its roots in mental or emotional stress. All teenagers face difficulties in growing up, and drugs may appear to offer an easy solution to loneliness, depression or anxiety.
• Try to be sympathetic and talk problems over.
• Direct the youngster's attention towards making friends away from the drug scene, and towards interests and activities which will help to boost his or her confidence.
• Try to arrange something he or she can look forward to, so that he or she does not slip back into depression or anxiety.
• In cases of long-term addiction, expert help may be needed to cope with withdrawal symptoms. But the care and attention of friends and family remain essential. Even when 'cured' at a drug addiction clinic, many addicts return to their habit after release.
• With heroin, the statistics are alarmingly high: the great majority of addicts return to the drug after clinical treatment, and more die than achieve lasting cures. Few among the survivors can kick the habit for good without the support and understanding of those closest to them.

HEROIN – THE SCALE OF THE PROBLEM

Once confined to the back streets of a few big cities, black market heroin has become available across the length and breadth of Britain. Estimates of users vary from 25,000 to 100,000 people and the figures are growing all the time.

On average, each addict takes about 1 gram (0.04oz) a week of adulterated heroin, and experts estimate that as much as 1.3 tons (1300kg) of the drug may be coming into Britain each year. The street value of the total is thought to be well over £50 million.

Street prices vary from around £50 per gram to more than three times that figure. Driven by the need to support the heroin habit, addicts may become involved in crimes ranging from petty pilfering to house-breaking, mugging and worse.

Drug traffickers eager for new clients sometimes offer teenagers and novice users impure heroin, suitable for smoking, at a cheap rate – or even free. Once initiated, the user may come to crave stronger doses – for which he will have to pay – and may want the swifter effects provided by injection.

Withdrawal – the price of giving up

Habitual users of heroin and other addictive drugs (including morphine, barbiturates and alcohol) become physically dependent on them. Missing two or three doses may precipitate a severe withdrawal crisis known among addicts as 'cold turkey'. Addiction treatment clinics and certain hospitals – family doctors will recommend where to go – provide specialist care for patients during such a withdrawal crisis.

The symptoms may come on within hours of a user being deprived of supplies.
• Typically, the onset of a withdrawal crisis begins with symptoms similar to those of a head cold: running eyes and nose, for example. These are often accompanied by acute anxiety and frantic drug-seeking behaviour.
• Stomach cramps, limb pains, headache, vomiting and intense anguish are likely to follow. In some cases, there may be minor convulsions as well.
• In severe cases, the symptoms of a drug withdrawal crisis may include fits. This is a particular feature of withdrawal from barbiturates.
• The crisis takes two or three days to pass. Then the symptoms gradually decrease in intensity over a week or two. But the craving for the drug persists and may stay with the user for the rest of his life.

Drugs and the law

Many drugs prone to abuse are restricted by law. Britain's Misuse of Drugs Act 1971 makes it a criminal offence to be in unauthorised possession of what the law calls a 'controlled' drug. It is also illegal to produce, import or export controlled drugs, or to supply them to others. The main controlled drugs are heroin, morphine and other opiates; cocaine; amphetamine stimulants; LSD, mescalin and other hallucinogens; and cannabis.

The controlled drugs are further divided into three classes – Classes A, B and C – according to how dangerous they are judged to be.

Class A

Drugs in this category are considered to be the most dangerous. They include heroin, morphine and other opiates, cocaine, LSD, mescalin, injectable amphetamines and cannabinol (the refined, active constituent in cannabis).

Class B

Drugs in this category are less dangerous and include several amphetamines, herbal cannabis and cannabis resin.

Class C

Drugs in this category include several amphetamines.

What the penalties are

In Britain, for trafficking in Class A drugs, the maximum penalties are 14 years' jail (though there have been plans to increase this to life imprisonment), an unlimited fine and seizure of the pusher's assets. Lesser penalties apply to simple possession, and to offences involving controlled drugs in Classes B and C. The proceeds of drug trafficking will be confiscated.

Similar laws exist in most countries. Drug trafficking has become one of the most profitable forms of organised crime all over the world, and severe deterrents are considered necessary. In some countries, drug offences carry the death penalty.

Evidence of possession

The Misuse of Drugs Act and similar laws abroad are directed mainly against criminal drug trafficking. But most of those charged with drug offences (around 15,000 each year in Britain) are in possession of small quantities for their own use.

Evidence of possession of a controlled drug is generally regarded as proof of guilt. The few exceptions involve cases where the defendant can prove that the drug was medically prescribed, or that he or she was totally unaware of possessing not only the drug, but also its container.

Simple possession may be dealt with leniently by the authorities, if the quantity is small. However, smuggling drugs – particularly those in Class A – usually attracts very severe penalties even if the defendant is an innocent courier who is merely carrying a parcel for a friend.

Search and arrest

The police and Customs and Excise officers have wide powers to search and arrest people for suspected drug offences. In the street, a person or a vehicle can be stopped and searched without a search warrant if officers have reasonable grounds for suspecting that the person or anyone in the vehicle is in unauthorised possession of a controlled drug.

However, the police do need a warrant to search private homes and other buildings, unless they are invited in to do so.

Customs officials have somewhat wider powers to search for drugs. They may search without a warrant not only at ports, airports and inside vehicles, ships and planes – but also inland and inside any building.

The courts can be asked to force a bank to disclose details of the accounts of someone suspected of drug trafficking.

If your home is used for drug offences

It is a criminal offence for a householder knowingly to permit the production, supply or unauthorised use of controlled drugs (including cannabis) on his premises.

It is not an offence, however, if these things happen without the householder's knowledge.

If you discover that drugs are being prepared, sold or used in your home or in any building you own, you are legally obliged to report the offence to the police. Failure to do so may result in your being charged as an accessory. It is also an offence to tip off a suspected trafficker.

Doctors, however, who treat victims of drug overdoses are not legally obliged to report their patients to the police, and they rarely do so.

If you discover a controlled drug in your home – or anywhere else – the law permits you to take possession of it to prevent an offence being committed.

You must, however, then hand it over to an authorised person, normally the police, or destroy it yourself without delay.

If a friend is charged with a drug offence

If someone close to you is charged with a drug offence, seek legal advice immediately. Ideally, contact a solicitor experienced in the field. Any local solicitor should be able to advise you on a suitable lawyer (see *Getting help with a legal problem*, page 370).

Not all drugs are controlled by the Misuse of Drugs Act, and possession may not constitute an offence. However, the law may change, which is one reason why expert advice is always necessary.

Additionally, there may be mitigating circumstances, and it is always essential for the defendant to know his or her rights.

Drink and drugs

Legal and financial emergencies

Getting help with a legal problem

There are three main sources of legal advice in Britain: Citizens Advice Bureaux (CAB); ·Law Centres; and solicitors.

Citizens Advice Bureaux

You can get free information and advice on a wide range of legal problems from local branches of the CAB, which is a national government-supported network of advice centres. Each bureau is staffed by trained volunteers who can help, for instance, with: divorce; disputes at work; disputes over property; social security questions; and consumer affairs.

• To find your nearest CAB, look in the local telephone directory or ask at a post office, public library or council office.

• You can telephone the bureau or call at the office. At some offices, a solicitor attends at regular times to give free advice.

• The CAB may also direct you to a legal advice centre, if there is one in the area. Legal advice centres – which are not connected with Law Centres – are independent charitable organisations which do not receive government funds.

Law Centres

There are about 50 Law Centres funded by central and local government in Britain. They offer free advice on legal problems, but only to people living within the districts they cover. Sometimes a Law Centre can also provide free representation in court. Each centre has at least one solicitor, and most centres have two.

Law Centres specialise in helping people who have problems over housing, Department of Health and Social Security benefit claims, child care and immigration.

• If you do not know of a Law Centre near you, you can find out whether there is one in your area by contacting The Law Centres Federation at Duchess House, 18-19 Warren Street, London W1P 5DB (telephone 01-387 8570).

• Telephone your local centre to make an appointment. Alternatively, ask the staff at the centre whether and when it holds advice sessions – for advice sessions no appointment is usually necessary.

Finding a solicitor

At any stage in dealing with a legal problem of any kind – whether or not you have been to a CAB – you may decide that you need or want formal legal advice.

• If you do not know a solicitor already, ask a knowledgeable friend to recommend one. Your bank manager might also be able to advise you.

• Alternatively, ask the local CAB for a list of local solicitors and ask the bureau to recommend one who specialises in the sort of problem you face.

• If there is no CAB near your home, consult the Solicitors' Diary and Directory in a public library. This gives a list of solicitors, with the kind of work they specialise in.

• Alternatively, look in the Yellow Pages of a telephone directory under 'Solicitors'. Telephone one near you and find out whether he deals with your type of problem. If not, ask him to recommend other local solicitors who may be able to help.

• Telephone two or three firms, ask for estimates and compare them. Many solicitors will give an initial half-hour consultation for £5. Ask if they will do this – it is called the Fixed Fee Scheme. But remember that any later work may well cost much more.

• If you become dissatisfied with your solicitor or feel that he has not acted in your best interests, you can complain to The Law Society, the solicitors' professional body. For advice on how to make a complaint, contact the Solicitors Complaints Bureau, Portland House, Stag Place, London SW1E 5BL (telephone 01-834 2288).

HOW TO GET LEGAL AID

If you need a solicitor's help but have a low income, it is possible to get legal aid to cover all or part of the costs – including the cost of having a solicitor or barrister to represent you in court.

• If you need advice, but no court action is involved, ask a solicitor for a £5 interview or ask for advice under the Law Society's 'green form' scheme. Any solicitor will be able to advise you on whether you are eligible for help under the scheme, and on how to apply.

• If a court case is involved, you need a legal aid form.

• In a civil case, get the form from a CAB or any local solicitor. A solicitor can help you to fill in the form. When the form is completed, send it to the area office of The Law Society. The bureau or the solicitor will have the address.

• In a criminal case, get the form from the magistrates' court which is to hear the case. Fill it in and return it to the clerk of the court.

• Because legal aid is means-tested, you may still have to pay some of your legal costs even if your application is approved. In addition, if you win your case and are awarded damages, some or all of the money you win may have to be paid back to the legal aid fund.

• If you lose the case, you may have to pay damages to the other side on top of your contribution to your own costs. Ask your solicitor how much this is likely to be before you decide to go to court.

Helping police inquiries

Under the Police and Criminal Evidence Act 1984, the police cannot stop and search someone without reasonable suspicion that the person has committed a crime or is about to do so.

• If you are stopped and questioned by police, you are not usually obliged to answer, or even to give your name and address. But it is usually sensible to help. They may, for instance, be looking for witnesses of an accident or crime and you may be able to provide useful evidence.

• You must give your name, address and date of birth if the inquiries involve a motoring case or are under the Official Secrets Acts.

• You can generally refuse to be searched, unless the police have a warrant. But this right to refuse does not apply if the police have reason to suspect that you have dangerous drugs, stolen goods, an offensive weapon or an implement that can be used for theft or burglary.

• If the police find anything that they think might be useful as evidence, they can confiscate it – though they may return it later.

• Before the police search you, they must identify themselves and tell you why they are searching you and what they are looking for. Then, or immediately afterwards, they must give you a note confirming these details in writing.

• If you are not sure whether the police are within their rights to search you, it is usually safer to allow the search anyway, and to complain later – through a solicitor, if necessary.

• You are not obliged to go to a police station unless you are arrested or unless the police want to continue the search.

• If you need a solicitor, telephone him if possible before going to the police station. If you do not know a solicitor, the police at the station will have a list of duty solicitors.

If a policeman comes to your home

A uniformed policeman who comes to your home should tell you his name and say why he wants to question you. An officer in plain clothes must show you his warrant card as well if you ask to see it.

• A warrant card is always in a sealed plastic case. It gives the policeman's name and rank, the name of his police force, and sometimes has a crest on it. It also has a photograph.

• Check that the photograph matches the person at the door. If you are not sure that he is a real policeman, telephone the station he is attached to for verification. Ask him to wait outside until you have made the call.

• You must let a policeman enter your house if he shows you a search warrant.

• Even if he has no warrant, you must also let him in if he says he wants to arrest someone inside, or if he says he wants to question someone he thinks is hiding inside.

• In other circumstances, you are not obliged to let a policeman into your house. If you do invite him in, you can ask him to leave at any time – and he must comply.

If you are arrested

If the police arrest you, they must tell you why they are doing so.

• Make a note of the reasons the police give you for your arrest. The note may help your solicitor later.

• Go quietly to the police station. If you do not, you can be charged with resisting arrest or obstructing a police officer. You can be jailed and fined for this offence even if you are later acquitted of the charge on which you were arrested. The police are entitled to use reasonable force, or handcuffs.

• Once you get to the police station, if you think you have been wrongly arrested, say so.

• You can refuse to answer questions. If you do reply, the police will note what you say and may repeat your words as evidence in court.

• You can ask for a copy of the Codes of Practice – which have replaced the old Judges' Rules. They say that, as soon as a police officer has grounds for believing that someone has committed a crime, the accused must be warned that he need not answer further questions.

• You can ask to see a solicitor. But if the offence is very serious the police may delay this for up to 36 hours if they think that it would lead to accomplices being alerted.

• However, nobody (except a suspected terrorist) can be held in a police station for more than 36 hours without the approval of a magistrates' court. This approval can be granted only after a hearing where both the suspect and his solicitor, if he wants one, are present.

At the police station

• The police may search anyone who has been arrested, and may take away items which are needed as evidence, or which could cause injury or damage. You will be asked to check a list of what is taken.

• If you make a voluntary statement, read it over carefully before signing it. Alter anything that is wrong or unclear.

• You can refuse to have your fingerprints taken. But the police can insist if an officer of the rank of superintendent or above has reasonable grounds for believing that your fingerprints will tend to confirm or disprove your involvement in an offence.

• You can refuse to attend an identity parade, and you can choose where you stand if you decide to attend one. If you want an identity parade, you can demand one.

Getting bail

• You must be given a copy of any charge against you. Once you are charged, the police will either release you on bail or keep you in custody until you appear before magistrates. Even if the police have refused to grant bail, you can ask the magistrates to overrule them and to grant it.

• If you have no solicitor, ask the court to arrange one for you.

If you are prosecuted

Unless you are warned at the time of an incident that you will be charged, your first knowledge of an impending criminal prosecution will normally be when you receive a Notice of Intended Prosecution from the police.

The notice will contain details of the alleged offence, and tell you the time and place of the court hearing.

• Check that the details in the formal notice of prosecution are correct. If there are mistakes, you may be able to get the charge dropped on technical grounds.

• Decide whether to plead guilty or not guilty. If you are innocent, you should always plead not guilty – even if (as in some driving offences) you can plead guilty by post without appearing in court.

• If in doubt, consult a solicitor (see *Getting help with a legal problem*, page 370). Do not be afraid to ring several – their charges and experience vary.

• If you decide to conduct your own defence without a solicitor, consult Stone's *Justices' Manual* (published by Butterworths) or some other legal reference book at a library. Stone's *Justice's Manual* gives the guidelines and penalties for the kinds of offences which are tried in magistrates' courts.

• Write down exactly what happened during the incident which led to the charge.

• If you are going to call witnesses, write down what they are going to say as well. You will need both these sets of notes when presenting your case.

• Visit the court beforehand and sit in on some of the trials being held there, so that you can get to know the procedure.

• If the case is at all complex, however, or if the maximum penalty you face is large, it is usually best to ask a solicitor to act for you.

• Consider, also, applying for legal aid (see *How to get legal aid*, page 370). You may be able to get enough aid to cover at least some and possibly all of the solicitor's fees.

If you are sued

Most civil disputes are settled by negotiations between the people involved in the dispute or their solicitors. If, however, the two sides cannot agree, the dispute can be referred to a court.

A civil dispute that goes to court may sometimes be heard by magistrates. More often, though, the case is dealt with by a county court or by the High Court.

Magistrates hear some actions over debts – non-payment of rates, for example – and disputes over the maintenance of wives and single parents.

County courts hear claims for debts of less than £5000, disputes involving landlords and tenants, undefended divorces, and disputes over hire-purchase transactions.

The High Court hears claims for damages for personal injury, breach of contract, debts of any amount, and libel and slander. It also hears defended divorces.

Whichever court hears the case, the person making the claim is called the plaintiff. The person he or she sues is called the defendant.

Most civil court cases begin with the plaintiff – or, more commonly, his solicitor – applying to the appropriate court for a summons or a writ. (The corresponding document in a divorce case is known as a petition.)

The summons or writ is likely to be your first formal notification that legal action has been started, but in most cases you will have been warned, through letters from the plaintiff, that the dispute could go to court.

If you do receive letters threatening legal action, and you dispute the claim, consider getting professional advice before legal action starts (see *Getting help with a legal problem*, page 370).

Paying a solicitor to negotiate a settlement out of court may be cheaper than fighting the case in court – even if you win.

Receiving a summons

If someone claims you owe him money, he may serve a summons (called a default summons) on you, or get a court official to do it. The summons may be given to you personally, or it may be sent by registered post or recorded delivery. It will show the amount claimed, including court fees and solicitors' charges. The summons also contains a form which allows you to admit the claim, defend it or make a counter-claim of your own.

• If you agree that you owe the money and can pay at once, send or take the money to the court office. The court will pay the plaintiff and that will end the action.

• If you admit the debt but cannot pay it, fill in the admission section of the form and send it to the court. You can offer to pay by instalments, or give a date when you can pay.

• If you dispute the debt, fill in the defence section. If the plaintiff owes you money, use the counterclaim section too.

• If you are not sure how to fill in the form, the clerk at the court office which issued the summons will often be able to give you advice free of charge. Alternatively, consult a solicitor.

• If the action is in the county court and is for an amount under £500, it will be dealt with by an informal procedure called Arbitration. Under this procedure, the case is normally heard in private and the formal rules of evidence need not apply – you can describe what someone else said, for example. Also, the loser does not have to pay the winner's legal costs.

Receiving a writ

If someone claims that he has been injured because of your negligence, he may issue a High Court writ against you. This could happen because of a car crash, for instance, or an accident at work.

The writ will say that an action is to be brought and give brief details of the reasons.

When you receive the writ, it is said to have been 'served'.

• With the writ will be a form for acknowledgment of service. Return the form to the court that issued the writ within 14 days.

• Consult a solicitor as soon as possible. You have 28 days from the date the writ was served to let the court know how you wish to answer the writ – by defending it, for instance, or by making a counterclaim of your own.

• If you are short of money, you may be able to claim legal aid. Ask your solicitor or a local Citizens Advice Bureau to help you to make the application (see *How to get legal aid*, page 370).

YOU AND THE LAW

Most people go through life without ever being involved in a court case. But the law still governs much of what we do. It is involved, for instance, when we take a job, get married, buy goods or drive a car. Knowledge of the law helps us to safeguard our rights and those of our families, and to protect our property.

There are two main branches: the criminal law and the civil law.

• Criminal law lays down penalties for breaking society's rules – from parking in the wrong place to murder.

• Civil law deals with disputes between individual members of society, businesses and organisations. It enables people to seek financial compensation or some other remedy from someone who may have been negligent, broken a contract, who may owe money or who may otherwise have acted unfairly.

If squatters move in

If you come home – from a holiday, say – to find that squatters have taken over a house you own, your legal rights depend on whether you live in the house or not.

Your rights are more extensive if you normally live in the house or if you intend to live in it (if, say, you have been working abroad and have just returned to Britain, or if you have just bought the house). Your rights are more limited if you do not normally live there (if, for example, it is a holiday home that you use for only a few weeks a year).

If you live in the house

• If you normally live in the house, show the squatters proof of this – a letter addressed to you there, for instance – and tell them to go.

• If they will not let you in, and insist on staying, call the police.

• You are entitled by law to use 'reasonable force' to enter your home or to eject squatters. What counts as reasonable, though, depends on the circumstances. And if you use what the courts regard as excessive force, you could be open to a charge of assault. For this reason, it is usually better to call in the police than to try to evict the squatters yourself.

• The police can evict squatters on the spot.

• Check your home insurance policy as soon as possible. Under most house and contents policies, it is possible to claim back from the insurance company the cost of temporary accommodation. In addition, it is usually possible to claim back the cost of any damage the squatters have done to your house or to your possessions inside it.

• The cover usually applies so long as the house had not been left empty for more than 30 days.

• If the policy documents are unreachable – perhaps because you left them in the house – contact the insurance broker or company which sold you the policy. They will usually have a copy of the documents. The policy may in any case require you to let the company know that you intend to make a claim.

• It is also possible to get the squatters evicted through the courts, and to sue them for the cost of your accommodation as well as for the cost of any damage they do. But since squatters are usually short of money and may be difficult to trace once they leave your home, this course is rarely worth pursuing.

• If you plan nevertheless to take court action – if your insurance policy does not cover the costs, say – get advice from a solicitor (see *Getting help with a legal problem*, page 370).

If the house is unoccupied

It is not a crime for squatters to move into an unoccupied house – such as an empty holiday home – unless they use violence to get into the premises, or unless they cause damage.

Provided the squatters do not use violence or

cause damage, they offend only the civil, not the criminal, law.

The police, therefore – who enforce only the criminal law – may often have no power to help. In addition, you do not, in these circumstances, have the right to use 'reasonable force' to eject the squatters.

• Ask the squatters to let you in, and tell them to leave.

• You can go in if they let you. But if they refuse, you are not entitled to force your way in.

• If they do refuse to let you in, wait until they go out – to go shopping, for instance. Then take possession. You are entitled to break in – by breaking a window, for example – if necessary.

• Stay out of sight while you are waiting. Otherwise the squatters may guess what you have in mind and make a point of leaving at least one person permanently in the house.

• If this tactic fails, get in touch with a solicitor. Ask him to apply to a county court for a possession order.

• Once the court order has been issued, a court official will evict the squatters – by force if necessary.

After the squatters leave

• Once you regain possession of the house, do not destroy any property the squatters have left behind. They are entitled to reclaim it – even after a number of years have elapsed.

• If their property becomes a nuisance, get a solicitor's advice on what to do with it.

If someone is evicted

People evicted from their home with nowhere to go should ask the local council's housing authority for help.

• The housing authority is legally obliged to provide accommodation for priority cases, such as pregnant women, families with children, and households where there is an elderly or handicapped person.

• The authority may send those evicted to a reception centre, give them a short-term lease on an empty house, or arrange a temporary stay in a guesthouse or hotel.

If the council refuses to help

Many councils classify tenants evicted for non-payment of rent as intentionally homeless, and may refuse to help for that reason.

• If the council refuses to help, those evicted should appeal to their local councillor or MP.

• If they have nowhere to store possessions, they should ask the housing authority to store them. It must do so, but may charge for it.

• If those evicted need money, they should ask their local Department of Health and Social Security office.

• Homeless people are as entitled to supplementary benefit as those who have a home. They should not be refused benefit because they have no fixed address.

Finding temporary accommodation

If evicted people have no friends or relatives with whom they can live, and the local council's housing department will not provide them with accommodation, a charitable organisation may be able to help.

Evicted people who find themselves without a roof over their head can contact Shelter at 157 Waterloo Road, London SE1 8XF (telephone 01-633 9377), or the Salvation Army at 101 Queen Victoria Street, London EC4P 4EP (telephone 01-236 5222). Both organisations run hostels for the homeless all over Britain.

The London head offices of both organisations will also know of local housing aid centres where evicted people can stay. Alternatively, a Citizens Advice Bureau should be able to supply a list of hostels in the area.

If you lose your job

An employee can lose his or her job in two main ways: by being dismissed; or by being made redundant.

When somebody is dismissed

• An employee who is dismissed should write to his employer. In the letter, the employer should be asked to give his reasons for the dismissal in writing, unless he has already done so. The employer is obliged by law to reply within 14 days of receiving the request.

• If the employer does not reply, or if the employee is dissatisfied with the reasons given or with the way in which the dismissal has been handled, he should talk to a local Citizens Advice Bureau, a solicitor or a trade union official (see *Getting help with a legal problem*, page 370).

• Any of these will be able to tell him whether he has a claim for unfair or wrongful dismissal, or for redundancy. They will also be able to advise him on how to pursue the claim in an industrial tribunal or the courts.

When somebody is made redundant

• An employee who is made redundant should contact the personnel department of his firm as soon as possible.

• If he is dissatisfied with the redundancy pay the employer is offering, he should discuss it with the personnel department.

• If still dissatisfied, he should get advice from a Citizens Advice Bureau, a solicitor, or a trade union official. They may be able to negotiate more generous redundancy terms, and can advise him about whether it is worth taking the case to an industrial tribunal.

• The legal minimum for a redundancy payment depends on the employee's age and how long he has been employed by the firm. For each year of service he should get one and a half weeks' pay if he is over 41, one week's pay if he is between 22 and 41, and half a week's pay if he is between 18 and 22. Some employers offer larger redundancy payments than these, but they are not obliged to.

If you are injured at work

More than 700,000 people are injured at work in Britain each year. The Health and Safety at Work Act 1974, and other measures which relate to specific industries, aim to limit this casualty toll and to protect the victims of industrial accidents.

The measures put a legal obligation on employers to provide: a safe place and system of work; safe plant and tools; and competent staff.

Anyone who is injured at work, or who becomes ill as a result of the work he does, can usually claim one or more of the state benefits administered by the Department of Health and Social Security. He may also be able to sue his employer for a lump sum in compensation if he can show that the accident happened because the employer or a workmate was careless in some way.

If you get hurt

• If you are injured in any accident at work, report the accident to a supervisor at once.

• A factory, mine or quarry, or any company that employs ten or more people on the premises, must by law have an accident book.

• If there is such a book where you work, record the accident in it.

• If you are too badly injured to write, ask someone else to record the accident in the accident book for you.

• Later, when you are able, write to the firm saying what happened.

• Take signed statements from witnesses, or get a workmate to do so.

• Make a note of the witnesses' home addresses as well, in case they leave the firm and you need to contact them later.

• See your doctor, even if your injury has been treated by first aid staff at work and the accident seems minor. There may be complications later.

Claiming benefit

Most employees who are unable to work because of industrial injury are entitled to claim sick pay from their employers in exactly the same way as they would if they were off work through illness.

Sick pay lasts for up to 28 weeks. Many firms pay full wages during this period. Thereafter, an employee can normally claim sickness benefit from the government.

• Claim sick pay in the same way as you would if you were ill.

• If you are still unable to work after 28 weeks, you are entitled to claim sickness benefit from the Department of Health and Social Security. Your employer will usually arrange this automatically.

• If you are not entitled to sick pay from your employer for some reason – the personnel department in your firm will tell you whether you are entitled – you can claim the state sickness benefit at once.

Legal and financial emergencies

Trouble at the shops

- To claim sickness benefit, get a 'self-certification' form SC1 from the local DHSS office. Fill it in and return it to the office. You do not need a doctor's certificate until you have been sick for more than seven days.
- If you are too ill to move, ask someone else to make the claim on your behalf. If you are claiming sickness benefit from the time of the accident, the claim should reach the social security office within six days of the accident; otherwise you may lose some benefit.
- You may qualify for other benefits as well, depending on the severity of the accident. If you lose a finger or toe, for instance, you can claim disablement benefit.
- If you are in doubt about what you are entitled to claim, ask the social security office for advice as soon as possible after the accident.
- Telephone or write to the office if you cannot get there yourself, or ask someone else to visit the office for you.

Going to court
You may be able to get compensation if your employer, or a workmate, has been negligent or your employer has broken safety rules. All employers are required to insure against this.
- If you think you have a case, talk to a union official or solicitor as soon as possible after the accident (see *Getting help with a legal problem*, page 370).

Surrounded by goods in a crowded store, it can be easy to knock something off a shelf and break it. With modern packaging techniques, you may not discover that you have bought faulty goods until after you get home. In both these situations, the law tries to strike a fair balance between the rights of the shopper and the shopkeeper.

What to do if you break something
- If you knock something over in a shop, or drop it, through carelessness, you are legally responsible for any damage you cause. If you feel that it was clearly your fault, it is best to pay for the breakage if the manager of the shop asks you to do so. The manager is entitled to ask for the full amount of the retail price – not just the cost price to the shop.
- If the accident was not your fault – because the goods were badly stacked, say – you are not liable for any damage. If you feel that this is the case, do not pay.
- If the manager of the shop disagrees with you, he may decide to take you to court (see *If you are sued*, page 372). If he asks for your name and address, you must give it to him.
- Before leaving the shop, collect the names and addresses of any witnesses – in case you need them to give evidence in your support.

How to complain
When making a complaint – about faulty goods, for example, or bad service – be systematic, reasonable and persistent. Have clear in your mind the reasons for your complaint and what you want done about it.
- Make your first complaint to the person you have been dealing with – the salesman or waiter, for example. Do not get angry. Contact the person as soon as you can. Undue delay will weaken your position. If this approach fails, ask to see the manager or the person in charge. Make it clear at each stage what you want done to settle the matter.
- If you still get no results, make your complaint formally in writing. Address it to the manager or person in charge of the office, shop or organisation that you have been dealing with. Get the address from the telephone directory.
- Set out your complaint in full. Give any relevant names and dates. Enclose photocopies of any documents. Do not send the originals.
- Set a time within which you expect a reply – 14 days, say. Make it clear that if you receive no reply you will take matters further.
- Send the letter by recorded or registered delivery. The organisation will then not be able to deny receiving the letter. Keep a copy.
- If you receive no reply within the time you have set, write again enclosing a copy of your first letter. Make it clear that you are also sending a copy of the letter to someone higher up in the firm such as the area manager, managing director or chief executive. If you do not know the address, you may find it in the local library.

Alternatively, ring the firm and tell the switchboard operator that you have to write to the company. Ask for the name and address of the managing director, but do not say why you will be writing to him.

• If you still get no response, consider taking your complaint to the firm's trade association, or to the local council's health officer or trading standards officer. Alternatively, contact the nearest Citizens Advice Bureau.

• As a last resort, consider consulting a solicitor. But weigh up first whether the cost of going to law is more than you are likely to get if you win your case. If your claim is small (less than £500) you will have to pay your own legal costs whether you win or lose.

IF YOU ARE FALSELY ACCUSED OF SHOPLIFTING

Anyone who intentionally takes goods from a shop without paying for them is guilty of theft. But absent-mindedness in a busy supermarket can result in someone accidentally putting goods in the wrong basket, or forgetting to pay. Being falsely accused of shoplifting is distressing. The main thing is to stay calm.

• If the store detective or a member of the staff asks you to go to the manager's office, you are not obliged to do so. If you refuse, he may let you go – or arrest you.

• Do not resist if the store detective arrests you – even if you are innocent. Go with him to the manager's office.

• You do not have to answer any questions at any stage. Nor does the store detective have any right to search you or your bag without your permission.

• Once you are in the manager's office, ask to make a telephone call. Get in touch with a solicitor and follow his advice. If you do not know a solicitor, ask a friend or relative to come to the shop.

• Make the call out of earshot of the shop staff, if possible. Anything you say may be repeated as evidence if you are prosecuted.

• Wait until the solicitor, or your friend, arrives before saying anything. The only exception to this rule might be if you realise that you have made a mistake. You may try to explain what happened – but remember that what you say may be taken down and repeated in court.

• If the manager decides to prosecute you, he will call in the police. He must do this as soon as possible after your arrest (see *If you are prosecuted*, page 372).

If a child causes damage

Whether a parent has to pay for damage his child causes depends largely on the age of the child. If a three-year-old ran out into the road and caused a crash after his mother left the front door open, the courts might make the parents pay the costs of the accident.

If a 16-year-old did the same thing, the chances are that his parents would not be held responsible because the child could have been expected to know better.

Similarly, if parents gave their normally sensible 15-year-old son an airgun and instructed him fully on how to use the gun safely, the courts would be unlikely to hold them responsible if the boy accidentally injured someone with it.

On the other hand, if the boy was often reckless by nature and the parents had given him the airgun without any advice on how and where to use it, the parents might well have to pay compensation to the injured person.

In general, the courts follow the principle that parents are responsible for their child's actions only in so far as they can reasonably be expected to have control over the child.

• If your young child causes minor damage – such as breaking a neighbour's window with his football – offer to pay for the cost of the repairs on the spot.

• If your child causes major damage or injury – suppose, for example, he lights a bonfire which gets out of control – and it looks as though court action could follow, the safest course is not to do or say anything which could be interpreted as an admission of responsibility.

• Instead, get advice from a solicitor as soon as possible (see *Getting help with a legal problem*, page 370).

When somebody dies

Even if the last illness has been long and death expected, coping with the formalities of a death is distressing. However, all the officials involved will be sympathetic and anxious to make procedures as simple and painless as possible.

As soon as a person dies, the first step is always to call a doctor, unless one is there already. Under certain circumstances, the doctor – or sometimes the registrar – will be obliged to report the death to a coroner.

Over the following days, five further responsibilities usually have to be faced: notifying the next-of-kin; arranging the funeral; registering the death; sorting out the dead person's affairs; and claiming financial help from the state.

Calling in a doctor

• If the death occurs at home, call a doctor – ideally the one who treated the dead person during his last illness. The doctor will complete an official medical certificate of death, identifying the cause of death. If the death occurs in hospital, the hospital will arrange this for you.

• The doctor may give you either the medical certificate or a tear-off slip from it called the Notice to Informant. Keep the document safely. You will need it for registering the death.

• If the dead person wished to donate parts of his body to be used for transplants, consult the doctor or the hospital authorities immediately.

• About 1 in 5 deaths in Britain are reported to the coroner, usually because the dead person was not seen by a doctor in the 14 days before he died. In the vast majority of cases, the fact that the coroner is informed does not imply any suspicion of foul play. If a coroner becomes involved – the doctor will tell you whether he will or not – you do not have to register the death within any particular time limit.

• No death certificate can be issued, nor can a funeral take place, until the coroner gives his permission. If he decides that a post-mortem and perhaps an inquest are necessary, there may be a few days' delay. You need do nothing for the time being. Any arrangements will be made by the doctor or the coroner's office.

• When the coroner has satisfied himself as to the cause of death he will either register the death directly, or ask the next-of-kin to do so.

Notifying the next-of-kin

• Let any close relatives and friends know of the death. You may also wish to put a notice of the death in a newspaper. Instructions on how to do this usually appear next to the paper's births, marriages and deaths column.

• Contact the executors of the dead person's will, if you know who they are.

Arranging the funeral

A funeral is usually arranged by the dead person's executors or his relatives.

If the dead person expressed a particular wish about his funeral, this is usually respected.

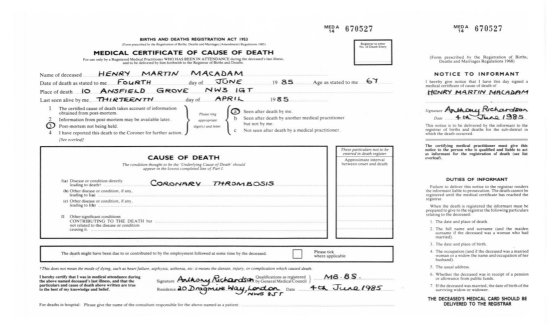

WHAT THE MEDICAL CERTIFICATE IS FOR
A doctor must fill in a certificate of the cause of death before the death can be registered. He will also sign the Notice to Informant (on the right of the certificate). This tells whoever is going to register the death what information he or she must give the registrar.

But the person organising the funeral is not legally obliged to follow the dead person's wishes, even if they are set out in the will.

• Call an undertaker. If you do not know of one, the doctor or hospital authorities may be able to suggest one to you. The undertaker will take the body away. Discuss with the undertaker what kind of funeral you would like him to organise and what the probable cost will be.

• If the body is to be cremated, a number of special forms have to be filled in. The undertaker will make the arrangements for you.

Registering the death

The person responsible for registering a death is specified by law (see box, page 380).

• Take the Notice to Informant – or the medical certificate of death, if the doctor has given it to you – to the local registrar of births, deaths and marriages. The doctor who completed the medical certificate will give you the address of the registrar. Otherwise it can be found in the telephone directory under 'Registration'.

• Take also the dead person's National Health Service medical card.

D. Cert.
R.B.D.

CAUTION—Any person who (1) falsifies any of the particulars on this certificate, or (2) uses a falsified certificate as true knowing it to be false, is liable to prosecution.

CERTIFIED COPY OF AN ENTRY
Pursuant to the Births and **Deaths Registration Act 1953**

DEATH	Entry No. 10

Registration district Sub-district	Hampstead St. Pancras Administrative area London Borough of Camden
1. Date and place of death	Fourth June 1985 10 Ansfield Grove, St. Pancras
2. Name and surname Henry Martin MACADAM	3. Sex Male 4. Maiden surname of woman who has married
5. Date and place of birth	7th September 1917 Basingstoke, Hampshire
6. Occupation and usual address	Accountant (retired) 10 Ansfield Grove, St. Pancras, NW3.
7. (a) Name and surname of informant Agnes Dorothy Macadam	(b) Qualification Widow of the deceased present at the death
(c) Usual address	10 Ansfield Grove, NW3
8. Cause of death	Coronary thrombosis Certified by Anthony Richardson MB.BS
9. I certify that the particulars given by me above are true to the best of my knowledge and belief. Agnes Macadam	Signature of informant
10. Date of registration Fifth June 1985	11. Signature of registrar P. Smithson Registrar

---

OBTAINING A DEATH CERTIFICATE
Ask the registrar for at least one copy of the death certificate (which you will have to pay for). You will need it to claim under a life assurance policy. The registrar will give you a free certificate of registration. You will need that to claim death grant and widow's benefit.

• You must visit the registrar in person within five days of the death. If you are unable to do so – because you are ill, for example – you must inform the registrar of the death in writing within five days. You cannot delegate this duty to the person next in order of responsibility.

• When you write, send the registrar the Notice to Informant or the medical certificate of death. You should then go in person to complete the registration within 14 days of the death.

• When you register the death, the registrar will want to know the full name of the dead person, his place and date of birth, occupation, place and date of death, usual address, whether he was receiving a pension or allowance from public funds, and, if he was married, the age of the surviving spouse.

• The registrar will give you a certificate of registration of death and a disposal certificate.

• Take the disposal certificate to the undertaker. Until he has it, the funeral cannot take place.

• If you are responsible for winding up the dead person's affairs, get copies of the death certificate as well (available for a fee). You may need to send one to a solicitor, and you will need one to claim under a life assurance policy.

WHO MUST REGISTER THE DEATH?

The law not only insists that every death must be registered, it also specifies who must do the registering.

• If the death occurs in a house or hospital, the first available person on the following list is obliged to register the death. He or she cannot delegate this duty to someone in another category. In order of precedence, the people are:

1. A relative who was present at the death.
2. A relative who was present during the last illness.
3. A relative who lives nearby or is staying nearby.
4. Anyone present at the death.
5. Anyone living in the same house as the dead person.
6. The person arranging the funeral.

• If the death occurs anywhere other than in a house or hospital, one of the following people is obliged to register the death. In order, they are:

1. Any relative who knows any of the details that need to be registered.
2. Anyone present at the death.
3. Anyone who found or took charge of the body.
4. Anyone arranging the funeral.

Sorting out the dead person's affairs

The responsibility for sorting out the affairs of someone who has died usually lies with the executor of his will. The executor is usually the widow or widower, or a close friend or relative. In some cases, especially if there is a large or complicated estate, there may also be a professional executor such as a solicitor, accountant or bank.

• The first step for the executor to take after the death is to find the will. If it is not immediately to hand, check with the dead person's solicitor or bank. The will may have been given to them for safekeeping. The will is the executor's legal authority to act.

• If there is no will or no executor – because the named executors are dead, for example – the nearest relatives should apply to the local probate registry for what lawyers call 'letters of administration'. These give you the same authority and duties as an executor. A local Citizens Advice Bureau will have the address of the nearest probate registry.

• To apply, ask the probate registry or a registrar for a copy of the form PR48, entitled Personal Application for Probate or Letters of Administration. The form also sets out the duties of an executor.

• If the estate is complicated and if no professional executor has been named in the will, it may be wise to engage a solicitor to help. His fees can be deducted from the estate.

• Find out what assets the dead person had. You will need to examine his personal papers and consult his bank manager, accountant or solicitor.

• Contact all the organisations with which the dead person had dealings – such as banks, National Savings, building societies and insurance companies. They will tell you which of the dead person's assets can be used at once – such as joint bank accounts – and which are frozen until the dead person's affairs have been sorted out and formally wound up.

Claiming financial help from the state

When somebody dies, his or her dependants may need financial help. There are various government benefits which can be claimed. The main ones are: death grant; widow's benefit; and industrial death benefit.

• Contact the local office of the Department of Health and Social Security. It will be able to tell you whether you are entitled to any of the benefits and how to claim them. Ask also for a copy of the leaflet What to do after a death (D49), which explains the benefits in detail.

If a Briton dies abroad

• Get in touch with the local British embassy or the consulate. The staff will advise on the local regulations for registering a death, and will help you to make arrangements for the funeral or for bringing the body back to Britain.

Making an insurance claim

If your home or car is damaged – by vandals or thieves, say, or simply by accident – and you decide to claim under your insurance, tell the insurance company as soon as possible.

Tell the company even if you are not sure that you want to make a claim – because you want to protect a no-claim bonus on a car, for instance. Otherwise you could lose the option of making a claim later.

Claiming on your home insurance

• Telephone the company as soon as possible after the loss or damage occurs, and tell the official you speak to what has happened. Find out the official's name and, at the same time, ask for a claim form.

• Get any emergency repairs done at once. Emergency repairs are those necessary to safeguard the property: covering a storm-damaged roof, say, or repairing a door that has been forced open by a burglar. There is no need to submit estimates for these repairs, or to wait for the company's approval.

• If you are in doubt about whether repairs you think necessary are urgent, telephone the company and discuss it with an official there. Again, get the official's name.

• Get at least two estimates for any non-urgent repairs. When the claim form arrives, fill it in with details of the damage and of any property that has been lost or stolen, attach the repair estimates and send it back to the company. Keep copies of everything you send. You do not normally have to submit proof of the value of stolen goods.

• If you do not hear from the company within a week, telephone. You may get approval over the phone to go ahead with the repairs. If you do, make a note of the official's name and ask him to send you a letter confirming what he has said. If not, ask the official when approval is likely to come through.

Claiming after a car accident

• If your car is damaged in an accident, tell the insurance company as soon as possible by telephone. Get the name of the person you speak to and ask for a claim form at the same time.

• Even if your car is undamaged and you decide you do not want to make a claim, report the incident to the company anyway in case someone else claims against you. A local council, for instance, might want to claim for damage to a bollard.

• Decide whether it is worth claiming under the insurance at all. The loss of all or part of a no-claim bonus may cost more than paying for the repairs yourself.

• Get at least two estimates for the repairs to your car. But do not get the repairs done at once. The company may want to inspect the damage first.

• When the claim form arrives, fill it in, attach

the estimates and send it back to the company. If you are not sure whether you want to make a claim, mark the form 'For information only' and explain in a covering letter that you are not at present making a claim, but that you might change your mind later. Keep copies of everything you send.

• Contact the company if you hear nothing after a week. If the official you speak to says you can go ahead with the repairs, get his name and ask for a letter of confirmation.

• If you do decide to make a claim under your insurance policy, pass on to the company at once any letter or writ you receive from anyone else who was involved in the accident. Do not reply to it yourself.

What to do if your car is stolen

A motorist whose car is stolen – in Britain or abroad – should contact the police, as well as his insurance company, as soon as possible after he discovers the theft. Insurance companies usually insist on the theft being reported to the police.

In addition, if the car is leased, or if it is covered by a hire-purchase or credit agreement, inform the loan company involved.

The chances are that you will not see your car again if it is stolen. Of the 380,000 cars reported missing in Britain each year, only about a quarter are recovered – and many of those have been damaged by the thieves.

• If you see the theft being committed but are unable to stop the thieves yourself, dial 999 (or the foreign equivalent) at once and ask for the police. If the theft has happened some time before, contact the nearest police station.

• Either way, tell the police your name and address, the car's make, colour and registration number – and the chassis and engine numbers, if you know them.

• Try to remember anything that makes the car easy to recognise, and tell the police about it. Details such as a large dent in the bodywork, a distinctive sticker in the window or an unusual aerial may help them to identify your car among all the others on the road.

• Once you have alerted the police, telephone your insurance company and ask for a claim form. If the theft happened in Britain, give the name of the police station handling it.

• Fill in the form with the same information that you have given the police and return it as soon as you can. If the theft took place abroad, attach a copy of the foreign police report.

• You will not hear from the insurance company for at least two or three weeks because many cars are recovered during this period. If your car is not found and there is no dispute over the claim, you should receive a cheque five or six weeks after you send in the form.

• If your car is found, you can claim for any damage done to it by the thieves in the same way as for damage caused in an accident.

Legal and financial emergencies

When an insurance claim is disputed

If your insurance company delays payment on any claim you make, or if it offers less than you have asked for, you have the choice of accepting the company's decision – or fighting it.

• The first step, if you decide to fight, is to complain to the company in writing, stating clearly what you want. Keep a copy of the letter, and of any others you send.

• If the letter does not produce a satisfactory response, phone or write to the company and ask if it has any standard arrangement for arbitration over disputed claims.

Going to arbitration

Most companies use one of three agencies to handle disputed claims in order to avoid the delay and expense of going to court: the Insurance Ombudsman Bureau; the Personal Insurance Arbitration Service; or a department of Lloyd's of London.

• If the company's arrangement is with the Insurance Ombudsman Bureau, contact the bureau at 31 Southampton Row, London WC1B 5HJ (telephone 01-242 8613). The bureau or the insurance company will tell you how to apply for a hearing.

• Under the bureau's scheme, disputes are decided by an independent solicitor, whose services are free. You can choose to accept or reject his decision.

• If you accept the solicitor's decision, the company is also obliged to accept, and to pay you what the solicitor recommends.

• If you reject the solicitor's decision, you retain the right to take the company to court.

• If the arrangement is with the Personal Insurance Arbitration Service, the arbitration is handled by the Chartered Institute of Arbitrators at 75 Cannon Street, London EC4N 5BH (telephone 01-236 8761). The insurance company will explain how to apply for a hearing.

• Under the arbitration service scheme, which is free, the arbitrator's decision is legally binding. This means that you lose the option to sue the insurance company in the courts if you disagree with the decision.

• If the amount in dispute is large – and you risk losing a lot if the arbitrator's decision goes against you – get the advice of a solicitor before deciding to use the scheme.

• If your insurer is a Lloyd's syndicate, contact the Manager, Advisory Department, Lloyd's of London (Insurance), Lime Street, London EC3M 7HA (telephone 01-623 7100). The department does not offer a formal arbitration service, but it will check to make sure that your claim has been properly dealt with. There is no fee for this service, and if you remain dissatisfied you retain the right to go to court.

• If your insurance company has no standard arbitration arrangement, write to the Association of British Insurers, Consumer Information Department, Aldermary House, 10-15 Queen Street, London EC4N 1TU (telephone 01-248 4477).

The association will investigate on your behalf and may persuade the company to improve its offer. There is no fee for this help and you retain the right to sue the insurance company if you are still dissatisfied.

Using a loss assessor

If none of these steps produces a satisfactory settlement of your claim, consider employing an insurance expert known as a loss assessor, who will look into the claim and try to negotiate a more acceptable settlement.

• Before a claim is considered – especially if it is a large one – the insurance company will usually want to inspect the damage to check that the claim is reasonable. It may either send a member of its own staff to carry out the inspection or an independent adviser known as a loss adjuster.

• A loss assessor does the same work as a loss adjuster, but he acts on your behalf. Loss assessors are, however, expensive and it is generally worth employing one only if there is a substantial difference between the amount the insurance company is offering and the amount you have claimed.

• To find out the names and addresses of loss assessors in your area, contact the Institute of Public Loss Assessors, 14 Red Lion Street, Chesham, Buckinghamshire HP5 1HB; telephone Chesham (0494) 782342.

• If you do contact a loss assessor, check what his fees are likely to be before asking him to start work.

Going to court

• If you still cannot agree a satisfactory settlement of your claim, the only remaining option is to take the company to court.

• Get the advice of a solicitor before deciding to take this course (see *Getting help with a legal problem*, page 370).

Lost credit card, cheque book or cheque card

If you discover that your credit card, cheque book, cheque card or cash card is missing, telephone the credit card company or bank involved as soon as possible. Follow up the call with a letter. To make it easier to report the loss, keep a separate note of all your card numbers safely at home. If you suspect theft, tell the police as well.

In most circumstances, provided you act quickly, you will not have to pay any bills a thief runs up on your account. And most home insurance policies will cover you against even this limited risk.

Because plastic money is becoming more common, some credit card firms in Britain are planning central schemes to help customers whose cards are lost or stolen. The first such scheme, called CardWise, was introduced for Access cardholders in 1985.

Under the CardWise scheme, customers file details of all their cards – including cash cards, and account cards issued by shops – with a central registry. Then if any or all of a customer's cards are stolen, he needs to make only one phone call to the registry, which is open round the clock 365 days a year.

As soon as he has called, his responsibility for any bills run up by a thief ends, and the scheme's staff make sure that all the companies whose cards he holds are notified.

What you stand to lose on a stolen card

CREDIT CARD You will not have to pay more than £25 of the bills a thief runs up with your card. If you report the loss before the card is used, you will not have to pay anything.

CHEQUE BOOK Unless you have been careless – by signing blank cheques, say – you will not have to pay for any forged cheques a thief passes. The bank or the shop that accepts them will have to bear the loss.

CHEQUE CARD You will not have to pay for any cash or goods a thief gets with your card.

If your cash card is stolen

Legally, you can be made to pay back any sums a thief withdraws using your card, up to the time you report the loss.

• Never keep a cash card and a note of your personal number (which does not appear on the card) together. The card is of no value to a thief without the number.

• Memorise your personal number if possible. If you must make a note of it, keep the note somewhere safe or disguise it as something else – a telephone number, say.

• The same rules and precautions apply to a credit card used as a cash card.

If you damage a banknote

If you accidentally damage a banknote – by putting it through a washing machine after leaving it in a pocket, say, or by partially burning it – you can get the note replaced.

• Take the remains of the note to a bank or post office and tell the staff you want a replacement.

• The bank or post office will ask you to fill out a form giving details of how the damage occurred, and will send the form – and the damaged note – to the Bank of England.

• If the Bank of England approves the application, it will repay you through your bank or will send you a payment order which can be cashed at a post office.

• Approval is not, however, automatic. The Bank of England may reject the application if the note is very badly mutilated. Alternatively – if, for example, only half the note has survived – the bank may delay replacing it for up to six months just in case the other half turns up.

IF YOU ARE ABROAD

• If you lose a credit card, cash card, cheque book or cheque card while you are abroad, telephone or cable the credit card company or bank as soon as possible.

• If the loss leaves you short of local currency, ask for an urgent transfer of cash to a convenient bank.

• Inform the local police of your loss and ask them for written confirmation that you have done so.

If you lose your passport

• If your passport is lost or stolen abroad, report the loss first to the local police. If you do not speak the local language, ask someone who does to come with you and help you to make the report.

• Ask the police for written confirmation that you have reported the loss. If they will not give you such a statement, make a note of the police station you visit and, if possible, the name of the officer you speak to.

• Once you have told the police, contact the nearest British consulate, embassy or High Commission. They can issue a replacement passport, or an emergency document to get you home. The police should be able to give you the consulate's address and telephone number. Alternatively, look in the telephone directory covering the nearest large town or the country's capital city.

• If you needed a visa for the country where you lose the passport, you will probably need to get a replacement visa stamped into a new passport. Ask the consulate whether this is necessary and, if so, how to apply.

Useful addresses

Advice on how to deal with or prevent particular emergencies is available from scores of organisations around Britain. The major ones are listed here.

Many of these organisations have branches or affiliated clubs throughout the country. In these cases, the head offices that are listed on these pages will be able to help you to get in touch with a local branch or club.

First aid and medical emergencies

BRITISH RED CROSS SOCIETY
9 Grosvenor Crescent, London SW1X 7EJ
Tel: 01-235 5454
Provides a wide range of services to the sick, elderly or handicapped. Runs courses in first aid, nursing and welfare services. Attends public events to provide first aid.

ST ANDREW'S AMBULANCE ASSOCIATION
St Andrew's House, Milton Street, Glasgow G4 0HR
Tel: 041-332 4031
Runs courses in Scotland on first aid, nursing and other welfare subjects. Attends public events to provide first aid.

ST JOHN AMBULANCE
1 Grosvenor Crescent, London SW1X 7EF
Tel: 01-235 5231
Runs courses throughout England and Wales on first aid, nursing and other welfare subjects. Members of the brigade also attend public events to provide first aid.

In the home and at work

AGE CONCERN ENGLAND
60 Pitcairn Road, Mitcham, Surrey CR4 3LL
Tel: 01-640 5431
Advises on the welfare of the aged. Branches throughout Britain.

BRITISH VETERINARY ASSOCIATION
7 Mansfield Street, London W1M 0AT
Tel: 01-636 6541
Keeps lists of all local vets in Britain.

CONSUMERS' ASSOCIATION
14 Buckingham Street, London WC2N 6DS
Tel: 01-839 1222
Publishes books and magazines with information and advice on consumer matters.

FIRE PROTECTION ASSOCIATION
140 Aldersgate Street, London EC1A 4HX
Tel: 01-606 3757
Advises on all aspects of fire and its prevention.

GOOD HOUSEKEEPING INSTITUTE
National Magazine House, 72 Broadwick Street, London W1V 2BP
Tel: 01-439 7144
Gives advice on household and consumer problems to readers of *Good Housekeeping* magazine.

THE KENNEL CLUB
1 Clarges Street, London W1Y 8AB
Tel: 01-493 6651
Keeps lists of local dog-training clubs.

MENCAP – The Royal Society for Mentally Handicapped Children and Adults
117-123 Golden Lane, London EC1Y 0RT
Tel: 01-253 9433
Offers a wide range of services to mentally handicapped people and their families. Local societies throughout the country.

NATIONAL SOCIETY FOR THE PREVENTION OF CRUELTY TO CHILDREN
67 Saffron Hill, London EC1N 8RS
Tel: 01-242 1626
Responds within 24 hours to calls charging that a child is being neglected or abused. Child protection teams and centres throughout England, Wales and Northern Ireland.

ROYAL SCOTTISH SOCIETY FOR THE PREVENTION OF CRUELTY TO CHILDREN
Melville House, 41 Polwarth Terrace, Edinburgh EH11 1NU
Tel: EDINBURGH 337 8539
As NSPCC, for Scotland.

ROYAL SOCIETY FOR THE PREVENTION OF ACCIDENTS
Cannon House, The Priory Queensway, Birmingham B4 6BS
Tel: 021-200 2461
Gives information on all aspects of safety.

ROYAL SOCIETY FOR THE PREVENTION OF CRUELTY TO ANIMALS
Causeway, Horsham, West Sussex RH12 1HG
Tel: HORSHAM 64181
Advises on animal welfare. Maintains animal hospitals and clinics and a network of inspectors throughout the country.

Emergencies on the road

AUTOMOBILE ASSOCIATION
Fanum House, Basingstoke, Hampshire RG21 2EA
Tel: BASINGSTOKE 20123
Operates a vehicle breakdown service for members, coming to the home and recovering vehicles broken down on the road. Offers touring and travel information and insurance benefits.

BRITISH MOTORCYCLISTS FEDERATION
129 Seaforth Avenue, Motspur Park, New Malden, Surrey KT3 6JU
Tel: 01-942 7914
Operates a breakdown service for members. Offers insurance benefits and information on all aspects of motorcycling. Runs a training scheme.

CYCLISTS' TOURING CLUB
Cotterell House, 69 Meadrow, Godalming, Surrey GU7 3HS
Tel: GODALMING 7217
Advises members on all aspects of cycling. Offers free legal aid and insurance benefits.

Publishes information on cycle touring.

DISABLED DRIVERS' ASSOCIATION
Ashwellthorpe, Norwich NR16 1EX
Tel: FUNDENHALL 449
Offers disabled people information and advice on how to keep mobile. Local groups throughout the country.

EUROP ASSISTANCE LTD
252 High Street, Croydon, Surrey CR0 1NF
Tel: 01-680 1234
Operates a Europe-wide breakdown and recovery service and a worldwide medical emergency service. Representatives worldwide can help subscribers in motoring or medical emergencies.

INSTITUTE OF ADVANCED MOTORISTS
359 Chiswick High Road, London W4 4HS
Tel: 01-994 4403
Runs advanced driving tests. Local volunteer groups run training courses.

ROYAL AUTOMOBILE CLUB
RAC House, Lansdowne Road, Croydon, Surrey CR9 2JA
Tel: 01-686 2525
Provides members with a vehicle breakdown service, both at members' homes and on the road. Offers touring and travel information and insurance benefits.

Emergencies in the water

BRITISH CANOE UNION
45-47 High Street, Addlestone, Weybridge, Surrey KT15 1JV
Tel: WEYBRIDGE 41341
Offers advice, guides to waterways, and insurance benefits to members. Affiliated clubs throughout the country. Many clubs run training courses.

BRITISH SUB-AQUA CLUB
16 Upper Woburn Place, London WC1H 0QW
Tel: 01-387 9302
Branches throughout the country and overseas. Publishes diving instruction manuals. Keeps lists of snorkelling and aqualung courses given by approved instructors.

BRITISH WATERWAYS BOARD
Melbury House, Melbury Terrace, London NW1 6JX
Tel: 01-262 6711
Administers over 2000 miles of rivers and canals in Britain. Sells maps and issues licences authorising craft to use its waterways.

ROYAL LIFE SAVING SOCIETY
Mountbatten House, Studley, Warwickshire B80 7NN
Tel: STUDLEY 3943
Branches throughout Britain. Runs courses in water safety, and rescue and resuscitation techniques. Provides lifeguards for certain beaches and some inland waterways.

ROYAL YACHTING ASSOCIATION
Victoria Way, Woking, Surrey GU21 1EQ
Tel: WOKING 5022
Affiliated sailing clubs throughout Britain. Keeps lists of recognised training schools. Covers motor as well as sailing boats, and windsurfing.

Emergencies on holiday and in the country

ASSOCIATION OF BRITISH TRAVEL AGENTS
55-57 Newman Street, London W1P 4AH
Tel: 01-637 2444
Provides financial safeguards for holidaymakers who have booked package holidays through ABTA travel agents.

BRITISH CAVE RESCUE COUNCIL
c/o The Secretary, Mr Brian Boardman, 8 Yealand Avenue, Giggleswick, Settle, North Yorkshire BD24 0AY
The secretary keeps lists of local affiliated cave rescue organisations.

BRITISH MOUNTAINEERING COUNCIL
Crawford House, Precinct Centre, Booth Street East, Manchester M13 9RZ
Tel: 061-273 5835
Local climbing clubs throughout Britain. Runs training courses. Advises on equipment. Publishes guides and instruction manuals.

THE CAMPING AND CARAVANNING CLUB
11 Lower Grosvenor Place, London SW1W 0EY
Tel: 01-828 1012
Runs campsites throughout Britain. Offers members breakdown and recovery services throughout Europe, and worldwide medical insurance cover.

THE CARAVAN CLUB
East Grinstead House, East Grinstead, W Sussex RH19 1UA
Tel: EAST GRINSTEAD 26944
Runs caravan sites throughout the country. Has a breakdown and recovery service for members. Advises on foreign touring.

CIVIL AVIATION AUTHORITY
CAA House, 45-59 Kingsway, London WC2B 6TE
Tel: 01-379 7311
Provides financial safeguards for holidaymakers who have booked package holidays through companies holding an Air Travel Organiser's Licence.

COUNTRYSIDE COMMISSION
Publications Dispatch Department, 19-23 Albert Road, Manchester M19 2EQ
Tel: 061-224 6287
Provides information on long-distance footpaths and on the rights and responsibilities of visitors to the countryside.

THE RAMBLERS' ASSOCIATION
1-5 Wandsworth Road, London SW8 2XX
Tel: 01-582 6878
Provides information on all aspects of walking. Local groups throughout the country.

THE SKI CLUB OF GREAT BRITAIN
118 Eaton Square, London SW1W 9AF
Tel: 01-245 1033
Provides information on ski resorts throughout the world. Representatives in many Alpine resorts. Advises on equipment and skiing courses.

THE YOUTH HOSTELS ASSOCIATION
Trevelyan House, St Stephen's Hill, St Albans, Hertfordshire AL1 2DY
Tel: ST ALBANS 55215
Runs hostels offering members cheap overnight accommodation throughout the world. Publishes handbook and maps for members.

Natural disasters

FIRE AND EMERGENCY PLANNING DEPARTMENT
The Home Office, 50 Queen Anne's Gate, London SW1H 9AT
Tel: 01-213 3000
Offers information on civil defence. For advice on local civil defence arrangements – including flood warning and prevention – contact your local council.

Crime

CRIMINAL INJURIES COMPENSATION BOARD
Whittington House, 19 Alfred Place, London WC1E 7EA
Tel: 01-636 9501
Awards financial compensation to the victims of crimes of violence.

RAPE CRISIS CENTRE
PO Box 69, London WC1X 9NJ
Tel: 01-837 1600 or 01-278 3956 or 021 233 2122 (Birmingham)
24-hour service offering advice and help.

Drink and drugs

AL-ANON FAMILY GROUPS UK AND EIRE
61 Great Dover Street, London SE1 4YF
Tel: 01-403 0888
Specialises in helping the families and friends of problem drinkers. Groups throughout the country.

ALCOHOL CONCERN
305 Grays Inn Road, London WC1X 8QF
Tel: 01-833 3471
Runs information, education and advice centres on alcoholism throughout the country.

ALCOHOLICS ANONYMOUS
General Service Office, PO Box 1, Stonebow House, Stonebow, York YO1 2NJ
Tel: YORK 644026
Helps alcoholics who want to stop drinking. Centres throughout Britain. Offers the support and companionship of reformed alcoholics.

MEDICAL COUNCIL ON ALCOHOLISM
1, St Andrews Place, London NW1 4LB
Tel: 01-487 4445
Voluntary body helping to educate the medical profession on alcohol and alcoholism, and alcoholics and their families to find specialist care.

NARCOTICS ANONYMOUS
PO Box 246, London SW10
Tel: 01-351 6794 or 01-351 6066 or 01-351 6067
A fellowship of drug victims, modelled on Alcoholics Anonymous, whose members help each other to stay free of their addiction.

SALVATION ARMY
101 Queen Victoria Street, London EC4P 4EP
Tel: 01-236 5222
Maintains hostels for the homeless throughout the country.

THE SAMARITANS
Head Office, 17 Uxbridge Road, Slough, Berkshire SL1 1SN
Tel: SLOUGH 32713 (office); 01-283 3400 (24-hour emergency line)
24-hour service listening to and befriending those in despair and with suicidal urges

Legal and financial emergencies

ASSOCIATION OF BRITISH INSURERS
Consumer Information Department, Aldermary House, Queen Street, London EC4N 1TT
Tel: 01-248 4477
Advises and assists with insurance problems.

BANKING INFORMATION SERVICE
10 Lombard Street, London EC3V 9AP
Tel: 01-626 8486

Offers information on bank facilities and practices.

THE CHARTERED INSTITUTE OF ARBITRATORS
75 Cannon Street, London EC4N 5BH
Tel: 01-236 8761
Arranges binding arbitration to settle commercial and consumer disputes.

INSTITUTE OF PUBLIC LOSS ASSESSORS
14 Red Lion Street, Chesham, Buckinghamshire HP5 1HB
Tel: CHESHAM 782342
Keeps lists of experts who will help to settle disputed insurance claims.

INSURANCE OMBUDSMAN BUREAU
31 Southampton Row, London WC1B 5HJ
Tel: 01-242 8613
Investigates some disputes between individuals and insurance companies.

THE LAW CENTRES FEDERATION
Duchess House, 18-19 Warren Street, London W1P 5DB
Tel: 01-387 8570
Keeps lists of centres in some major cities and towns offering free legal assistance and advice.

SOLICITORS COMPLAINTS BUREAU
Portland House, Stag Place, London SW1E 5BL
Tel: 01-834 2288
Deals with written complaints about solicitors.

LLOYD'S OF LONDON (INSURANCE)
Advisory Department, Lime Street, London EC3M 7HA
Tel: 01-623 7100
Checks that a claim on a Lloyd's insurer has been dealt with properly.

Index

All about CHILDREN

All about ELECTRICITY

F

Escaping from a fire
    If you are trapped on an upper floor........ 145
    action summary 24
    How to rescue a victim of smoke
    inhalation.................................... *124*
    If a house is on fire............................**142-7**
    Getting out of a blazing house..............*142-4*
    If the exit is blocked...........................*144-6*
    Escaping from a high rise building.......... 146
    Using a rope ladder...........................*146-7*
    Rescuing someone from a fire..............**148-9**
    How to do a fireman's lift.....................**148-9**
    Escaping from a sleeping bag................*294*
    Escaping from a forest fire.................. **328-30**

Fire prevention
    The causes of house fires....................... 147
    How to protect your home against fire..... 152
    How to use fire extinguishers.................. 152
    Choosing a fire alarm............................. 152
    Preventing chip pan fires...................... 164-5
    How to use fireguards............................ *168*
    Guarding against fire on a boat............ 262-3

First aid for fire victims
    How to treat burns.................................**66-7**
    first aid summary................................7-10
    Treating blisters caused by burns.............64
    Removing burnt clothing...........................*66*
    Treating chemical burns 66
    Treating burns or scalds in the mouth.......67
    Treating electrical burns...........................93

G

When the windscreen shatters..................**213**
If you feel drowsy at the wheel................**214**
Staying awake during car journeys..........214
If the car catches fire...............................**215**
Getting out of deep snow.........................217
How to drive through floodwater..............**220**
If you are threatened by a hitchhiker.......**226**
If you are stopped by the police..............**227**
If you suffer from car sickness.................284
If your car is stolen.................................381

Stranded in a car
    If you are stuck on a level crossing.........215
    If you are stuck in sand, mud,
        snow or ice...**216-17**
    If you are in a snowbound car.................217
    Trapped in a car underwater...............**218-19**
    If you are caught in a thunderstorm.........298
    Lighting a fire with a car battery..............*313*
    Motorist's survival kit...............................320
    If you are caught in an earthquake..........327
    If you are caught in a forest fire..............328
    If you encounter a hostile crowd.............343

Emergency repairs
    If the fan belt breaks.............................221
    If the petrol gets low............................221-2
    If the windscreen wipers fail....................222
    If you lose the wheel nuts......................222-3
    If the engine is flooded with petrol..........223
    If the engine fades out because of
        vapour lock..223
    If the accelerator jams..........................223-4
    If the distributor cap is cracked...............224
    If a fuse blows...................................224-5
    Thawing a frozen door lock.....................225
    Spare parts for everyday motoring..........225

U

These panels are for you to write in the telephone numbers you might need in a crisis. Write the numbers large and in a strong colour – you might have to read them in poor light.

CITIZENS ADVICE BUREAU

....

COASTGUARD

....

CREDIT CARD COMPANIES

....

....

....

....

DENTIST

....

BANK

....

DOCTOR

....

CHURCH

....

ELECTRICITY

....

Making a

- **Before making the call, work out where you are, if possible. The operator will need to know this if he is to get help to you promptly. He will also ask for your telephone number. It will enable the emergency services to find you if you are cut off.**

- **Call 999. On a pay phone, do not put any coins in. In the dark, find the number on a dial by feeling for the stop. The 9 is the second hole to the left of the stop. On a push-button phone, the 9 is the right-hand bottom button on the panel.**